CW00566231

Channel Tunnel transport system

INSTITUTION OF CIVIL ENGINEERS

Channel Tunnel transport system

Proceedings of the conference organized by the Institution of Civil Engineers and held in London on 4–5 October 1994

Edited by Charles Penny

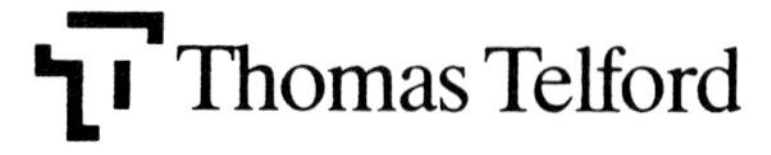

Organizing committee: Charles Penny, Balfour Beatty Civil Engineering Ltd (Chairman); Ian Fugeman, Costain Group; Bernard North, North Transport Consultants; Allan Smith, Consultant; John Taberner, Eurotunnel; Rex Vickers, Mott McDonald Group.

Conference organized by the Institution of Civil Engineers and co-sponsored by the Chartered Institute of Transport, the Institution of Electrical Engineers and the Institution of Highways and Transportation.

Published by Thomas Telford Publishing, Thomas Telford Services Ltd, 1 Heron Quay, London E14 4JD

First published 1996

Distributors for Thomas Telford books are
USA: American Society of Civil Engineers, Publications Sales Department, 345 East 47th Street, New York, NY 10017-2398
Japan: Maruzen Co. Ltd, Book Department, 3–10 Nihonbashi 2-chome, Chuo-ku, Tokyo 103
Australia: DA Books and Journals, 648 Whitehorse Road, Mitcham 3132, Victoria

A catalogue record for this book is available from the British Library

Classification
Availability: Unrestricted
Content: Collected papers
Status: Refereed
User: Transport engineers

ISBN: 0 7277 2515 7

Printed in Great Britain by The Cromwell Press, Melksham, Wilts.

Contents

Session 6: Operation of fixed link

Session 7: Safety

The Eurotunnel overview

Address by Sir Alastair Morton, Co-Chairman of Eurotunnel

May I thank the opening speakers for their comments and congratulate the ICE for bringing this conference together.

Last Wednesday evening, I sat in my hotel room in Madrid going over my address to the Project Finance Summit which preceded the IMF/World Bank Annual Meetings. In it, I was preparing to draw some lessons from the Channel Tunnel project. As part of my preparation, I read a feature article in a recent issue of a French magazine 'Genie Industriel'. The article was by Pierre Parisot, the last and best of the Chairmen of TML's Executive Board.

Pierre answered the rhetorical question 'Si c'était à refaire?'. If you had to do it again, would you? It is the fashionable question these days — my partner André Bénard wrote a piece on that question for the French press a few months ago and I get asked it often. André and Pierre both answered Yes, definitely, but not quite that way! I would say the same.

Pierre Parisot drew six lessons from the Channel Tunnel project. Pierre is a delightful man and, although I would look at some of his rhetorical flourishes through the opposite end of the telescope, I would agree with the broad intent of five of his six points, namely:

- one, get the two governments to respect the intention and form of the Concession in framing their demands on the design;
- two and three, start with a strong and experienced client, answerable to an articulate and risk-taking financial interest;
- four, keep the promoters together in their commitment to the project until it is complete: don't let them separate into opposing and external factions as our contractors and banks did;
- five, restrict the number of parties to every decision; for example, don't have ten contractors each with 10% of the vote and 220 voting banks!

Further, I agree very much with Pierre that the parties to this project deserve high praise for avoiding Franco-British or Anglo-French disputes — whatever else was in dispute. I do not go on from there to his sixth point that the culture of the project could or should have remained a private party for British and French invitees only.

Great credit goes to many people for the achievement of the Channel Tunnel.

- To the entrepreneur contractors who conceived it and, as promoters, won the contest for the vastly valuable Concession to build and operate fixed links across the Channel.
- To Margaret Thatcher and François Mitterrand for launching it and keeping out of its ownership or financing to the end.

- To the lead bankers and investment bankers who had the courage at the outset and in 1990 to develop with us the huge financing, now totalling £10.5 billion.
- To the engineers on site who overcame the difficulties extant in the opening stages of the project to finish the civil engineering so splendidly. They had more difficulty with the kitting out of the transport system, but among them were some magnificent specimens of the engineering contractor breed.

Credit also goes to

- the civil servants, consultants and advisers who did their best to support a sometimes tottering project, often without clear terms of reference; and, dare I say it, to
- the team that André Bénard and I had the honour to build up and lead in Eurotunnel.

But giving great credit does not — as Pierre Parisot, André Bénard and, I am sure, Neville Simms will agree — imply blessing the structure, the terms and conditions, and the external impositions under which we laboured.

I am not alone in describing the launch of the Channel Tunnel project without a competent, strong client as the 'original sin' of the project. A design and build contract formulated without a client is a recipe for trouble — doubled and redoubled when the bluff and counterbluff between contractors and bankers, in the absence of a client, results in a difficult contract for a not-yet-detailed design being lump sum in large part! Latham is not needed to know what the contractor will do when he gets truly scared of what he has signed onto there — in our case a lump sum contract for the terminals (no great problem) and the fixed equipment, including what TML called 'the clever systems' with evident fear. And difficulties duly followed, as night follows day!

The structured flaws in the contract, in the design process, in the financing and in the relationship of the governments to the project were serious and will repay lots of study. Also deserving study and, as I have said, praise are the courage, determination and sheer endurance of those in TML and Eurotunnel who produced the solutions.

Not every aspect of the outcome is flawless and the process of debugging the system and identifying what must be rectified, replaced or rearranged is still going on. But a 200 year dream has been realised and everyone, of the thousands who actually did it, has a right to be proud to have been part of it.

Lifting our eyes from the sites, the drawing offices, the lawyers' and bankers' meeting rooms, let us be aware of what has been achieved. The greatest imaginable piece of infrastructure has been inserted into the Single European Market by private enterprise working in partnership with two governments and other national interests represented from Brussels. A lead has been given towards the networks of infrastructure and services that an integrated Europe needs for the 21st Century. Lessons from it are available, if the parties to further projects will learn them. Skill and technologies have been developed to higher levels, confidence has grown. We are better placed to build a stronger Europe.

And the capitalist system has been strengthened — not quite as Mrs Thatcher intended. She wanted to prove private enterprise could do *anything*, if left *completely* alone by government.

Well, what we did was prove there are limits to that proposition. We have proved that projects at the interface of public and private sectors — shall I say the provision of public services by private capital and management — must be blended partnerships between governments, capital market and industry. Each has risks to take that are within its sphere of control. Each has powers or capabilities that the other does not have — for example, the power to boost a public interest project into existence by loan funding over more than 25 years is not available in the private sector.

We learned the lesson that the Channel Tunnel is a private sector enterprise between two public sector initiatives — the provision of national road and rail systems to the Tunnel — all within a framework of national laws and tax systems, binational treaties and multi-national European obligations, the whole focused onto our shareholders and bankers through the mechanism of a 65 year Concession.

Great risk has been undertaken by the private sector but the Channel Tunnel, in the end, is a public/private partnership — the aches and pains of which are still being worked upon by negotiation and litigation. Looking ahead, Her Majesty's Government will be ill-advised to ignore the impact of the Channel Tunnel Rail Link on

- first, the French taxpayer, who invested hundreds of millions of pounds in a highspeed rail link and three motorways to Calais
- second, 225 banks with a prior charge on the Tunnel, and
- third, the 650 000 shareholders of Eurotunnel.

All those taxpayers, bankers and shareholders are HMG's partners now, and partnership imposes obligations as well as entitlements. Will any of those who have read the Department of Transport's quarter-ton of paper stand up and say that this has been recognised in Whitehall?

Indeed, I will close on that note with a reminiscence. André Bénard and I used to say to the ten owners of TML and to 220 banks, 'We are partners: we are condemned to get on with each other!'. It is not an ignoble situation. By immense effort and some tolerance, much has been achieved in the spaces between London and Paris and between public and private sectors over the past nine years.

The TML overview

N. I. SIMMS, Group Chief Executive, Tarmac PLC,
and joint Chairman Transmanche-Link Members Assembly

Some fourteen years ago, way back in 1980, Alan Osborne, my predecessor as Chief Executive of Tarmac Construction, happened to be having a working lunch. While waiting for the soup, he chatted, as one does, to the gentlemen beside him — who turned out to be Lord Shackleton, then Deputy Chairman of RTZ. They talked about the Channel Tunnel Scheme into which RTZ had put a lot of work some years earlier but which had been abandoned for political reasons.

History does not record if either man ordered Dover sole, but something must have set them thinking because, while waiting for the main course, the germ of an idea began to surface. If, they asked themselves, the Government was not prepared to stand alone in supporting and funding a channel tunnel, then perhaps it would do so in partnership with the private sector. I have to say that in 1980 this was a truly radical thought bordering on heresy.

Nevertheless, they explored the idea further and, or so legend has it, by the time the last of the jam roly poly has been cleared away the tablecloth was covered in calculations and an outline proposal. Legend also has it that this tablecloth is stored safe for posterity somewhere in the vaults of our Wolverhampton offices. I cannot comment on this but I like to think it might be true.

What is certainly true, however, is that from that day on Tarmac took a leading role in promoting and building the world's largest privately funded infrastructure project. The eventual contractor was called Transmanche-Link.

So, nearly fifteen years later, what are the lessons that have been learned by TML and its partners? The rest of the book is devoted mainly to operational and technical matters so I would like to focus my remarks on the key organisational and commercial issues surrounding the project. Under organisational issues, I would like to concentrate on *sponsorship, partnership* and *people*, commercially, I want to look at the importance of *time* and *re-negotiation*: these are all issues that Sir Alastair Morton and I are still closely involved with in our work on the Government's Private Finance Initiative.

The initiative currently aims at a partnership of money and management from both the public and private sectors. It follows (although we did not immediately realise this) that each sector needs a dedicated *sponsor* or champion with the necessary leadership, authority, and skill. The sponsor of the private sector must bring together the private sector skills and financial expertise; the champion of the public sector has to achieve commitment and backing from every relevant Government department — this is no simple matter as many projects, by their very nature, do not fit neatly into the remit of a single Department. Both sponsors have to work together to drive the project forward.

The eventual UK public sector sponsor for the Channel Tunnel was Mrs Thatcher, and it is quite clear to me that without the foresight, energy, and commitment of a few key sponsors in the private sector in the early 1980s, the project would not have got off the ground.

The recent Treasury document 'Breaking New Ground' contains an explicit invitation to the private sector to promote its own ideas as candidates for the private finance initiative. I welcome this invitation, but how are public sector champions to be found for these ideas? Not every project will have a prime minister's active involvement. A way must be found so that good private finance opportunities are not lost and to ensure that the Private Finance Initiative does not just rely on the private sector's imagination.

As I have said, Tarmac was the initial sponsor of the Channel Tunnel, but very soon we were joined by our British partners and advisors. This leads me to my second point — *partnership.*

A successful partnership is like a good marriage — it needs the right partners, mutual confidence and trust, and a willingness to pull together to achieve a common goal. I'll push the analogy a step further — you can't rely on luck, you have to work at it. That was certainly true for TML.

The British end of what was to become TML was formed between early 1981 and mid-84. In October 1984, the British Government then accepted that private funds could be raised to fund the Tunnel. This was the cue for a period of intense activity. By May 1985 we had a French partner on board and in July 1985 agreement was reached between the Channel Tunnel Group and France Manche. Europe's big ten were combined with a common objective — the completion of the Channel Tunnel.

The Channel Tunnel Group and France Manche then became the operator while a joint venture between Translink and Transmanche, foreshortened to Transmanche-Link, was formed to design and construct the fixed link. This arrangement was partly because the financial institutions lining up behind the contractors thought those who build the link should not be the ones to own and operate it.

We tried hard to find operators to join us but not one was prepared to invest in the Link — a decision I am sure they will regret in the fullness of time. And with hindsight, I regret both the failure to get an operator on board and also the subdivision of the original sponsors into client and contractor groups. I am sure this was a source of many problems later on.

However, I believe we have learnt from this and that it is now recognised that sufficient time and effort must go into bringing together the right partners. They must have the right mix of experience and expertise to ensure that any project (public or privately financed) has the best opportunity to succeed. The right mix is everything.

The third and last organisational issue I would like to look at was, in fact, the most important ingredient in TML's achievements and progress. *People.* When formed in 1986, TML had a total staff of ... six. Just four years later, we had more than 14 500 employees and many thousands more working for our subcontractors and suppliers. Every person in TML, from senior executives to the most junior operative should be proud of what has been achieved, but inevitably a number stand out. One of those was Jack Lemley, an America, who took on the role of Chief Executive early in 1989. At that time, the rate of progress was causing considerable concern but Jack soon introduced a number of organisational changes. In less than a year, the tunnel boring machines so improved their progress that world records were being achieved and all the tunnel breakthroughs were achieved on or before their programme dates. Clear proof, I think, that even with sponsors and partnership in place, an organisation still needs to find the right people to push the job through to a successful conclusion.

Time is one of the key commercial issues on any large project — and there is never enough of it. You need time to pull partnerships together; to research those variables that can make or break a proposal; to convince your bankers the proposal will achieve what you say it will; perhaps you even need time to convince the Government to make the necessary changes in legislation - and all this, of course, without even starting on construction and commissioning.

Let's look back at our timetable. The Anglo-French treaty was signed in February 1986. The contractual programme started in May 1986 and TML signed a contract with Eurotunnel in August that year. But, and it's a big but, the last legislative hurdle was not overcome until July 1987 when Her Majesty The Queen gave assent to the Channel Tunnel Bill thus creating the Channel Tunnel Act. It took nearly seven years to get the construction work started — which means that the lead-in took longer than the construction. And frankly, that lead-in was not well used and was, as ever, rushed in its larger stages.

There is a school of Evolutionary Science which believes that progress is made in short, rapid, bursts punctuated by long periods of apparent inactivity — running into hundreds of millions of years. It certainly felt like this in our case! I recognise that, when new ideas and new approaches are evolving, progress if often slow until, suddenly, everything moves at once. However, I believe this is not only frustrating but also dangerous. A better approach is to look for scheduled and continuous progress. For example, the prospects for the private finance initiative could be delayed by the Government if it fails to push through changes in legislation in the departments of Education, Environment and Transport. Urgent parliamentary action is vital. We risk losing momentum and wasting the lead-in time.

Time, as we all know, costs money and unscheduled time costs most of all! And this, my final topic, is one that the Anglo-Saxon culture finds unduly difficult to accept — although the French appear to embrace it more willingly. I believe that, particularly for large, long-term, projects, there must be opportunities for *re-negotiation* of the terms of the project. These must be built into the agreed procedures at key staging points. This must benefit both parties since a concession that turns out to be financially nonviable will not work and is not in the interests of the concessionaire. Similarly, the one that yields excessive profits prematurely is equally unwelcome.

One can only hypothesise about both the improved relationships and also the time and cost savings if, within, the contract between Eurotunnel and TML, there had been an opportunity to re-negotiate peaceably the terms of the project at key points. But, I am certain of one thing — there would have been savings in both time and money.

A short overview like this can only scratch the surface of the key lessons we all learnt in bringing this magnificent transport system to a successful conclusion. But in my view, the success was due, in no small measure, to paying real attention to the major organisational and commercial issues.

In the early days, the Channel Tunnel project had dedicated *sponsors* and was the catalyst for the creation of a cross-border *partnership* with all the necessary financial, managerial and engineering skills. These were vital factors without which no project will get off the ground.

Once the project was underway, other factors came to the fore; we strove to bring out the best in the *people* involved. And we kept a very proper focus on end cost and completion date.

The Channel Tunnel is a landmark project which marks a turning point in the history of the construction industry. I am delighted to have been asked to share with you a few of the key factors surrounding it. I hope some of the lessons of the Channel Tunnel will be taken on board for future projects whether they be traditionally or privately financed.

Discussion on session 1

R. Barnes, *Retired*

The Channel Tunnel has cost about £10 billion to build while the initial estimate was, I believe, £4 billion. This large difference between the initial estimate and the final cost seems to be a typical feature of large projects these days. The difference is so large that it calls into question the credibility of the initial estimating process. What is the point or value of these wildly inaccurate initial cost estimates and why are they taken seriously? Is it because these large projects are led by political and financial considerations with scant regard for physical and engineering reality and uncertainty?

Sir Alastair Morton
Reply to R. Barnes

The question uses the wrong numbers. Excluding rolled-up interest, the 1987 Prospectus estimated £3.9 billion. Outturn, excluding rolled-up interest, has been £5.8 billion.

The original estimates were the work of the promoters of the project. In the absence of a client/operator at the outset, there had to be a possibility they would be exceeded, but at the time that possibility was not thought to be large.

Regional road traffic predictions and traffic flows

Alastair Dick FEng FICE FIHT FCIT
Director of Group Planning
National Express Group PLC

1. Introduction

This paper deals with the development of traffic forecasts that have been used for the Channel Tunnel and its related transport systems. It does not deal with the mechanics of the traffic forecasting procedures used for the Channel Tunnel, as this has been dealt with at a previous conference.[1] It therefore concentrates on the special requirements for traffic forecasting in the development of a major transport business to be created by the private sector. A major need of the private sector is the estimation of likely cash revenues. These requirements are materially different from those conventionally required by Governments who tend to be primarily interested in the economic justification for transport infrastructure investment.

2. Background

Eurotunnel is a private sector transport business and its success will be measured in its ability to generate net revenues and thus being able to pay dividends to its investors. Thus Eurotunnel has to attract paying customers in sufficient numbers to cover its operating costs and to at least pay off its debts. To achieve this, there has to be a sufficiently large market, either already existing or to be created **and** Eurotunnel has to offer a service that is capable of attracting customers from competing services. In addition the providers of these competing services will not willingly give up market share and they will develop their own competitive responses.

The transport market is the movement of people and goods, and in this particular instance, between Britain and the Continent. The journeys made by the people and the freight movements have their origins and destinations far removed from the physical terminals of the Tunnel. It is therefore crucial to realise that the Tunnel is only a 50 kilometre length of a pair of rail tracks, and that this, in itself, is not that relevant to the movement of people and goods. It is nevertheless a crucial link in that it connects the transport networks of Britain with those on the Continent, and therefore has a potential for significant use.

It is only a minor part of a more complex infrastructure of networks and systems which are used by transport operators and individual travellers. Eurotunnel has had to become involved in the debate on the adequacy of transport infrastructure and services on both sides of the Channel, but

---

[1] DICK, A.C., A. BLANQUIER and D. DANFORTH, Expected Traffic Demands. Presented at a Conference on The Channel Tunnel, organised jointly by the Institution of Civil Engineers and Societé des Ingénieurs et Scientifiques de France, in London and Paris during 20-22 September 1989.

particularly between the Tunnel and the rest of the United Kingdom. This required a deep understanding of the existing and political national and international traffic demands. However, the first stage was for Eurotunnel to be awarded the Concession by the Governments of the United Kingdom and France.

3. The Bid: October 1985

The desire for a fixed link by means of a Tunnel had been in existence for some time.[2] The latest previous attempt had been unilaterally terminated by the British Government in 1975. Part of the reason for that termination was the problem of gaining Parliamentary Approval for a Hybrid Bill for a high-speed rail link between the Tunnel and London.

However, the desirability for a fixed link was brought forward again at an Anglo-French summit meeting on 10/11 September 1981. At that meeting it was agreed that a Study Group should be formed to report[3] on the viability of a fixed link across the Channel. The major conclusions reached by this Group included;

- The Group suggests to Ministers that the only decision they can immediately take is, if it is to be in favour of a fixed link, one of principle: on both sides of the Channel it must be subject to the ability of the market to raise finance on terms acceptable to both Governments.

- It is the Group's judgement that the best solution from the point of view of both countries would be one which combined a fixed link of the kind proposed with a thriving maritime industry still carrying as much as, or more than, the traffic it now carries, in conditions of healthy and constructive competition.

This report was followed by a report[4], commissioned by the UK and French Governments and prepared by a Group of Banks which specifically considered the issue of the market's ability to raise the necessary finance of the project. The report outlined the possibility for a private investment together with a non-recourse bank loan (ie without external guarantees) funding of the link but concluded that this could only be tested and verified by carrying out a "market test". This test would have to clearly set out the Governments' positions and how the various risks are to be allocated. They also concluded in their report that:

"The project has no natural sponsoring investment group and an owner will not emerge

---

[2]A good background description of the history of the Project is given in "The Tunnel: The Story of the Channel Tunnel 1802-1994" by Donald Hunt. ISBN 1 89781735 5/7.

[3]Fixed Channel Link. Report of UK/French Study Group, published by the Department of Transport, June 1982. HMSO

[4]Finance for a Fixed Channel Link. A report prepared by the Franco-British Channel Link Financing Group (National Westminster, Midland, BNP, Indo-Suez and Credit Lyonnais Banks), May 1984.

without adequate encouragement and backing from Governments".

In April 1985 the two Governments issued[5] an invitation to promote for the construction of a fixed link across the Channel. The first paragraph of this document made clear one of the fundamental ground rules; viz.

> "The two Governments rule out all support from public funds or Government financial guarantees but agree to provide the necessary political undertakings. Failure to respect this condition will render any proposal unacceptable".

The consortium which was to become Eurotunnel was one of the promoters that submitted a bid. Its bid was a development of the scheme that was stopped in 1975. That is, it was for a rail link tunnel that enabled traffic on the motorway systems of UK and France to be carried between those countries by a Shuttle Train, as well as the rail link being used by Conventional Train services. The motorway traffic would "board" the Shuttle Trains and "disembark" at Terminals at either end of the Tunnel. It was considered that the Shuttle Trains could operate at a capacity equivalent to a motorway traffic lane.

The dual mode approach, ie catering for motorway traffic and rail traffic was considered by many as a low risk option because it meant that it was not fully dependant on the outcome of the road/rail debate for the long term movement of people and goods. As long as there was travel between Britain and the Continent, the Tunnel had a role. The balance between road and rail based demands could be reflected by the allocation of paths between Shuttle Trains and Conventional Trains.

The estimation of traffic revenues was a key element in the preparation of the Bid. The construction cost could be visualised with some precision and the financing plan could be developed by incorporating some heroic assumptions about inflation rates, interest rates and exchange rates. However, the derivation of the revenue forecasts incorporated even greater uncertainties inasmuch that they had to take into account a wide range of factors that included;

- **growth in traffic** between Britain and the Continent; this would depend, inter alia on; the growth in the economies; the effect of the then developing European Single Market; the cost of travel.
- **market shares** obtained by the completing cross-Channel forms of travel; ie Ferries, Airlines, Tunnel.
- **creation of additional** cross-Channel traffic due to the new opportunities that would be possible with the transport services using the Tunnel <u>as well as</u> the competitive improvements in the competing Ferry and Air Services ("the halo effect").
- **tariffs/fares** to be charged by transport operators using the Tunnel as well as those directly charged for private cars. Obviously the charges made by transport operators (eg through passenger and freight trains, coaches, trucks) would reflect the tariffs paid to

---

[5]"INVITATION TO PROMOTERS: for the development, financing, construction and operation of a Channel Fixed Link between France and the United Kingdom". DoT, April 1985.

Eurotunnel. Theses tariffs would obviously have to relate to those likely to be charged for cross-Channel travel on the competing services. Also, in general, the lower the tariffs, the greater the expected traffic volumes. (Note: it is thus obvious that a variety of predicted traffic volumes can be produced depending upon the tariffs that are assumed).

Sir Nicholas Henderson, the then chairman of "Eurotunnel", describes in his book[6] the period of major concern about the traffic revenue estimates when their financial advisers were "getting cold feet" in their ability to finance the project. However, he managed to restore confidence by stating that all estimates were bound to be hazardous, and that nothing had fundamentally changed in the projects cost\revenue characteristics. He also took confidence from my assertion that nobody, especially the Government, would be expecting precise traffic forecasts before deciding whether a scheme is financiable. Their criteria would be whether the figures were "not unreasonable". This double negative was not just a reflection of official caution but was intended to allow a certain degree of flexibility and to reflect the inherent impossibility of predicting the future.

The traffic forecasts and consequent revenue estimates were subject to a wide range of "reasonability" tests reflecting a wide range of possible scenarios. In the end a single "most likely" set of forecasts were produced for the Bid. These forecasts were considered to be "Bankable",that is, very likely to occur. However, higher traffic volumes could occur and the Tunnel's transport system should be capable of handling these greater traffic flows. In any event the forecasts would be kept under review. This was a prime requirement of the financial credit agreement which needed a check that future revenues always were estimated to be greater than the expected maximum deficit.

The traffic forecasts included in the Bid are given in Table 1 together with the traffic figures used by the Anglo-French Study Group and by the Banking Group. It can be seen that the Bid had a substantially higher estimated traffic volume than those used previously. The comparable figures for 2000 being:

Estimate	**Tunnel Traffic**	
	Passenger (mppa)	**Freight (m. gross tonnes)**
Anglo-French S.G.	19.8	11.1
Banking Group	16.0 to 20.9	10.1 to 11.7
"Eurotunnel": basis	27.8	17.2
(with high speed link Paris-Tunnel)	34.8	17.2

The major difference being a higher expected use of through rail services and a higher amount of freight traffic. In addition the Bid stressed the importance of the construction of a "Ligne de Grande Vitesse" (LGV) between Paris and the Tunnel. This would, with TGV train technology, enable a journey time between London and Paris to be achieved within three hours, even with

[6]"Channels & Tunnels: Reflections on Britain and Abroad" by Nicholas Henderson. Weidenfeld and Nicholson, London 1987 ISBN 0297 790765.

the train travelling at normal line speed between London and the Tunnel. The additiona revenues that this would produce were considered to be very important to the financiability of the Project.

4. Approval, Construction and Development Period: 1985 to 1994.

The decision to construct the LGV Nord was taken by the French Government before the Parliamentary procedures in both countries were completed. The initial finance was thus able to be raised which enabled the construction of the Project to formally start on 1 November 1987.

Table 2 sets out the series of traffic forecasts that have been released by Eurotunnel in its public documents. These show a generally consistent picture for the magnitude of expected traffic. The major difference being;

- a recent reduction in the expected through rail passenger figures. I presume this is because of uncertainties in the future for rail transport.
- additional growth in truck freight traffic. I understand that the increase in expected volume is due to an increase in the expected market rather than any change in assumptions on market share.

Table 3 summarises the passenger traffic volume between United Kingdom and France, Belgium (including Luxembourg) and the Netherlands. This traffic is the prime market for the potential use of the Tunnel. Of course, some passengers travelling to other European Countries will also use the Tunnel services, but the expected market capture will be less for these trips. This table shows that there has been a substantial increase (some 155 per cent) in this cross-Channel traffic between 1974 and 1992. This growth, however, has occurred in three phases;

- rapid growth (6.8 per cent per annum) between 1974 to 1983
- feeble growth (1.2 per cent per annum) between 1983 and 1988
- rapid growth (7.4 per cent per annum) between 1988 and 1992

These three periods, just happened to be perverse for the forecasting procedures. The robust growth data was used for the initial forecasts, which were then tested by the financial community and others (eg Ferry operators), during a period of stagnation in the cross-Channel market. However, the recent growth has demonstrated that the market is there. The question still remains on whether the Eurotunnel services can win the relevant market share.

It is of interest to consider the initial estimates within the Bid with the actual 1992 cross-Channel volumes between UK and France, Belgium and the Netherlands.

1993:	Expected Tunnel Traffic	24.7 mppa without LGV Nord
	(forecast in 1985)	29.7 mppa with LGV Nord
1992:	Actual Traffic in Prime Market	40.6 mppa

This implies that Eurotunnel needs to achieve about two thirds of that market, if one assumes some created traffic. This is not unreasonable especially, if the Eurostar trains can divert the major part of the air traffic market.

5. Conclusions

The core traffic forecasts for Eurotunnel have been derived from a relatively simple consideration of likely market shares of a future overall traffic demand which is a "trend" forecast of the existing volumes. The future overall traffic volume is easy to establish, especially for the short term, as it is only an extension of the current situation. How this market then chooses to use the various competing cross-channel mode then becomes the key issue. This will depend on many factors, few of which can be accurately modelled as they depend upon the Board decisions of existing private sector companies, for example, Ferries and Airline.

A crucial factor will be a consideration of relative tariffs and perception of quality of service that is provided by the competing modes. In addition, however, the choice of mode of travel is often decided by other issues such as car availability, accessibility of transportation interchanges etc. The actual tariffs that can be achieved depend upon market pressures by other operators and which operator dominates the various niche sections of the market.

The consideration of these factors for the production of traffic volumes and related revenue estimates are considered by many to be an "art" rather than a science. However, decisions have to be produced. This situation is not unknown to Engineers who have to develop artefacts in an imprecise world and therefore it may be appropriate for them to be involved in using "Engineering Judgement" for the establishment of traffic volumes. This could well be the case when the traffic figures are needed in the subsequent design and development phases of the transport infrastructure and services. In that case the Engineer needs to be confident in being able to justify their views to Bankers, Lawyers, Politicians and the Media.

TABLE 1: FIXED LINK: TRAFFIC FORECASTS

	Anglo-French S.G.[1]		Banking Group: 2000[2] Low-High	Eurotunnel (submission)	
	1991	2000		1993	2003
Passenger (mppa) By Rail	7.7	9.2	6.2	10.9[3]	12.9
By Car	4.4	6.0	4.7 - 7.0	6.3	7.3
By Coach	3.2	4.6	4.0 - 5.9	4.4	5.5
Day Trips	(Included in Rail Figures)		1.1 - 1.8	3.1	3.4
Freight (m.gross tonnes) By Rail	3.1	3.8	3.8	7.2	11.4
By Shuttle	5.5	7.3	6.3 - 7.9	6.0	7.5

[1]Anglo-French Study Group. Double 7m Tunnel with Shuttle Trains Scenario B: neutral to fixed link. HMSO Cmnd 8561 1982.

[2]Banking Group Report - see note 4 in main text for reference.

[3]Plus an additional 5.0 and 7.9 mppa in 1993 and 2003 respectively if High Speed Line were to be constructed between Paris and the Tunnel.

TABLE 2: EUROTUNNEL: TRAFFIC FORECAST

Date of forecast	PASSENGER (mppa)						FREIGHT (m. gross tonnes pa)					
	RAIL			SHUTTLE			RAIL			SHUTTLE		
	"1993"	2003	2013	"1993"	2003	2013	"1993"	2003	2013	"1993"	2003	2013
1994	-	17.1	22.2	-	18.6	23.6	-	10.4	15.5	-	14.8	21.8
1992	-	24.9	30.2	-	19.1	24.3	-	11.7	17.4	-	14.7	21.9
1991	n/a	25	33.3	n/a	18.6	23.3	n/a	12.6	18.9	n/a	15.3	22.5
1990	14.0	24.7	28.9	14.6	19.9	25.0	7.2	12.2	18.1	7.2	14.6	19.9
1989	13.6	21.0	25.0	15.8	22.9	29.0	6.4	10.6	15.6	9.0	14.2	19.2
1988	15.4	19.8	22.4	15.3	21.5	27.4	7.4	11.4	16.4	8.1	12.2	16.2
1887*	16.5	21.4	26.1	13.2	18.1	20.5	7.3	10.6	14.6	7.5	10.5	13.3
1985/6+	15.9	20.8	-	13.8	16.2	-	7.2	11.4	-	6.0	7.5	-

* Equity 3 + Submission document

Source: The Channel Tunnel Project: A Digest. The Channel Tunnel Group, Oct. 1985 and subsequent Annual Reports issued by EUROTUNNEL Plc.

TABLE 3: GROWTH IN THE CROSS-CHANNEL PASSENGER TRAFFIC MARKET & BETWEEN UK AND FRANCE, BELGIUM & THE NETHERLANDS (mppa)

Year		1974	1975	1976	1977	1978	1979	1980	1981	1982
By Sea		10.7	12.9	13.7	15	16.3	17.6	19.7	21.4	22.4
By Air		5.2	5.2	5.6	5.7	5.9	5.9	5.8	5.7	5.8
Total		15.9	18.1	19.3	20.7	22.2	23.5	25.5	27.1	28.2
Year	1983	1984	185	1986	1987	1988	1989	1990	1991	1992
By Sea	22.8	22.2	22.3	22.9	22.3	21.4	25.1	26.2	27.4	28.8
By Air	5.9	6.5	7	7.1	8.1	9.1	10.2	11	10.5	11.8
Total	28.7	28.7	29.3	30	30.4	30.5	35.3	37.2	37.9	40.6

Source: Cross Channel Passenger and Freight Traffic. DoT. Transport Statistics Report, May 1994, and earlier reports.

Managing road traffic in the Kent Corridor

Martin Rogers BSc C Eng M.I.C.E, M.I.H.T
Highways Agency
Dorking
England

1. INTRODUCTION

The roads and cross channel connections, which link London with Paris, Lille and Brussels, make up a Corridor of strategic trade and leisure routes whose importance will increase with increasing European Integration; all the more so now the Channel Tunnel has come into operation. With this increasing demand we face the challenge of ensuring the maximum efficiency and safety of travel along the strategic approach roads to the cross-channel facilities.

A major part of the Department of Transport's commitment to ensuring that the national network will meet this challenge has been the improvement of the motorway and all purpose trunk road network in Kent. Since the passing of the Channel Tunnel Act in 1987 the M20 has been completed all the way to Folkestone (summer 1991), the A20 has been dualled between Folkestone and Dover (December 1993) and the oldest section of M20, between junctions 5 and 8 around Maidstone has been widened (November 1993).

Although the M2/A2 route will be replaced by the M20/A20 as the main road artery to the ports and the Channel Tunnel it will remain an important route serving East Kent and will offer an effective alternative route to the M20/A20. The existing dual 3-lane section between the London boundary and the M2 has already been improved by adding hard shoulders and there are schemes in the road programme to widen the existing dual 2-lane section of the M2 between junctions 1 and 4, to improve junction 2 of the M25 with the A2, and to dual the last single carriageway length on the A2 on the outskirts of Dover.

To cope with the additional traffic demands in Kent arising from the Channel Tunnel and our closer ties with Europe, Kent County Council are undertaking a major programme of new construction on their own roads. The Department is providing considerable support to this programme of schemes with Transport Supplementary Grant.

This all amounts to a considerable investment in the roads infrastructure in this part of the country. However, the Department, through the Highways Agency, also seeks to optimise travel convenience and the use of road space. Following a decision in 1988 by the then Minister for Roads and Traffic, that a Variable Message Sign (VMS) system would be installed on the M20 to cater for closures of the Channel Tunnel or the M20, the Department embarked on a programme of work to provide such a system. However, at an early stage in the project it became clear that the original concept of a localised VMS system in the vicinity of the Channel Tunnel should be extended to a strategic signing system throughout the Kent Corridor. The Highways Agency is now completing the installation and commissioning of the system. This paper describes the objectives of the system, how it will operate and the benefits there will be to road users.

2. THE ROAD NETWORK

The 'Kent Corridor' is made up of the M20/A20 route from Swanley (M25) to Dover, the M26 and the A2/M2/A2 route from Dartford (M25) to Dover, together with the cross links which can be used to switch traffic between them in the event of difficulty on one or the other. These cross links include the M25 between the M26 and Dartford, the A229 between Maidstone and Chatham, the A249 between Maidstone and Sittingbourne, the A260 between Folkestone and Barham, and the A20 between Folkestone and Dover (see Figure 1).

Whilst traffic growth in the UK has in general been similar to that experienced in other parts of Europe, transport studies in Kent have shown that vehicle growth on Kent roads has been much faster than the European average. The 30% average growth rate over ten years for road vehicles in Europe was experienced in Kent in six years (1986-92). For heavy goods vehicles the average 20% growth rate in Europe over ten years was achieved in seven years (1985-92).

Traffic flows on the M20 will increase significantly as a consequence of normal traffic growth, the growth in cross Channel traffic, the completion of the motorway and it's signing as the main artery to the ports and Channel Tunnel. For example, flows on the section west of Maidstone have increased from 65000 vehicles per 24 hour average day in 1991 to 80,000 vehicles now and can be expected to rise to well over 100,000 vehicles by the year 2000. Traffic flows on A2/M2, although initially relieved by the completion of the M20, will also climb to and beyond existing levels as we move towards and into the next century.

The availability of the cross-routes for transfer purposes shows the scope there is for variable message signs to optimise the use of the motorways while at the same time avoiding the severe junction congestion that could result from indiscriminate traffic responses to incidents or heavy motorway congestion. The high traffic volumes predicted on the motorways, means that queues and delays will develop rapidly in the event of any incident. The cost of these delays to business and the community could be considerable.

3. THE KENT VARIABLE MESSAGE SIGN SYSTEM

The Kent VMS system will allow the display by remote means of a variety of messages at set locations, permitting the quick and efficient diversion of traffic in the event of road incidents and/or congestion. The overall objective is to maximise the use of road space and derive the full benefits of the large investment made in the Kent road infrastructure. The objectives are to:-

(i) respond quickly to incidents or changes in traffic patterns on the main routes in the corridor;

(ii) minimise congestion and delays and their consequential costs to commerce and industry

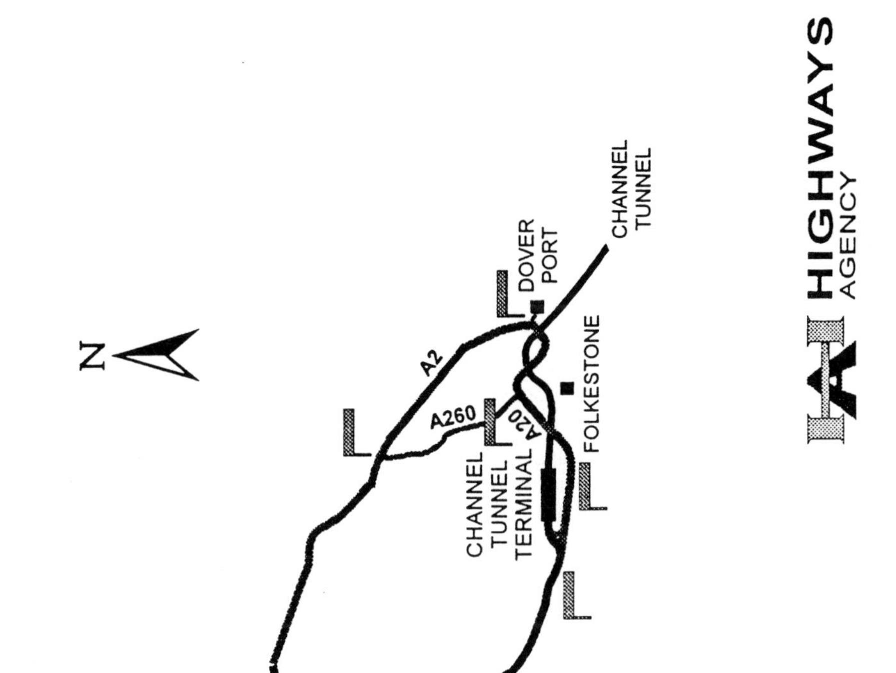

Fig. 1. Kent Corridor strategic traffic management locations

(iii) optimise road safety on a network which carries very heavy traffic volumes and a concentration of foreign drivers unfamiliar with our conditions; and

(iv) provide emergency signing and information in the event of problems occurring at the Channel Tunnel or Dover port.

The major components of the system are:-

(i) variable message signs capable of providing alternative route information. These take the form of a matrix display which can show an almost infinite number of messages or of a rotating plank or prism design giving a much more limited range of messages. All are located at key decision points on the network.

(ii) the cabling system which forms part of the National Motorway Communications network for the transmission of data to roadside equipment; and

(iii) a control centre, operated by the police, providing an overview of the network and with the ability to provide information to the driver and to initiate and monitor a route change.

Other systems being installed in the area and connected with the communications infrastructure will assist with monitoring and surveillance of traffic on the network. These include Closed Circuit Television (CCTV) and automatic incident detection systems when these become available.

4. PROJECT PROGRAMME

Implementation of the strategic signing system is being carried out in two Phases.

The installation of Phase 1 of the VMS system commenced in December 1993 and was completed in March 1994. (See Figure 2.)

This stage caters for:-

(i) delays or closure of the M20/A20 in the immediate vicinity of the Channel Tunnel and Dover Docks. It's aim is to advise drivers of alternative routes, in order to disperse traffic leaving the facilities and to advise of alternative local routes to reach Dover and the Channel Tunnel;

(ii) signs to be operated in the event of an emergency occurring at the Channel Tunnel or ports and allow vehicles, in particular heavy goods vehicles and coaches, to be directed to an emergency parking area at Ashford. Rotating prism type signs and symbols on static signs will direct traffic to the actual parking facilities;

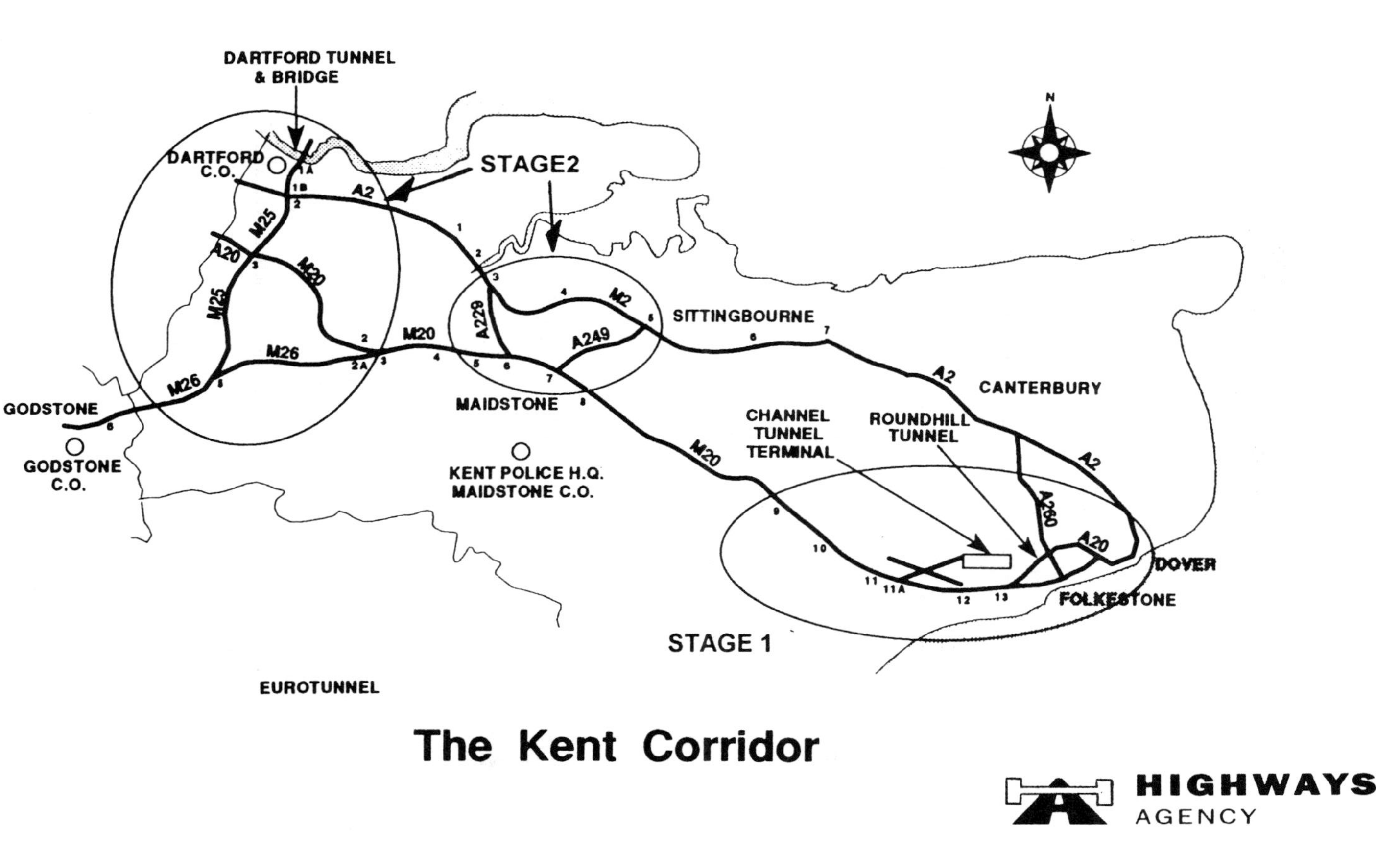

Fig. 2. Kent area strategic traffic management system

(iii) advice to drivers if heading for the Channel Tunnel or Dover Docks of closure or delays. The aim is to advise drivers of the duration of delays or the closures;

(iv) advise drivers of accidents, congestion, poor weather and other information to allow them to anticipate problems and improve road safety.

Installation of Phase 2 of the VMS commenced in August this year and extends the system back as far as the M25. This will be fully operational in early 1995. Phase 2 will provide complete coverage of the Kent Corridor and will cater for:-

(i) delays or closure anywhere on the Kent Corridor. The aim is to provide drivers with information on long range strategic diversions to re-route traffic on alternative routes, in either direction;

(ii) Channel Tunnel or Dover Docks closure or delays. Its aim is to advise drivers further afield of the duration of delays or closures;

(iii) advise of the situation at other channel crossing facilities in the event of a Channel Tunnel or Docks closure;

(iv) a wide range of information to drivers on road and weather conditions and other information well in advance of the incident point on the network.

5. OPERATION OF SYSTEM

The system will be controlled by the Kent police from their control centre in Maidstone (Figure 3). The VMS will be operated from a stand-alone controller until it is connected to the National Motorway Communications System (NMCS2) in mid 1995.

The Maidstone control centre is being equipped with the latest control systems with the capability to operate matrix signals, VMS of all types, Closed Circuit Television (CCTV) coverage from cameras located at key points on the network, and tunnel monitoring facilities for the Roundhill Tunnel on the A20 near Folkestone. The control room is also equipped with a dynamic display diagram capable of displaying general network overview maps and detailed status information on the signalling, VMS and CCTV systems.

The system will provide road users with information by displaying fixed text messages using a number of strategic plans providing pre-determined diversion routes (Figure 4). All choices will be selected by the operator at the Maidstone Control Office. It will not be possible to set two conflicting plans for separate incidents. Plans may be displayed on an operator's map to indicate what messages are displayed on each sign.

In the event of a incident on the Network, the operator will be able to input into the controller the location and nature of the problem and from this information, a selection of available strategic plans will be made available to him. The operator will then select the most appropriate plan to deal with the incident and signs will be set automatically throughout the Kent Corridor network. It will also be possible to display information on individual signs from a menu of previously approved messages.

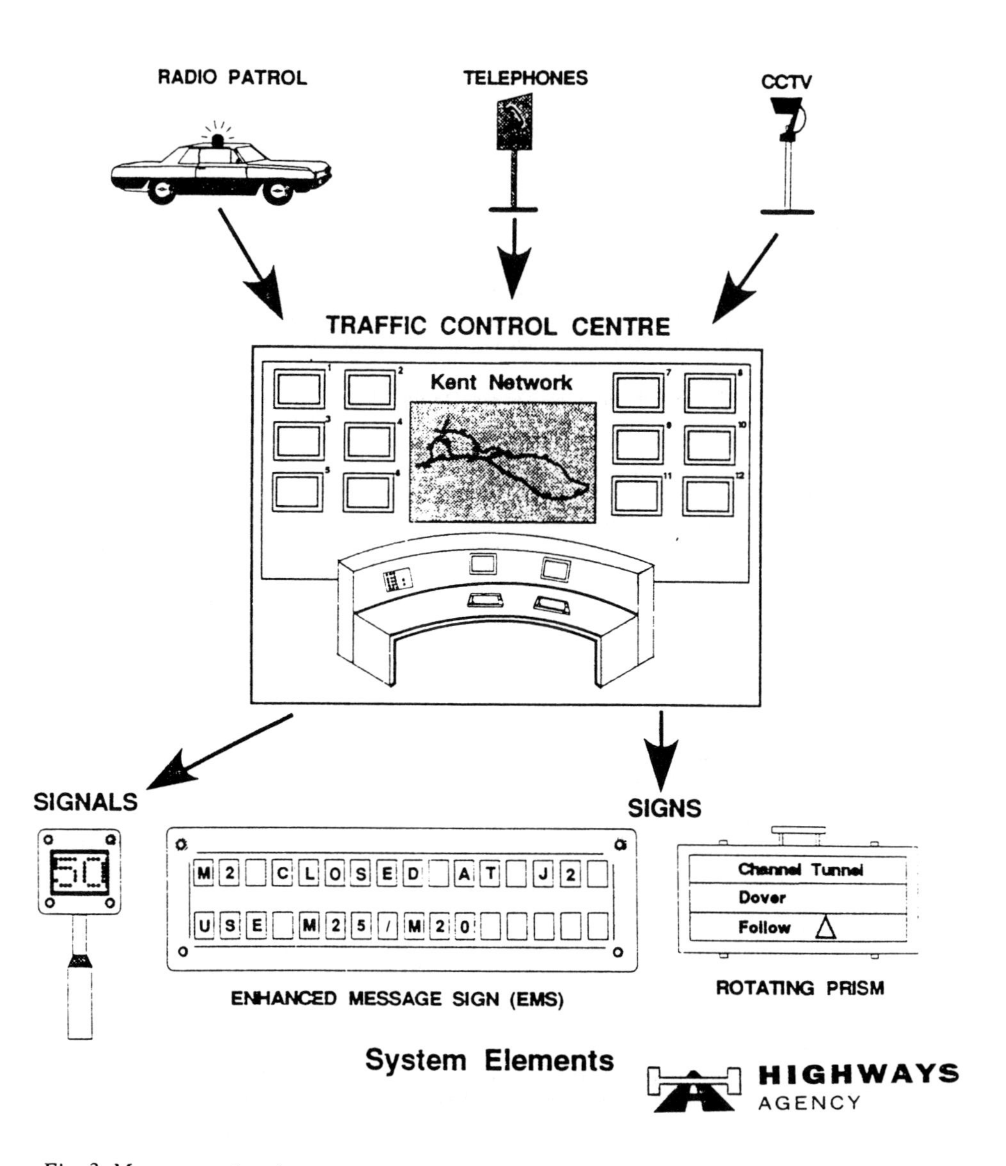

Fig. 3. Management system

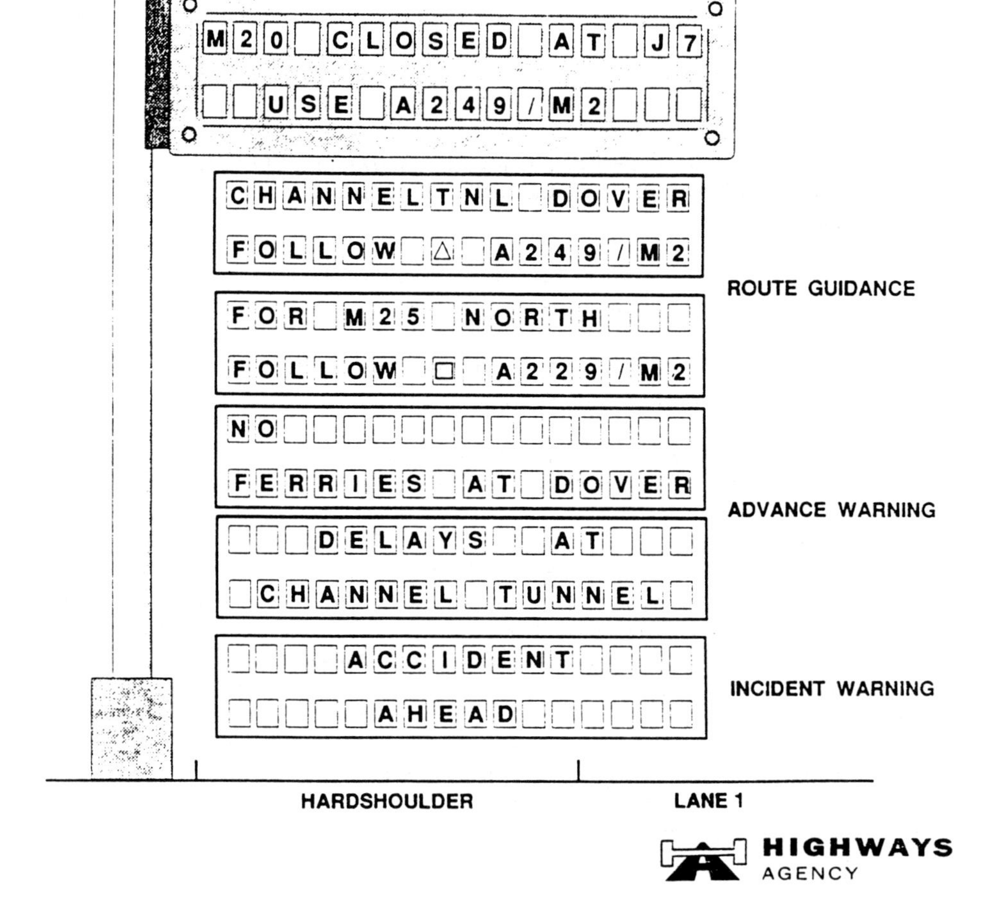

Fig. 4. Enhanced message sign 2 x 16 typical messages

6. DRIVER INFORMATION - A LONGER TERM VIEW

Maximising the safety and efficiency of travel along these routes is a major concern for the future and Advanced Transport Telematics (ATT) systems, of which variable message signs (VMS) forms an important part, will have a key role to play.

The Strategic Traffic Management System and VMS infrastructure in the Kent Corridor forms an important contribution towards the European Commission's DRIVE II programme. A consortium comprising infrastructure owners and operators, information providers, system manufacturers and transport and communication specialists from the UK, France and Belgium are working together to realise a project in the important Corridor connecting London to Paris. The Department of Transport, Eurotunnel, the AA, BBC and Ford's are major UK partners in this project.

The London-Paris Corridor project (see figure 5) is known as PLEIADES (Paris London Corridor Evaluation of Integrated ATT and DRIVE Experimental Systems). The project has three principle aims:

(i) to develop and demonstrate state of the art traffic monitoring and control facilities for use throughout the Corridor,

(ii) to develop and demonstrate Traffic Information Centres in England and France using real-time information on travel conditions in the Corridor,

(iii) to provide and evaluate a range of information services for drivers both before and during their journeys along the Corridor.

There are two main work areas: Integrated Inter Urban Traffic Management and Travel and Traffic Information. The first work area builds on the existing development plans of the infrastructure owners and operators in the Corridor. The Kent Corridor strategic management system with its VMS, communication links, CCTV and control centre forms the platform for the development in UK. A validated traffic model of the network in Kent has been prepared. This is being used to study the effects of a wide range of potential problems which may occur in the Corridor and help prepare appropriate signing plans to minimise disruption. The project will also evaluate the impact of the VMS and the effect of the strategic signing plans and develop mechanisms that ensure the system will keep pace with changing traffic patterns. (In France similar traffic modelling is being used in combination with short term forecasting tools with the aim of peak spreading on major routes to and from the coast at peak holiday times).

The second work area concentrates on improving facilities for gathering and handling data at Traffic Information Centres in England and France. An automatic link has been installed between the motorway Control Office in Maidstone and the AA Traffic Information Centre in Stanmore. This link will help ensure that relevant information is effectively and speedily passed between the two centres thereby helping to ensure that drivers receive consistent information throughout their journey. The information will be passed to drivers using the conventional radio broadcasts and the project will also demonstrate improved methods of transmitting traffic information using RDS-TMC, Paging and cellular telephones. These new dissemination methods will feed in-car vehicle navigation and information systems and these will also be demonstrated and evaluated on the Corridor. (The AA Traffic Information Centre is being linked to the French Regional Centre near Lille so that up to date information

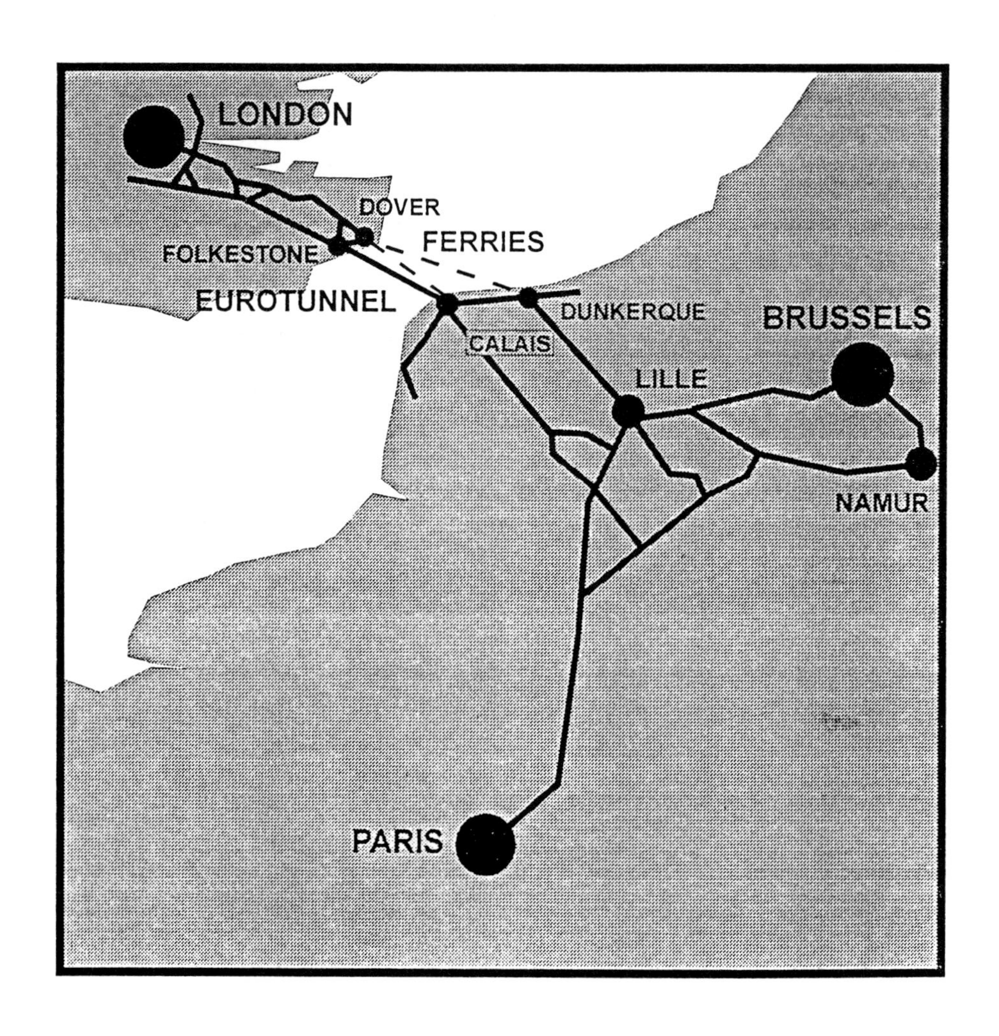

Fig. 5. The London to Paris Corridor

on the whole of the Corridor can be passed to drivers where appropriate).

The PLEIADES project commenced in early 1992 and field trials of the various systems have been underway this year with results of the evaluation coming forward soon.

7. CONCLUSION

The Kent Corridor strategic traffic management system is a major advance in providing information to make the best use of our roads and improve driver safety. It came into operation in a limited form when the Channel Tunnel opened and will come fully into use as cross-channel traffic expands through the South East. The systems and concepts deployed are flexible and therefore will be capable of developing to reflect the changing needs in the future. Strategic traffic management systems together with tactical control systems, such as the automatic incident detection and speed control systems now being installed on the M25, should ensure that we are able to effectively manage traffic on the major roads to the Kent coast for the foreseeable future. Such systems also form part of a wider vision for the future, where the adoption and implementation of Advanced Transport Telematics can be expected to significantly enhance the performance of transport systems and ease the driving task.

THE LOCAL CONNECTIONS

DR. ALASTAIR JEFFORD
Kent County Council

INTRODUCTION

The Channel Tunnel as a transport system will function because it forms part, albeit a vital part, of a much larger transport system in both the UK and mainland Europe. It will complement and enhance existing transport systems, for example, the rail networks of England and France are at last connected. It will, however, also compete with other transport; aircraft and the 'roll on roll off' (RoRo) ferries. As a transport system, therefore, it has brought about a number of changes to the built environment, the countryside and travel patterns. As far as the UK is concerned most of these changes will occur in Kent and this paper describes therefore the impact of this transport system on Kent and how Kent County Council in particular sought to influence its construction and use. Brief mention is also made about road connections in France.

Phases of Development

There have been four distinct phases in achieving the tunnel, all of which had significant local contexts.

1985-86	Choosing the Promoter
1986-87	Bill Promotion
1987-93	Construction
1994	Operation

CHOOSING THE PROMOTER 1985-86

Options for a fixed-link were put forward and considered in UK and France. Schemes involved rail and/or road transport, tunnel or bridge or a combination bridge/tunnel.

The County Council and district councils argued that the proposal that had least overall impact on Kent's environment should be selected. They considered that this should be a rail option. It was judged that the Channel Tunnel Group (Eurotunnel) proposal comprised compact sites compared to other alternatives. Rejection of other schemes which would have had more damaging implications for much of South East Kent was urged of Government. The County Council believed that the Channel Tunnel Group's proposals would provide the best chance of fostering economic opportunity in the County of any of the alternative schemes. It met the objective of assisting in relieving Kent's roads and attracting a greater use of rail rather than road traffic. The Government subsequently selected the Channel Tunnel Group's proposal.

BILL PROMOTION 1986-87

During 1986 and '87 the Channel Tunnel Bill was considered by Parliament. This involved Select Committees of both Houses hearing evidence from petitioners and holding some of their proceedings in Kent. The Channel Tunnel Act received Royal Assent on 24 July 1987. The County Council petitioned against the Bill on a number of important issues including:

- the effects of the Tunnel on the economy of the County, particularly East Kent;
- the funding and timing of the necessary infrastructure;
- the need for controls on the construction works and traffic;
- the lack of provision for the disposal of spoil.

Several additions and modifications to the Bill were negotiated as a consequence which were of considerable local importance.

KCC successfully opposed the provision of utilities or supporting development in the Ashford-Folkestone corridor, which in part is designated as an Area of Outstanding Natural Beauty (AONB) and Special Landscape Area, to minimise the landscape intrusion. See Figure 1. This resulted in some sites being dropped from the Bill, and rail sidings being provided at Dollands Moor adjacent to Cheriton terminal, the International Passnger Station (IPS) being located in central Ashford and the inland clearance depot for freight customs clearance being sited at Ashford. It also resulted in the electricity supply to the terminal being provided, at extra cost to Eurotunnel, by underground cable from Sellindge rather than by overhead pylons as originally proposed.

Construction Sites

Joint representations with Shepway District Council ensured protection for Frogholt, Newington and Peene by cut and cover tunnel over the rail loop at the western end of the site. An amendment to the terminal access road was negotiated to avoid these three villages being surrounded by roads and traffic. See Figure 2.

At Holywell, the tunnel works alignment was amended to avoid key scientific and archaeological interests following joint representations with Shepway District Council and English Nature. Cut and cover over the tunnel rail lines, with a viaduct over Holywell and a tunnel through Round Hill for the A20 extension to Dover were secured at the Bill stage after a Select Committee site visit. See Figure 2.

The provision of the Eurotunnel Exhibition Centre was justified partly to avoid traffic being attracted via inadequate lanes to the North Downs scarp to look down on the terminal construction site. The Centre is now well established as a major information and visitor centre.

A reduced number of construction related sites was negotiated from those originally in the Bill to avoid undue environmental impact.

Planning Clause

While the Channel Tunnel Act essentially granted outline planning permission for Eurotunnel's works, Schedule 3 of the Act provides significant control over the manner in which those works should be carried out eg. noise limitations, handling of bulk materials, restoration of construction sites, landscaping etc. A comprehensive set of controls were

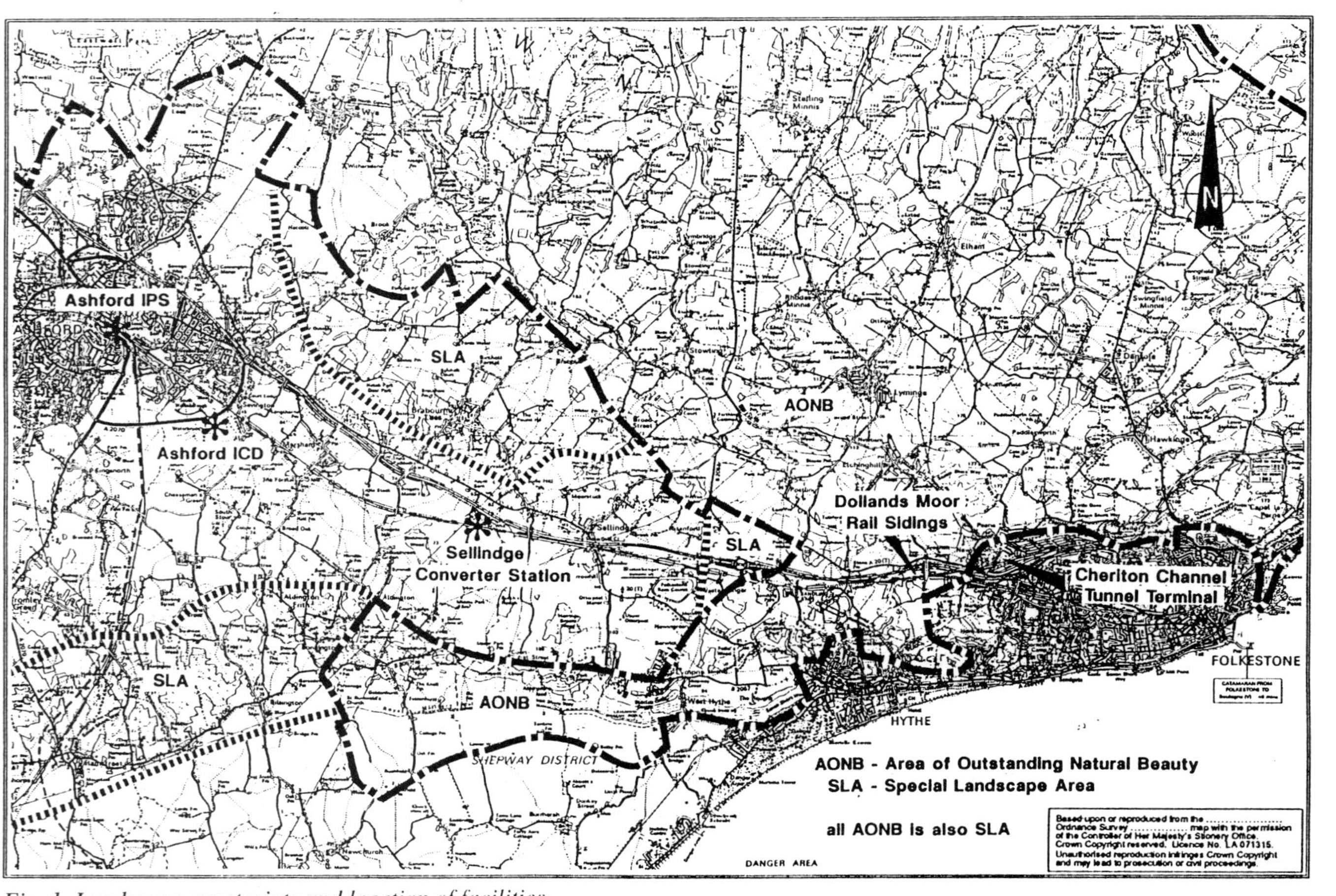

Fig. 1. Landscape constraints and location of facilities

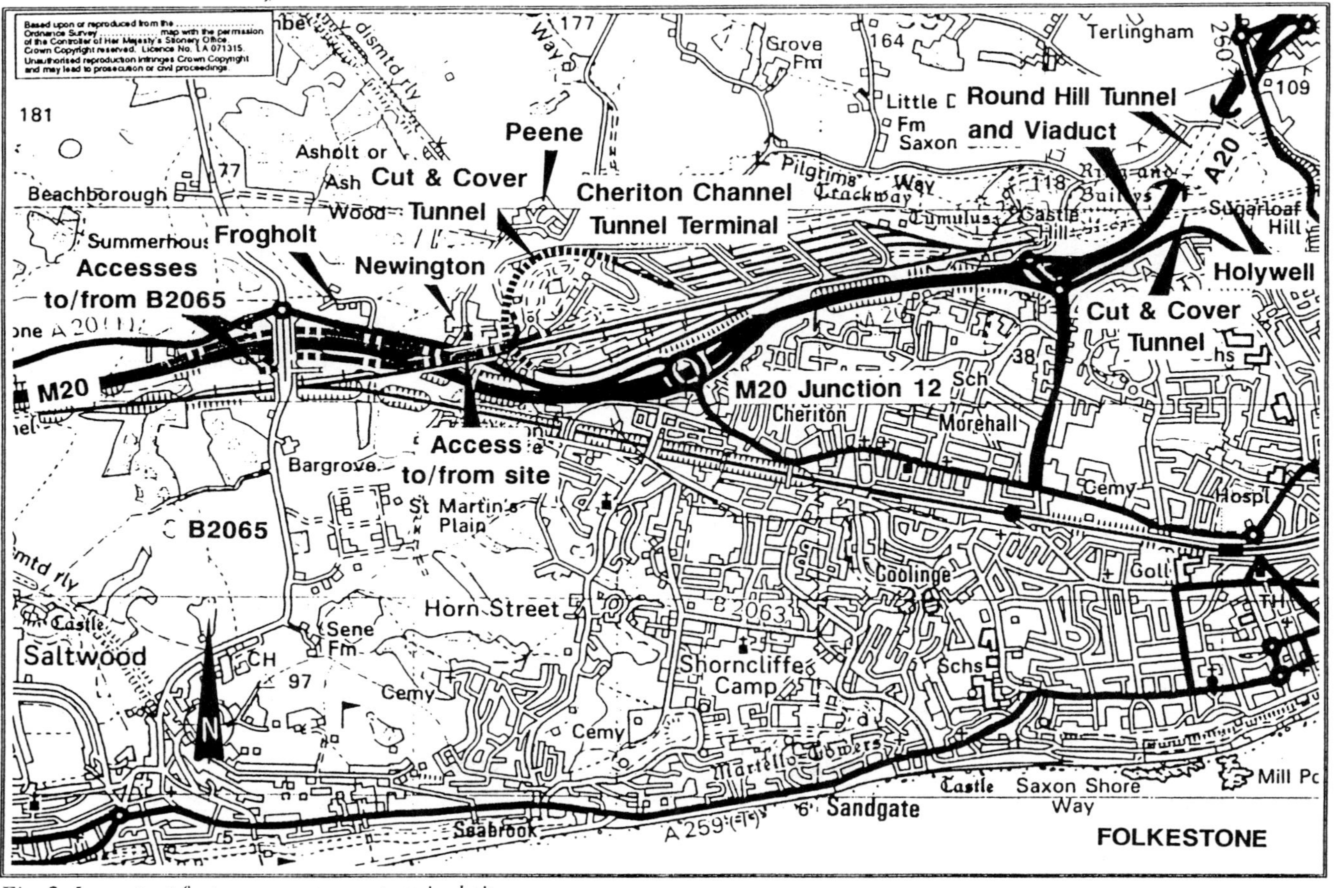

Fig. 2. Important features on or near terminal site

included in the Act as a result of negotiations during the Bill stage over the inclusion of a "Planning Clause". A related Memorandum of Agreement between the four local planning authorities and Eurotunnel was signed to add detailed understanding and interpretation of these planning provisions.

International Passenger Station

The location of a central Ashford station was proposed with Ashford Borough Council support. This location is at the hub of the East Kent rail network, including a line to East Sussex. It will enable Kent and East Sussex residents to access high speed international rail services linking London to Paris, Brussels and beyond. The station will also act as a focus for economic development in Ashford and East Kent. This partly depends on its accessibility and the Ashford South Orbital Road (part Eurotunnel/part KCC funded) and access arrangements into the station were therefore promoted in the Act; these also provided early access to the South East Ashford development area.

Access to East Kent

With the location of the shuttle terminal at Cheriton on the edge of Folkestone, the issue of access to much of East Kent was addressed at the Bill stage by negotiating the provision of a junction with the B2065 immediately at the terminal exit. With an exit slip road, incoming visitors would be encouraged to access East Kent, and not all would seek the quickest route to London and beyond via M20. See Figure 2. Beyond the terminal site access to East Kent generally was a crucial issue addressed by the County Council strategy discussed later.

The fixed link has fundamental implications for the operation of the ports and cross-Channel sea traffic, especially via Dover. The extension of the A20 from the end of the M20 to Dover was included in the Bill to enable a more level "playing field' for the ferries with Eurotunnel shuttles.

Channel Tunnel Joint Consultative Committee

This Committee was established in February 1986 by the Minister of State, David Mitchell, following the County Council representations to Government. Its terms of reference were to "maximise the economic benefits and minimise the environmental impact" of the Channel Tunnel in Kent. More recently it has been chaired by the Minister for Public Transport, Mr. Roger Freeman. It includes British Rail (European Passenger Services), Eurotunnel, all relevant Kent local authorities, Kent Association of Parish Councils and representatives of Government departments, DoE, DoT, DTI, and Employment.

The JCC has been a valuable clearing house for co-ordinating actions and settling differences. It has provided regular direct access to the responsible Minister and commissioned the Kent Impact Study (KIS). KIS (1) sought to identify ways in which Kent could maximise the benefits of the Channel Tunnel and minimise adverse employment and other economic effects. KIS, for example, endorsed the County Councils strategy for accommodating the Channel Tunnel related traffic.

(1) The Channel Tunnel Joint Consultative Committee: The Kent Impact Study, 1987, HMSO.

The last JCC meeting was held in July after the formal opening of the Tunnel. Through its seven years it has considered a variety of aspects. In the early years it dealt with topics such as required infrastructure, planning clause, spoil disposal, environmental impacts, lorry routing for construction, labour availability and compensation.

Latterly, the main topics have been emergency planning, progress reports on highway and rail infrastructure, progress on Channel Tunnel construction and Channel Tunnel complaints.

Complaints Commissioner

This is a unique appointment, established in 1986. It was agreed that the Commissioner's role would be that of a an independent arbiter to assist local residents at the construction stage. Costs would be shared by the promoters, including Eurotunnel and KCC. The Commissioner provides the public with a direct point of contact rather than attempting to chase Eurotunnel, TML or their contractors/sub-contractors if something has gone wrong in three District Council areas. The Commissioner has authority and rigour to seek to ensure effective action is taken eg. to label construction lorries for identification purposes and generally to provide public confidence in avoiding problems or putting right unnecessary adverse impacts associated with the construction project.

Road Access Strategy

Following Parliament's decision in January 1986 to proceed with the Channel Tunnel, the County Council reacted swiftly by drawing up a strategy to cater for Tunnel-related traffic. This was published in May 1986 (2). The strategy sought to improve selected routes, making them more attractive to through traffic and, at the same time, to discourage the use of unsuitable local roads through the Kent villages and countryside which, if overused, would cause environmental problems; for example, the route from Tunbridge Wells to Ashford via A262 and A28 was not identified for improvement. See Figure 3.

A quick response was required, as the lead time for major highway projects is effectively many years, and it was important that the infrastructure was in place when the Tunnel opened.

The strategy concluded that the Tunnel would increase the proportion of total cross-channel traffic passing through Kent in the future. It also emphasised that there would be a significant local impact by creating another focal point of movement to Cheriton in addition to the main focus of Dover for the ferries. Ashford would be a further focus, because of the International Passenger Station and the Inland Clearance Depot for customs.

The strategy identified improvements to the motorway and trunk road network, which is the responsibility of the Government, and to County roads. On the M20/A20 trunk road which was to be the main route to the Tunnel (and the port of Dover) from London and the M25, the strategy highlighted the need to improve the M20 Maidstone Bypass and the A20 between Folkestone and Dover.

(2) Kent County Council, Channel Tunnel: A Strategy for Traffic in Kent, May 1986.

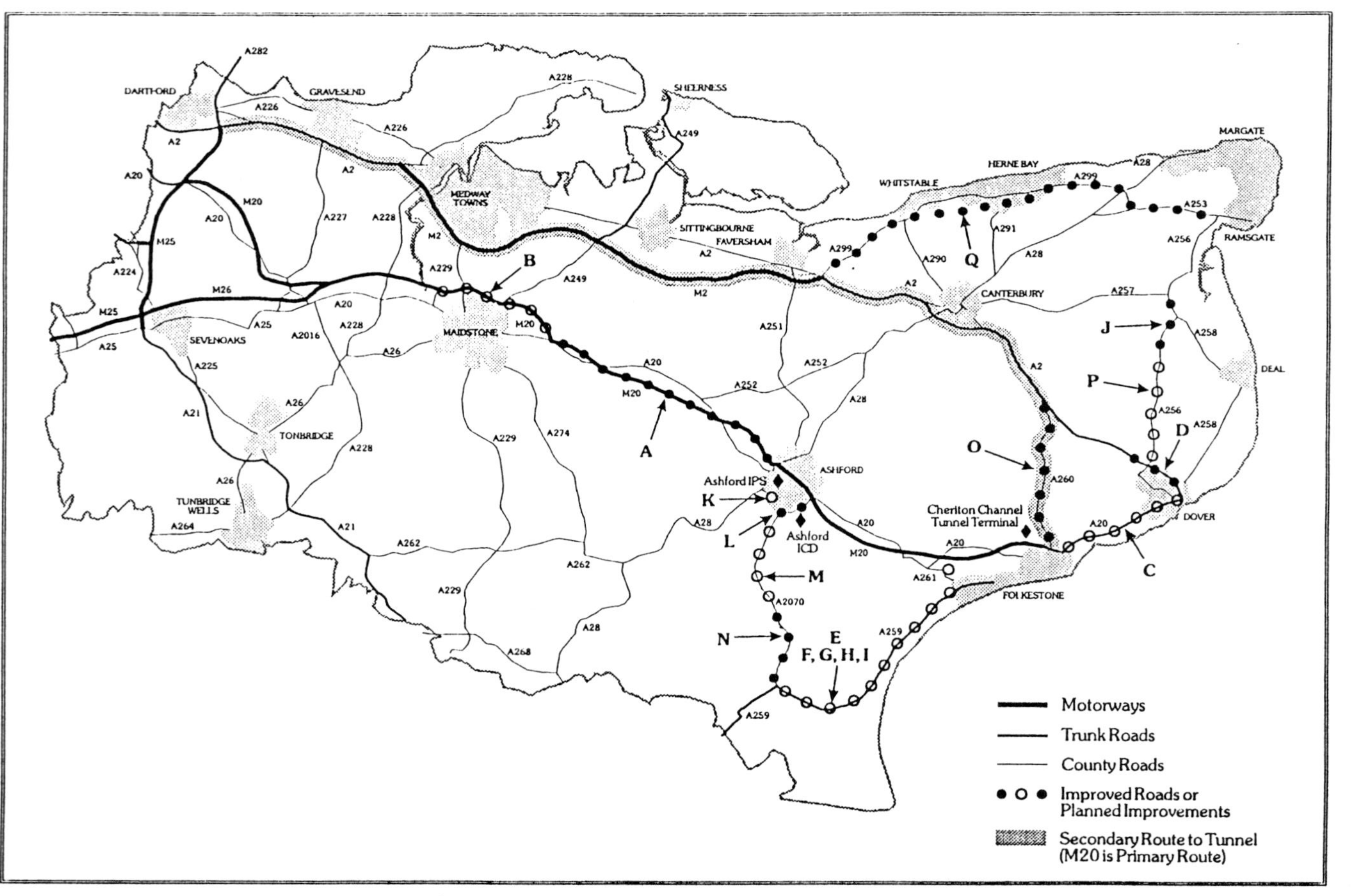

Fig. 3. Key road access routes and required improvements

The other important trunk road in the area is the A259 South Coast Road. The strategy identified the need for major improvements to this route and, primarily as a result, the Government announced its intention to provide bypasses to the holiday areas of New Romney, St. Mary's Bay and Dymchurch, and to link the A259 direct to the M20 junction.

On the County roads, the strategy identified the need for improved roads in Ashford to serve the International Passenger Station (IPS) and Inland Clearance Depot (ICD). It also identified that improvements were required to three other County roads, the A2070, A260 and A256. The Government subsequently accepted all these schemes for Transport Supplementary Grant (TSG).

The A2070 Brenzett to Ashford road would be an important link between the A259 South Coast Road and the Ashford IPS and ICD (now for Non-EU Countries only).

The existing route is sub-standard in width and alignment. Improvements to the route, including bypasses to the villages of Hamstreet and Kingsnorth, were proposed to overcome the existing problems.

The A260 Barham to Folkestone road would provide a link between the M2/A2 trunk road and the Channel Tunnel Terminal at Folkestone. The existing poor quality road passes through several villages and it was proposed to construct a new A260 route bypassing the environmentally sensitive areas.

The A256 Thanet to Dover road already carries heavy traffic created by the port operations at Ramsgate and Dover. Improvements were proposed, including bypasses to the villages of Eastry and Whitfield, to improve access to the Tunnel terminals from the Thanet/East Kent area for tourists, workers and servicing traffic.

In addition the KIS identified the importance of improving access to Thanet to help job creation. It stressed particularly the importance of improving the Thanet Way A299 from the M2 to Ramsgate. Subsequently, following a submission by the County Council, this improvement was accepted by Government for TSG.

The Kent Impact Study

The original Kent Impact Study, commissioned by the Channel Tunnel JCC, was published in 1987. It confirmed the importance of actions on both the road and rail networks to improve the accessibility of East Kent in order to help counteract job losses. Whilst the 1987 review was relatively optimistic in the longer term that between 9,000 and 13,000 jobs would be created in East Kent as a whole, this hid substantial reductions in jobs in the Dover area, in particular of up to just under 7,000 jobs lost. Even with the increase in jobs in the Folkestone area due to the Tunnel the direct effects of it would be up to 3,400 jobs lost. The study concluded that the indirect effects would eventually cause an overall net gain of jobs, but this assumed a substantial increase in manufacturing and wholesale/distribution employment. It also assumed that road and rail access would be improved to encourage this increase. KIS stressed the importance, therefore, of the County Council's road access strategy, the Thanet Way improvement and several other schemes to assist in generating jobs. It also stressed the importance of the International Passenger Station at Ashford and the need to construct a high speed rail link.

In 1991 the JCC commissioned a review of the 1987 KIS (3). This took into account the creation of the Single European Market (SEM) and updated information on the likely economic and employment effects of the Tunnel. It also took into account that development plans and especially infrastructure improvements were progressing better in Nord-Pas de Calais compared to Kent.

The review's main points were:-

- The adverse employment effects of the Tunnel in the short and medium term were expected to be larger that envisaged in 1987.

- Greater rationalisation in port and ferry industries was now more likely whilst anticipated new employment in Tunnel and rail operations would be less due mainly to scaled down operations of the ICD at Ashford.

- The overall direct detrimental employment impact was forecast to be almost twice as big as the 1987 KIS at some 5,500 jobs lost. The impact in East Kent, especially Dover would be severe.

- The beneficial secondary job creation effects of the Tunnel and related infrastructure would be less than the 1987 estimate; some 5,800 jobs compared to 13-14,000. This was because there were now advantages of locating Nord-Pas de Calais.

The review concluded, therefore, that there was even more importance now to complete transport infrastructure projects than there was in 1987 because the job consequences of the Tunnel would be less favourable even in the long-term.

The French Connection

Very soon after the French and British Governments announced the Tunnel's go-ahead in January 1986, the French Government adopted a special programme of infrastructure improvements to serve the Tunnel. At that time access from the coastal strip inland was poor and the connections between three important ports of Dunkirk, Calais and Boulogne were very inferior. The coastal linkages were considered very important because of access to the Tunnel and the economic well-being of the Region Nord, Pas de Calais (4). A coastal motorway was proposed - A16 Rocade Littorale - between Boulogne and the Belgian Border. (See Figure 4.) This was intended to improve local access along the Channel coast with the strategic objective of maximising the economic and social benefits of the Tunnel in areas of high unemployment. For this reason it was not to be tolled and would be financed by central and local government. Other roads were proposed as well; to the south east A26 via Rheims and Chalons-sur-Marne and to the south west A16 from Boulogne via Abbeville to Rouen and Paris. These were to be tolled.

(3) The Channel Tunnel Joint Consultative Committee: Kent Impact Study: 1991 Review, Kent County Council

(4) Christian Parent*, Highway Improvements for Cross Channel Traffic in Northern France, 1992,. Unpublished paper.
*Director, Pas de Calais, Direction Departmentale de l'Equipement

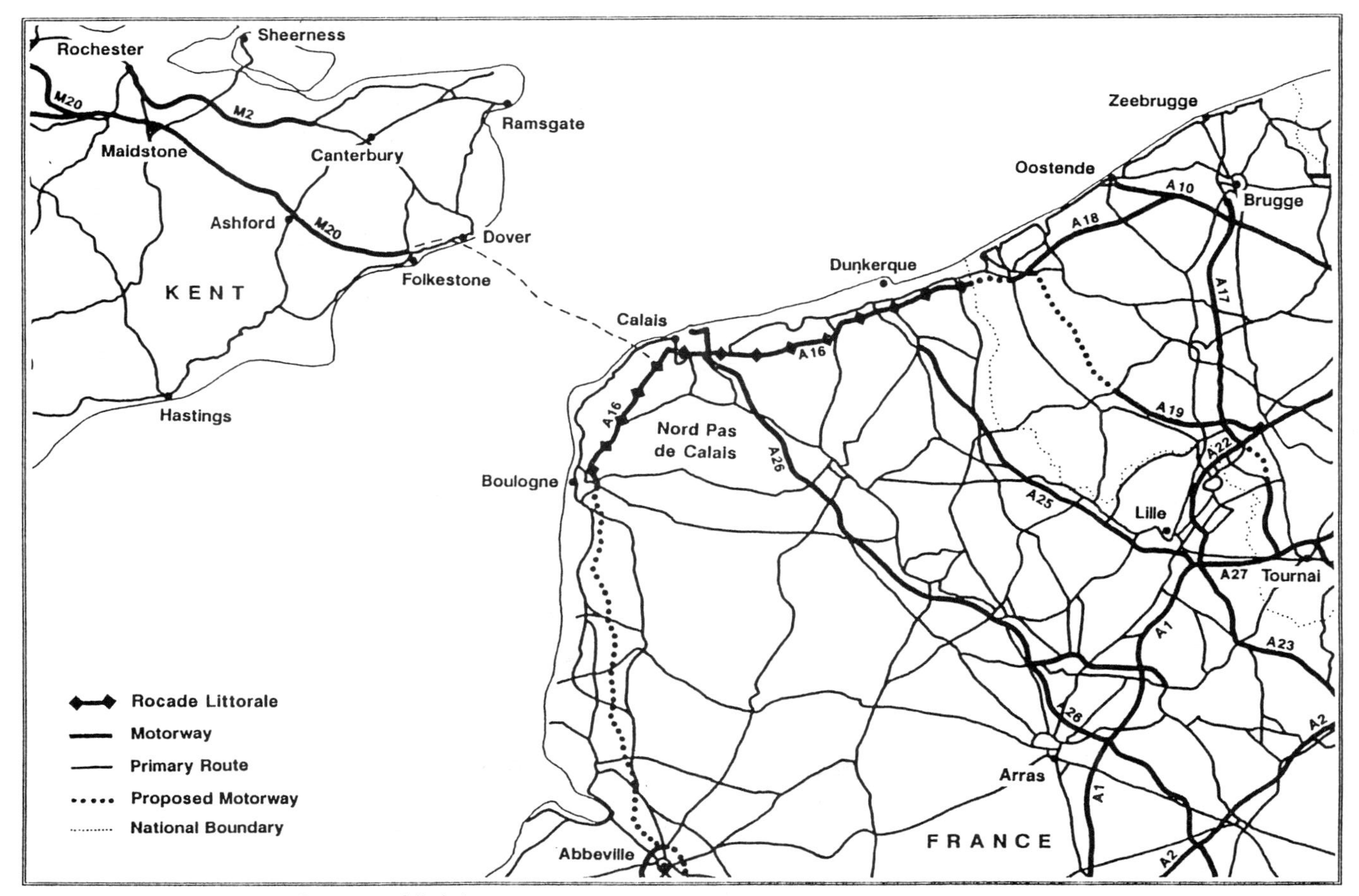

Fig. 4. Main roads in UK, France and Belgium

There is a direct parallel because of their local access and employment generation roles between the A16 Rocade Littorale in France and the County roads proposed in Kent, particularly the Thanet Way, A299.

CONSTRUCTION 1987-93

In addition to the construction of the Tunnel the period has seen a considerable amount of work improving UK (DoT and KCC) and French roads. Substantial works on the rail network are also being carried out but this will be covered elsewhere.

The Tunnel

As far as the Tunnel construction is concerned local considerations had a dramatic impact on a number of factors, particularly importing of bulk materials, spoil disposal and planning applications for tunnel related work.

As Minerals Planning Authority the County Council convinced the promoters that Kent itself did not have the resources to supply materials for constructing the Tunnel, and that bulk materials brought into Kent need to be controlled to minimise their impact on the environment and local communities. KCC negotiated, and subsequently operated, controls over the source, means of transport and routing of all bulk materials, resulting in major benefits to Kent. Some 80% of construction aggregates (over 10 million tonnes) came from outside the County, thereby avoiding severe depletion of Kent's resources. 90% of all bulk materials were moved by rail, sea or pipeline to the terminal or tunnel construction sites, thereby avoiding congestion on Kent roads. This included some 3 million tonnes of sea-dredged sand pumped to the terminal site to raise the levels, while all the concrete tunnel lining segments were manufactured in Kent (at Grain) and taken to the construction site by rail.

The arrangements for disposing of tunnel spoil were considered by a working party chaired by a KCC officer in recognition of the County's overview as Waste Disposal Planning Authority. After an exhaustive look at all alternatives including possible movement of spoil off site by rail or sea to restore derelict and despoiled land elsewhere in Kent, Shakespeare Cliff was agreed as the best available option. Provisions were made in the Act for KCC to control the deposit of 3.75 million tonnes to form a new platform at the foot of the cliff. No spoil was taken off site, avoiding attendant transport problems, while the platform provided the major tunnel construction site, and an opportunity for public after use. After-use of the platform has been negotiated with Eurotunnel and Dover District Council to provide part recreation and conservation uses with public access secured.

Progress on Roads

Progress on DoT schemes which improve access to both Dover and Folkestone is described in Table 1 and shown in Figure 3.

Table 1. DoT roads which improve access to Tunnel, Ports and East Kent.

Ref. Fig. 3.	Scheme	Status
A	**M20 Link - Maidstone to Ashford**	Opened to traffic in June 1992
B	**M20 Widening - Junctions 5 - 8**	Opened to traffic in November 1993
C	**A20 Trunk - Folkestone to Dover Improvement**	Completed December 1993
D	**A2 Trunk - Lydden - Dover**	DoT Priority 2
	A259 Trunk	
E	New Romney Bypass	DoT Priority 1
F	Dymchurch - M20 - Junction 11 Improvement	DoT Priority 2
G	St. Mary's Bay and Dymchurch Bypass	DoT Priority 2
H	Brookland Diversion	DoT Regional Programme
I	Walland Marsh	DoT Regional Programme

As regards County schemes, progress is described in Table 2 and the roads are shown in Figure 3.

Table 2. County Roads which improve access to the Tunnel, Ports and East Kent.

Ref. Fig. 3.	Scheme	Status	Cost
J	**A256 Eastry Bypass**	Opened to traffic June 1991	£3.7m
K	**A2042 Beaver Road Diversion (Ashford)**	Phase 1 completed June 1992 Phase 2 delayed because of IPS - completion February 1995	£24.3m
	A2070 Ashford to Brenzett		
L	Ashford Southern Orbital	Opened to traffic September 1992	£10.6m
M	South Ashford to Hamstreet Bypass	Opened to traffic June 1994.	£17.0m
N	Stockbridge to Brenzett	Completion expected September 1994	£5.4m
O	**A260 Hawkinge and Denton**	Awaiting Public Inquiry outcome likely completion July 1996	£18.1m
P	**A256 Eastry to Whitfield Bypass**	Awaiting Public Inquiry outcome. Completion date May 1997	£28.2m
Q	**A299 Thanet Way**	Part completed, middle section awaiting Public Inquiry outcome. Completion early 1997.	£137m

In Nord, Pas de Calais the 18 sections of the Rocade Littorale between the Belgian Border and Boulogne were completed between 1991 and 1993 at a cost of some £286m (1990 £ assuming FF/10, (4)). The A26 tolled motorway and the access into Calais port has also been comepleted.

Whilst considerable progress has been made by both the DoT and the County Council towards providing a high standard of road access to Dover, Folkestone and Ramsgate (A299), more needs to be done. The completion of the A16 in France is particularly impressive.

THE OPERATION OF THE TUNNEL 1994-

It is too early to measure the impact that the Tunnel will have on travel patterns. Four things are clear, however. Firstly, there have been a significant increase in cross channel movements in Kent in the last few years. For example, between 1990 and 1993 the number of cars passing through East Kent ports grew by 35%. There is little doubt that this market and also the freight and coach market will continue to grow past the turn of the century. The key issue is the balance of use between the tunnel, ferries and other seaborne modes.

Secondly, the improvement and completion of the M20/A20 route in Kent to Dover has switched traffic from the A2/M2 route to the M20 route.

Thirdly, the operation of through trains in the Tunnel, both passenger and freight, means that for domestic rail services in Kent not to suffer there is an imperative for a new dedicated line to the Tunnel as soon as possible.

Fourthly, Ferry operators have improved their "product" over the last four years so that checking in times have been reduced substantially, fares are lower and on-board facilities have been improved greatly. As a consequence there is far more confidence in the industry that they will be able to compete with the Tunnel.

CONCLUSIONS

The local impact of the Tunnel as a transport system is likely to be significant, not only because of increased cross-channel traffic through Kent but also because of job losses in the ferry industry, exacerbated by losses due to the SEM.

Nevertheless the physical impact of the Tunnel has been minimised both during construction and operational phases by careful discussion between the promoters, the County Council and District Councils.

Every opportunity has been taken to seek infrastructure improvements in East Kent to assist job creation and whilst many schemes have been implemented several still need promotion, not least the Channel Tunnel Rail Link in order to maximise employment and sustain the economy of East Kent.

The key "local" objectives remain. Firstly, to maximise rail use and minimise road use in accessing the Tunnel. Secondly, to ensure that two competing systems of crossing the Channel remain in being - the Tunnel and the Ferries.

CHANNEL TUNNEL - FIXED EQUIPMENT TERMINAL TRAFFIC FLOWS

D MEREDITH Master Mariner, F.I.H.T., M.N.I., M.C.I.T.
Eurotunnel - Folkestone, England

R NAPTHINE BSc., C.Eng., F.I.C.E., M.A.S.C.E
TML - Folkestone, England

EUROTUNNEL TERMINAL TRAFFIC FLOW

INTRODUCTION

The main purpose of the Channel Tunnel is to act as a conductor for the transportation system connecting the UK and French road systems and railway networks.

Conceptually, the Channel Tunnel is considered to be a rolling roadway as far as road traffic is concerned requiring a quick and efficient transfer facility to be provided at the terminals in each country.

While the principles are the same, the design of the traffic management facilities are different in the UK and French terminals. This paper describes the layout and procedures in the UK terminal.

FEATURES OF THE PROCESS.

The main essentials of the traffic management process are that they be:

Quick
Simple
Reliable

and that they should in consequence:

Provide the customer with a good experience
Project the company image
Encourage customers to use the system again.

Success with the first three objectives will lead to achievement of the latter three goals.

THE SHUTTLE SYSTEM

Before describing the road traffic handling system the following is a brief description of the shuttle characteristics.

Tourist Shuttles - Tourist shuttles consist of 2 rakes, each rake contains 12 carrier wagons with loading and unloading wagons at each end arranged with a single deck rake at the front, a double deck rake at the rear, and a locomotive at each end of the shuttle. Each wagon length will accommodate 1 coach or up to 5 cars, double decks will be limited to vehicles below 1.85m in height. Passengers will remain with their vehicles, motor cycles and riders are carried in the loading and unloading wagons.

HGV (TIR) Shuttles - Freight vehicles will be allocated one per wagon, drivers are required to leave their vehicles and will be transported down the platform by bus to a club car at the front of the shuttle, a maximum transit of 650 metres. Small lorries and vans will be carried 2 or 3 to the wagon and vehicles carrying hazardous goods, permitted in accordance with a restricted list, will be separately identified in the shuttle.

Special Requirements - In addition to those requirements, certain safety features are required to be observed such as: the placing of vehicles carrying disabled passengers at the front of a rake (on the lower deck in the case of double deck wagons), isolation of large coaches to one per wagon and the loading of medium and small coaches, so that maximum limits for passenger numbers are not exceeded.

A general requirement is the assurance that no vehicle obstructs the area adjacent to fire barrier doors.

TICKET TRANSACTIONS

Ticket purchases will be possible using cash, cheque, credit card or by the surrender of a prepaid ticket or the presentation of a post-payment account card.

FRONTIER CONTROL

The concession agreement allows for the principle of juxtapositioning frontier control formalities for both countries. This means that formalities for each country can be completed in the terminal of departure and passengers will then be free at the terminal of arrival to drive off directly without further formality.

LAYOUT

Many of the objectives are met by carefully thought out arrangements of layout, where route selection by the user is made easy.

The process in the UK starts on the three lane approach road where traffic is segregated into HGV, through tourist and tourists wishing to use amenities. In France HGV traffic has a dedicated approach road to the separate freight terminal.

By the time customers arrive at the tolls, vehicles will be in the lane leading to the toll booth best positioned for onward travel.

In the UK, HGV traffic is fed to the left, whilst tourists turning off into customer services are directed to the middle approach lanes, through tourists proceed via the right-hand lanes.

HGV traffic proceeds to the dedicated parking area on the HGV route which embodies a small customer services building. Alternatively the driver may elect to proceed directly to the frontier control booths.

Tourist traffic (coaches, caravans, trailers and cars) consists of two streams; one takes a direct route, the other turns off into the Amenity parking area for customers to use the services building for meals, purchase of duty free goods, toilets or information. Following this, the latter returns to the tourist route and rejoins the direct route traffic to the frontier controls.

The Concession agreement allows for the juxtaposition of UK and French frontier controls. These are separated by about 150 metres. Parking arrangements are provided for both coaches and cars in this area for the use of HM Customs & Eurotunnel security should an examination of a vehicle be necessary.

After the French frontier controls, vehicles are directed into one of two lanes, leading to a shuttle allocation. The initial 2 lane sort is to separate low vehicles (<1.85m), to be directed towards double deck wagons and high vehicles to single deck wagons.

Up to this point all decisions are made by the driver and consist of the choice of one out of two available routes at any stage. From here, drivers will be given clear instructions on where and when to proceed.

Following allocation, drivers will be directed to reservoir or holding lanes in the order of their final position in the shuttle. From the reservoirs, convoys of vehicles in shuttle order will be called forward by the operation of barriers and variable message signs on the route to loading platforms via overbridges 1 and 2 and associated ramps. They will then load into shuttle wagons via side entry doors or special loading wagons in the case of double deck tourist and freight shuttles. Upper decks of double deck wagons are accessed by fixed internal ramps in the loading and unloading wagons.

Vehicles proceed inside the shuttle to their parking position where passengers are free to remain in their vehicles or move around within the wagon.

The HGV route is similarly arranged with the exception of the vehicle allocation. In this case, one vehicle is allocated to each shuttle carrier wagon and marshalling is a simple queue arranged in shuttle order. Security inspection for freight vehicles consists of an X-Ray scan in the 'Euroscan' facility, a large purpose-built structure containing a vehicle conveyor and scanner. A percentage of freight vehicles will be selected for security inspection. The driver will position his vehicle on a conveyer wagon, after dismounting the wagon and lorry will be transferred into the building, the lorry will be scanned and will emerge from the other end where the driver will

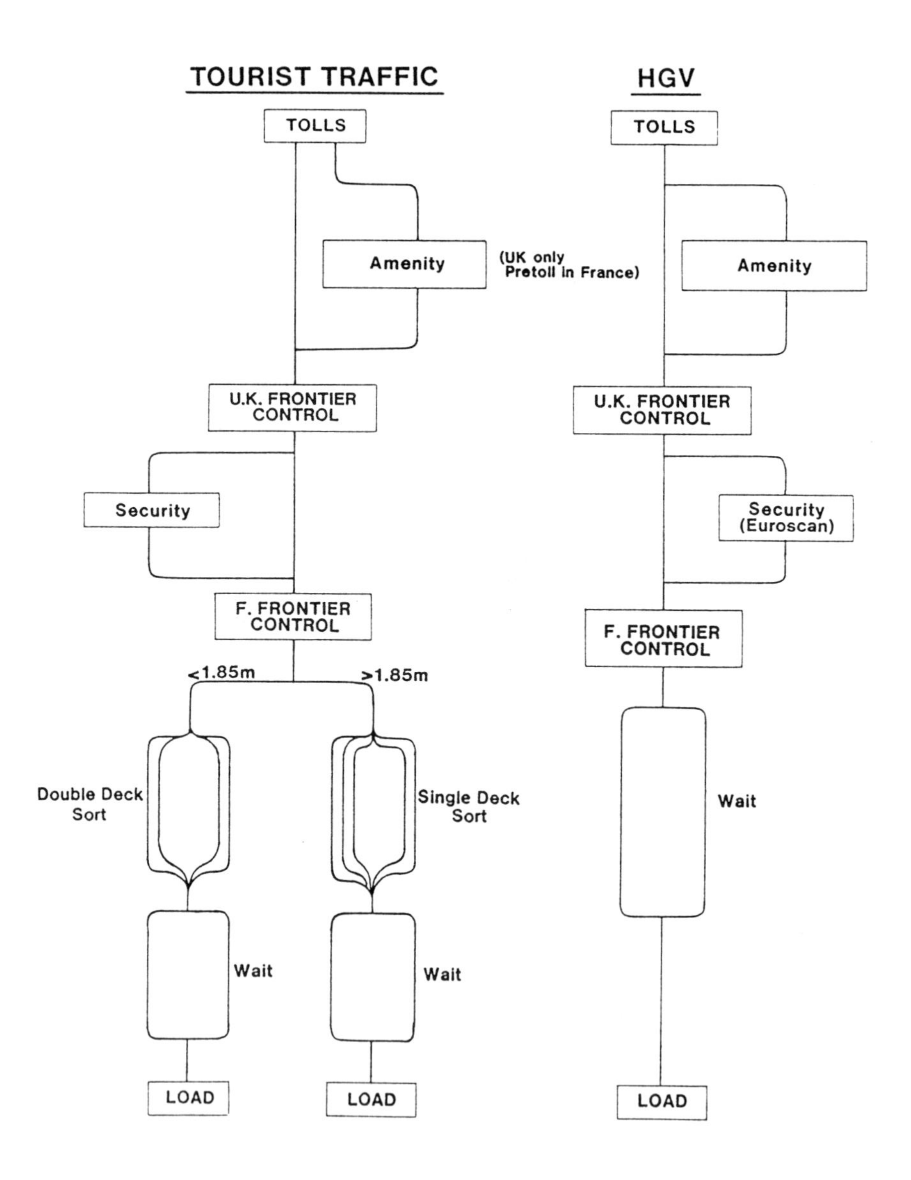
TOURIST TRAFFIC
TOLLS
Amenity
(UK only
Pretoll in France)
U.K. FRONTIER CONTROL
Security
F. FRONTIER CONTROL
≤1.85m
≥1.85m
Double Deck Sort
Single Deck Sort
Wait
Wait
LOAD
LOAD
HGV
TOLLS
Amenity
U.K. FRONTIER CONTROL
Security (Euroscan)
F. FRONTIER CONTROL
Wait
LOAD

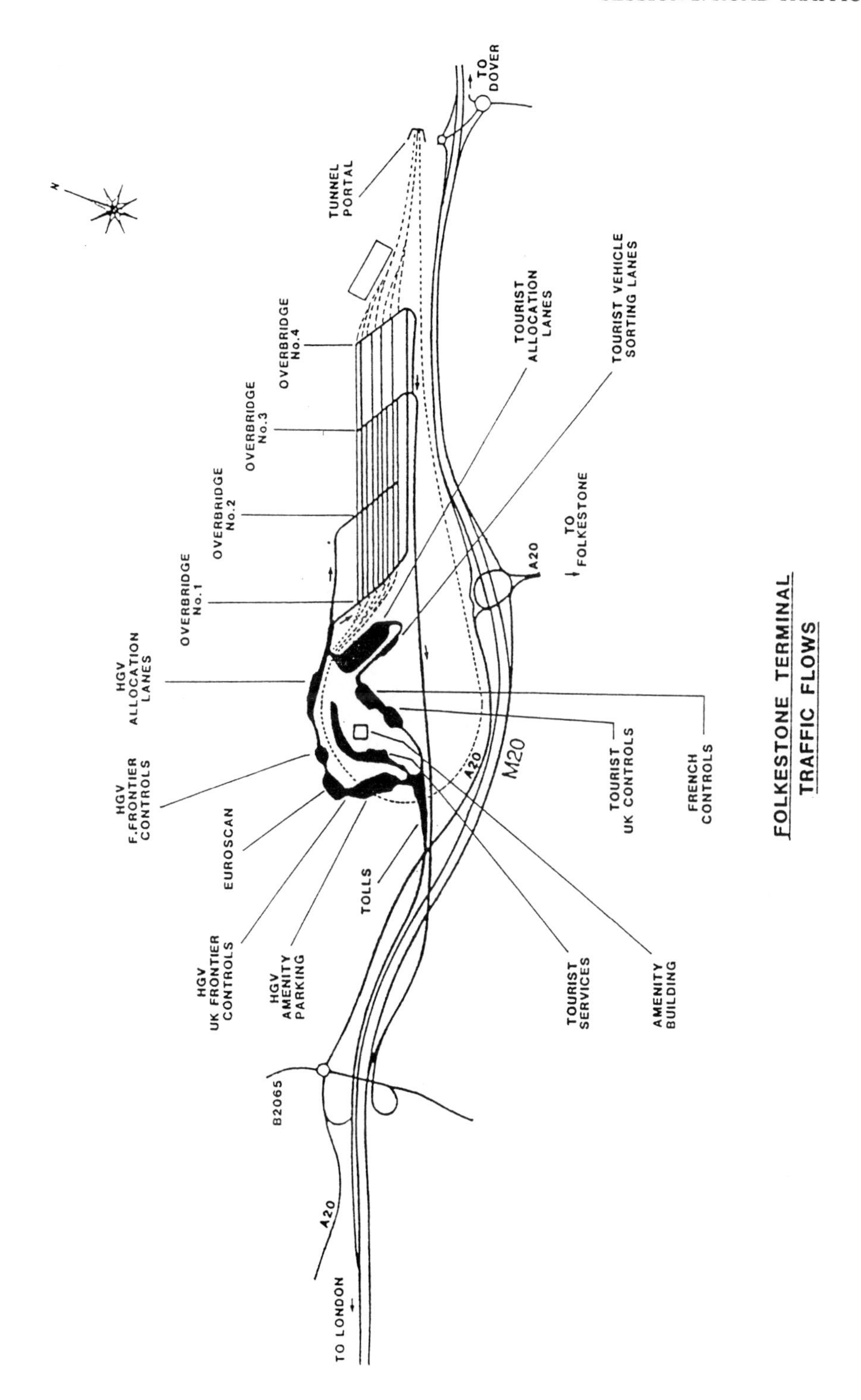

TO DOVER
TUNNEL PORTAL
OVERBRIDGE No.4
OVERBRIDGE No.3
OVERBRIDGE No.2
OVERBRIDGE No.1
TOURIST ALLOCATION LANES
TOURIST VEHICLE SORTING LANES
TO FOLKESTONE
A20
HGV ALLOCATION LANES
HGV F.FRONTIER CONTROLS
EUROSCAN
TOLLS
HGV UK FRONTIER CONTROLS
HGV AMENITY PARKING
TOURIST SERVICES
AMENITY BUILDING
TOURIST UK CONTROLS
FRENCH CONTROLS
A20
M20
B2065
A20
TO LONDON
FOLKESTONE TERMINAL
TRAFFIC FLOWS

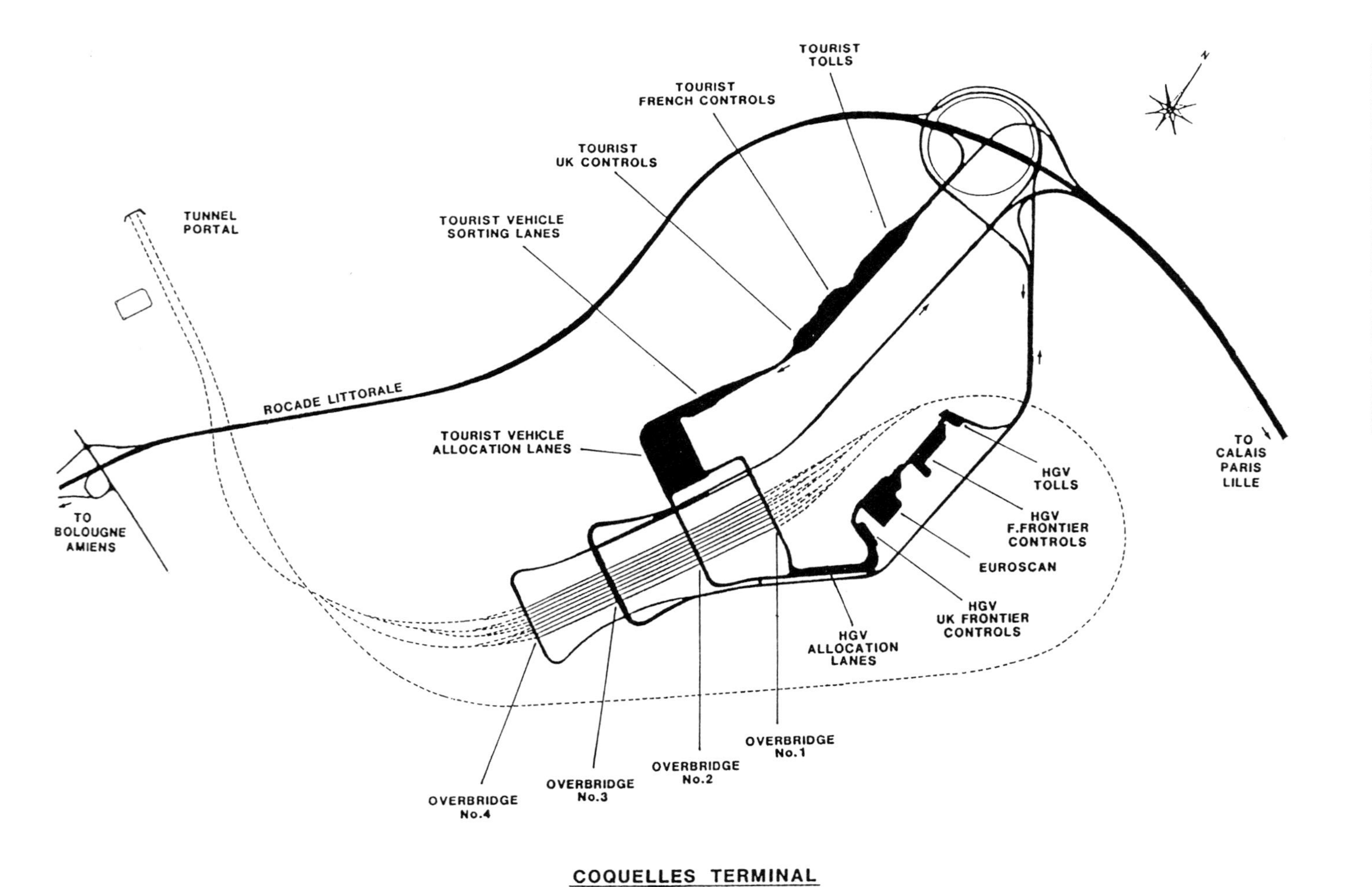

TOURIST TOLLS
TOURIST FRENCH CONTROLS
TOURIST UK CONTROLS
TUNNEL PORTAL
TOURIST VEHICLE SORTING LANES
ROCADE LITTORALE
TOURIST VEHICLE ALLOCATION LANES
TO BOLOUGNE AMIENS
TO CALAIS PARIS LILLE
HGV TOLLS
HGV F.FRONTIER CONTROLS
EUROSCAN
HGV UK FRONTIER CONTROLS
HGV ALLOCATION LANES
OVERBRIDGE No.1
OVERBRIDGE No.2
OVERBRIDGE No.3
OVERBRIDGE No.4

COQUELLES TERMINAL
TRAFFIC FLOWS

rejoin his vehicle. An analysis will be made of the x-ray picture which will either give the all clear and allow the driver to proceed or may require a series of further security checks.

Traffic arriving from France drives directly off the Shuttle using overbridges 3 & 4.

When the initial shuttle fleet is fully operational offering up to 4 tourist departures and 3 freight departures per hour, traffic will flow freely from motorway to shuttles with little or no waiting time. During periods of peak demand waiting times are bound to increase but these will be kept to a minimum by addition of shuttle capacity as necessary.

SYSTEM PERFORMANCE CRITERIA

The contract required the design to cater for the following traffic flow (vehicles per hour):

* By 2003

		2003	
		At Tourist Peak	***At Freight Peak***
a)	Cars, less than 1.85m high	665	220
b)	Cars, 1.85m high and over	120	40
c)	Coaches	74	25
d)	Lorries	55	130

based on forecasts of the 30th peak hour traffic level during each year.

* At ultimate capacity assuming 24 Shuttles/hour

		At Tourist Peak	***At Freight Peak***
a)	Cars, less than 1.85m high	2680	1200
b)	Cars, 1.85m high and over	450	400
c)	Coaches	225	100
d)	Lorries	100	370

The peak traffic levels above do not occur simultaneously in both directions. In the lesser direction, the traffic is assumed to occur at approximately 50% of the quoted peak figures.

In addition to the flows specified for the design, the layout was also tested at other traffic levels. Peak and shoulder traffic flows were tried on a 'what if' basis to confirm the sizing of the reservoirs and numbers of lanes. Shuttle timetables were examined to check overbridge lane occupancies.

To facilitate this a probabilistic mathematical model was developed for each terminal's traffic flows: times, queuing lengths and numbers of booths derived within the model were used in finalising layout, routes and reservoir sizes.

Examinations of expansion schemes for traffic build up beyond 2003 were conducted and incorporated into the present facility, e.g. provision for up to eight further tracks.

Further expansion to system capacity has been examined in outline only and the site capacity tested for typical layouts. It is assumed that major changes will be required in layout of tolls as a prime example but future parameters are difficult to quantify due to uncertainties in relation to the development of European Community frontier control formalities.

The sites have also been tested for vehicle storage requirements following a 3 hour delay and assuming unrestrained arrival of travellers.

SYSTEM CHARACTERISTICS (TOURIST ROUTE)

Outside World

Users approaching the terminals will be kept informed on current status by radio and by variable message signs controlled by the Police who will, in turn, be informed by Eurotunnel.

Access to Concession

Signs on the approach road will segregate traffic into 3 streams. Lanes are equipped with queue detectors (presence only).

Detectors counting traffic are installed at the Tolls and information is fed to the Terminal Traffic Control Centre to advise on traffic volume.

Tolls

Each lane can deal with all types of traffic and arriving vehicles may be directed by variable message signs at the tolls, displaying booth status.

Two lanes will be equipped to accept authorised vehicles equipped with dynamic tags, allowing immediate access which will be invoiced through a customer account at a later date, whilst six other lanes can be configured to accept prepaid tickets automatically. In addition all lanes can be operated manually as required.

Height acceptance or rejection is checked and is entered (Double deck shuttles are limited to <1.85m and HGV or single deck shuttles to <4.20m).

After payment or verification of pre-paid ticket a transport ticket is issued, the barrier raised and a green light displayed.

On leaving the booth a height check and axle counter verify the vehicle classification entered at the toll. An alarm is raised to the Supervisor in the case of a discrepancy. From this point on, fixed signs will indicate lanes associated with height limitations i.e. <1.85m.

Data from toll position are routed by the local toll computer to the Traffic Control Centre computer as are vehicle count and queue detector. Additionally the current state can be reported by telephone or radio and verified visually by CCTV.

Reject vehicles will be led out of the system using designated routes.

Amenity Area

Parking facilities are provided adjacent to the Passenger Terminal Building. These are divided into areas for cars, vehicles with trailers, coaches and motorcycles.

Counters on the access and exit roads will indicate its state of occupancy.

Security and Frontier Control

The design principle for the frontier control zone for both tourist and freight vehicles is the same on both terminals. The zones cover an area approximately 150 metres in length and comprise facilities for UK authorities (HM Customs, HM Immigration and Police Special Branch) and the French authorities (Douane and Police de l'Air et des Frontiers). The Eurotunnel security search area is located between the two national authorities control points. In the UK security inspections are conducted by Eurotunnel staff, in France inspections are conducted by the French authorities (Douane).

Traffic operates in free flow in these areas except when stopped or diverted for frontier control purposes and/or a security check.

The Channel Tunnel crosses an internal EC border and consequently frontier control checks on both tourist and freight traffic are "light weight" following the introduction of the Single Market on 1st January 1993. There has been no effective outward (departure) control from the UK into the rest of the EC since 1st February 1994.

Vehicles carrying liquefied propane gas (LPG) will be selected for a safety check when passing the Eurotunnel security control point. Gas bottles will be inspected to check that valves are turned off..

Allocation and Pre-ordering

Having left the Frontier Controls, vehicles are directed to one of two lanes: one for vehicles <1.85m and the other for those >1.85m. Motor cycles are <1.85m.

A second check on height will detect any high vehicles in the wrong lane and a flashing light will request drivers to change lane. An attendant is present at this point to deal with problems.

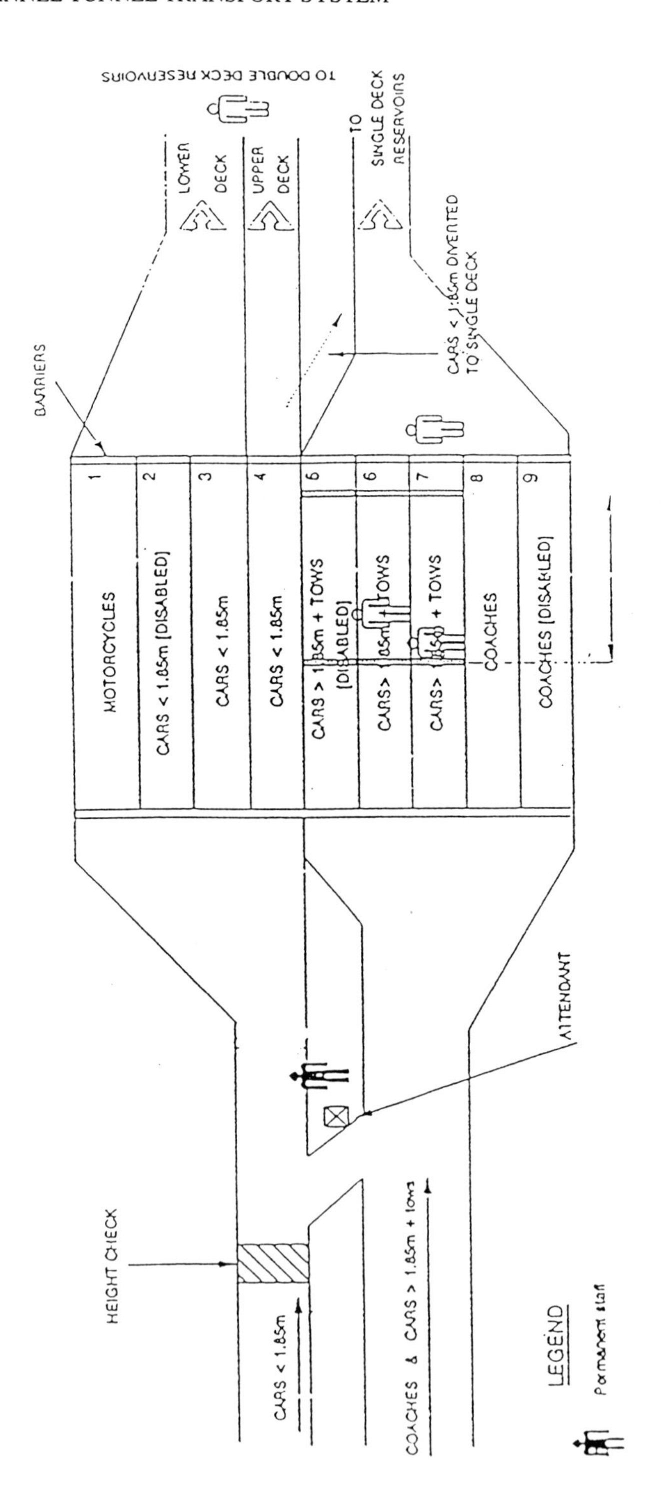
TO DOUBLE DECK RESERVOIRS
LOWER DECK
UPPER DECK
TO SINGLE DECK RESERVOIRS
CARS < 1.85m DIVERTED TO SINGLE DECK
BARRIERS
1 MOTORCYCLES
2 CARS < 1.85m [DISABLED]
3 CARS < 1.85m
4 CARS < 1.85m
5 CARS > 1.85m + TOWS [DISABLED]
6 CARS > 1.85m + TOWS
7 CARS > 1.85m + TOWS
8 COACHES
9 COACHES [DISABLED]
ALLOCATION
ATTENDANT
HEIGHT CHECK
CARS < 1.85m
COACHES & CARS > 1.85m + tows
LEGEND
Permanent staff

Pre-ordering will segregate
* motor cycles
* vehicles below 1.85m in height
* vehicles below 1.85m in height carrying disabled people
* coaches
* coaches carrying disabled people
* vehicles over 1.85m in height with trailers and disabled people
* vehicles over 1.85m in height with trailers

Each lane will be fitted with a vehicle detector, axle counter and barrier with associated red/green light.

Marshalling Area and Transit to Loading Point

The marshalling area is divided into two zones i.e. double-deck and single-deck, each zone is divided into dedicated reservoirs for deck lengths each with two lanes. Vehicles remain in the same order as they were positioned in the ordering lane. Loading lanes are opened in sequence and released in the same sequence.

Two shuttles can be loading at the same time and care is taken to avoid crossing traffic flows. Lane exit is controlled by barriers and lights allowing controlled release of vehicles for loading, platform numbers are displayed at this point. The lane to be followed to the loading ramp is indicated by variable message signs along the route. In general, loading of single deck rakes is via overbridge No. 2. Rear rakes are configured as double deck, loading from overbridge No.1.

If the shuttle is not ready for loading the first vehicle will be stopped to wait at the foot of the ramp.

Loading

A member of staff will be stationed at each loading door. He/she will be in radio contact with the train crew stationed at various positions down the shuttle. Vehicles will be directed into the shuttle and will be marshalled into position by the train crew walking back through the rake until the last vehicle has been parked. Once in position the train crew and the internal information system (dot matrix signs, public address system, notices and the internal shuttle radio) will keep the passengers informed of all safety regulations and current points of interest.

HGV VEHICLES

Heavy goods vehicles will follow a similar flow route the only differences being:

* Examination by security may take the form of automatic scanning at the Euroscan facility
  and
* No ordering is required, each lorry being dedicated to one wagon.

UNLOADING AND EXITING

Train crew will control unloading and direct vehicles to exit ramps on overbridges 3 and 4 where they will be directed by lanes to the egress road.

Fixed signs will indicate EXIT: local and distant destinations will be signed on the 2km long egress road leading to the boundary of the site, where it will lead to the M20 and local road connections.

SIGN PATHS

It was decided to use the signing system as a means of projecting Eurotunnel's corporate image and this, together with an overall design strategy for the terminals and Eurotunnel uniforms all form part of the development of a Corporate Identity.

There are basically three types of sign:

a) National road signs with faces set by statute.
b) Information signs
   - Directing Traffic flow
   - Providing Customer information
c) Pedestrian signs - giving local access information

The latter two categories have been designed using Eurotunnel's corporate colour system, but those in the first category have legal significance and could not be modified.

THE CONTROL SYSTEM UTILISED

General Description

The control facility installed to direct, marshal and designate freight and tourist vehicles to shuttles leaving every 3 minutes (ultimately 2 minutes) has a single source. This is a master computer constantly feeding and in turn being fed data by a network of subsystems. The master computer controls an automatic operation based on a mathematical queuing algorithm which has in-built variable factor programming which allows for supervisory decision making agreement.

The division of the five discreet sub-system responsibilities through the progression from tolls to disembarkation is:

a) Traffic Control Supervisor Computer - Overall supervision of Terminal Traffic Management (TTM).
b) Supervisory work stations - Supervisors/machine interface to TCSC.
c) Marshal Consoles-Control of local equipment and selection of equipment in area.
d) Security and Frontier Control (SFC) consoles - Control of equipment in area.
e) Data base Preparation - Provision of data for update to control and organise on a continuous basis.

The Traffic Control Supervisor Computer (TCSC)
The TCSC provides overall control, coordination and management of its sub-system whilst interfacing with external systems such as Road Traffic Management (RTM), Tolls in UK and France and the National Motorways Control centres.

It consists of a "secure" system of a pair of Digital VAX/VMS 4000 computers, one live and the other in standby mode with duplicated communication links, receiving daily shuttle schedules from which deck loading allocations, loading/unloading platform details are initiated and required resources identified.

Five functional areas of input on which the decision process is reliant are embodied: tolls, security and frontier controls, embarkation, field equipment and the monitor/controls of traffic supervisory functions.

The supervisory Workstation links provide the man/machine interface control and normal operation is a mix of automated supervisory operations which in general require confirmation by the responsible personnel.

Abnormal or Emergency conditions rely on manual action from TCSC prompts.

The Supervisory Workstations
These consist of Digital VAX 3100 computers with Windows displays of status for field equipment, alarms, allocation and embarkation.

The embarkation supervisor takes responsibility for confirming reservoir assignment to shuttles, allocation, loading and unloading, whilst the traffic supervisor monitors traffic flows, queues and controls abnormal or emergency situations and any necessary freeing of routes.

Both supervisors have the facility to overide the TCSC and take control manually in the event of crippled operation due to failures of equipment, communication or vehicle breakdown. However, the TCSC still retains the right to check the validity of the route and in cases of conflict, prioritise.

Key Safety Criteria are:

1) Vehicles are directed such that driver delay is minimised,
2) Traffic columns are prevented from crossing each other and
3) Access for emergency vehicles is maintained at all times.

Security and Frontier Controls Consoles
These allow local control of field equipment in the area and provide access to National Security systems terminals for the Security Authorities use. There is also an interface with the TCSC for data on lane status.

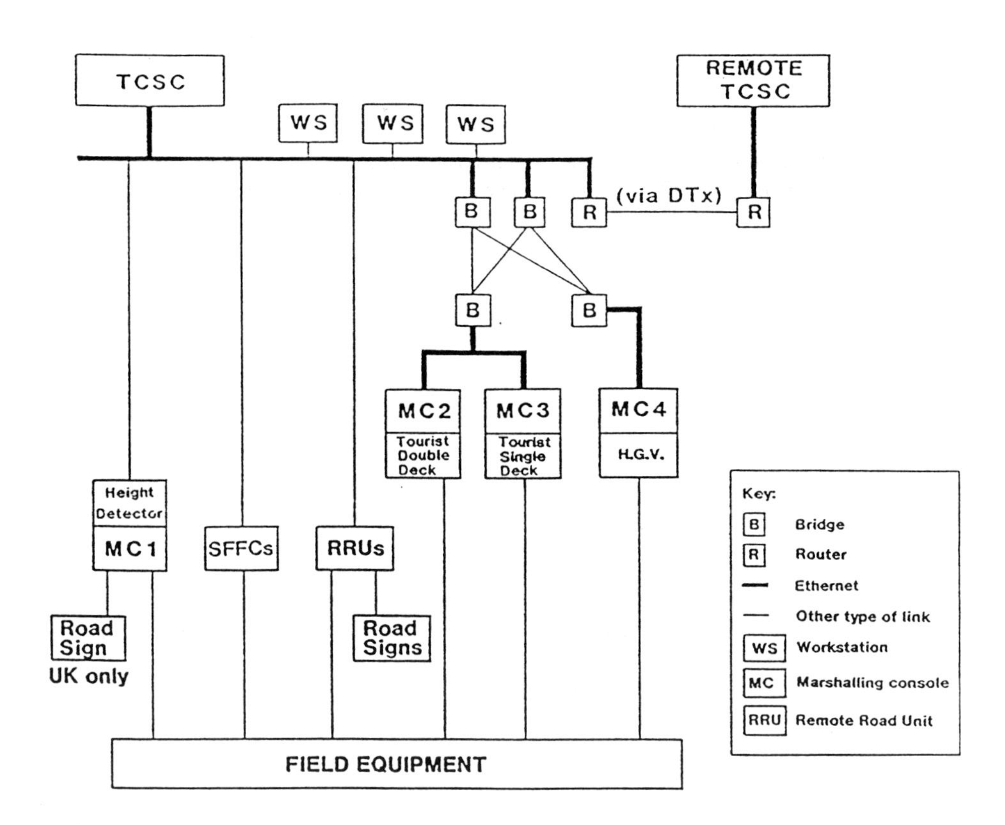

Communications links within the Traffic subsystem

The Marshalling Allocation Consoles
Satellites of the TCSC are located in the field at the freight, single deck, double deck allocation position and in addition there is a height detector location at the entry to the double deck lane.

The TCSC calculates in advance what allocations are required and when they should be performed using the information on shuttle schedules. From the data contained of the geography of the terminal routes, the routing from the marshalling area to the reservoirs and onward to the platform is planned and the required field equipment is set up.

Messages to commence or abort allocation are communicated to the consoles from the TCSC by serial links. Data models of the constituent deck loads are built up and this data is displayed at the consoles so that vehicles can be released in the requisite numbers from the marshalling lanes and the information reported back to the "load model". Vehicle identification is by make and registration number.

These consoles can, if necessary, be run manually independently of the TCSC should there be a physical link failure. In addition the associated field equipment is monitored automatically and in the event of a failure the affected lane will be closed down and TCSC informed.

Normal operation will be in unmanned mode and situations such as vehicle, or equipment breakdown and emergencies or maintenance can be dealt with in this mode.

Data Exchange With Other Systems
The exchange of data between other systems is necessary for the Traffic system decision making process to be effective. The main ones are:

1. Rail Traffic Management - the automatic provision and receipt of information on shuttle schedule and 'actuals',
2. The Tolls - the provision of toll lane traffic flow reports, equipment status and the receipt of requests lane clearance, and
3. The National Motorway Control Centres UK and France - the exchange of information on traffic flow to and from access roads and terminal status.

CONCLUSION
The Eurotunnel Road Traffic Management system is unique and has been designed and produced following close liaison between Eurotunnel, Eurotunnel's main contractor, TML and TML's Sub-contractor, the Unitraffic consortium consisting of Logica (with Siemans-Plessey), SEMA and Elsydel. The system is unique insofar as it must present traffic to the shuttles safely, in a highly ordered sequence in very high volumes at a very high frequency.

It would have been easy to assume at the outset that it is necessary to provide every driver with a foolproof system but this would have been enormously expensive, it would have been highly reliant upon fallible technology and it would probably not have produced traffic flows at adequate speed. Instead, a simpler system has been provided which it is believed will work adequately most of the time but may have weaknesses. The early days of operation will identify unforeseen problems, a process quite normal in new transportation projects and the necessary resources will be made available to evolve a competent and successful traffic management system, using lessons learned from operations and the changing demands of the travelling public.

Acknowledgements - The authors acknowledge the assistance of Mr K Bisset C.Eng., M.I.MechE. in the preparation of this paper, in particular his contribution of the section on the control system. In addition they would like to thank Eurotunnel for their permission to publish the paper.

Discussion on session 2

R. Ford, *Modern Railways*

Currently there are 7500 seats per day on aircraft between London and Paris. Eurostar will provide 11 900 seats per day. Where will these passengers come from?

L. Chapman, *London Underground Limited*

What moves are being made, in terms of a liaison with London traffic authorities, to ensure consistency of directional signing throughout the journey from the Channel Tunnel to London?

N. Roth, *London Transport Planning*

I was very interested in the PLEIADES message system in paper 6 and noted that all the examples of messages in Fig. 4 were in English.

What proposals are there to give messages in foreign languages and how would it be decided which foreign languages to display? I believe that foreign messages are essential to the achievement of the PLEIADES objective of providing information to motorists unfamiliar with Britain's roads.

D. Gray, *Heathrow Express*

How does Eurotunnel control the movement of cars while the train is travelling along, and how does it ensure that the general public follows the rules, for example, putting the handbrake on as requested?

M. J. Chatelard, *Transmanche-Link*

Regarding the efforts made to clarify the messages to the customers, surely putting the continental time on the UK terminal causes more confusion than anything else?

A. C. Dick
Reply to R Ford

The traffic forecasts for future rail passengers resulted from an analysis based upon the following process

- an examination of the current cross-channel passenger flows between Great Britain and mainland Europe and its expected growth into the future, if the Channel Tunnel was not constructed,
- the proportion of this expected traffic that will be captured by the transport services that use Eurotunnel,
- allowing for the additional traffic that will be created because of the significant enhancement in the quantity and quality of the cross-channel transport service.

The number of seats being provided on the Eurostar Service has been decided by the three operating rail companies, European Passenger Services, SNCF and SNCB. I am sure that this has been based upon not only the expected number of passengers but also the fares to be charged, together with a consideration of seasonal factors and the operational aspects relating to the utilization of their fleet of trains.

It will be interesting to note the number of seats being offered by the airlines once the Eurostar operations are fully developed.

M. P. Rogers
Reply to L. Chapman

Under the London Primary Route Signing Project, the Highways Agency will be re-signing the whole of the motorway and primary route network (PRN) within the M25, requiring the replacement of about 10 000 signs. A primary route is designated by the appropriate Secretary of State as the most satisfactory all-purpose route for through traffic between two or more places of traffic importance.

Outside the M25 considerable changes to signing have already been made on all the major approach roads to the Channel Tunnel and ports to ensure consistency and clarity for the road user.

This, with the London Primary Route Signing (when completed), will provide clear directional signing from central London to the south coast, ports and Channel Tunnel.

Reply to N. Roth

The Kent Corridor Strategic Traffic Management system is only one part of the PLEIADES concept, and is concerned with the effective management of traffic in the A2/M2 and A20/M20 corridors. It will shortly be fully operational, but there is no intention to give messages in foreign languages.

The PLEIADES project is much wider in its scope, and is intended to demonstrate and evaluate the application of Advanced Transport Telematics (ATT) systems for providing an integrated driver information and network management system within the Paris-London corridor. The project will provide a valuable contribution to the understanding of issues related to the practical implementation of ATT systems and standards. Within the several in-vehicle and other systems tested within PLEIADES there are opportunities in their development for messages to be received in the driver's own language.

Shuttles

B. Driver, FCIT, Formerly Rolling Stock Director, Transmanche-Link

THE ORIGINAL BRIEF FOR SHUTTLES DESIGN

Historical Background

It is both interesting and relevant to refer, initially, to the 1974 Channel Tunnel Project, before embarking upon the theme of the development of design for the Shuttles as we now know them. The 1974 Project was a rail tunnel sponsored directly by the British and French governments. In developing the early stages of the rolling stock design proposals it was envisaged that heavy goods vehicles (HGVs) should be conveyed through the tunnel on open sided flat wagons. These wagons would have a light roof structure to protect the overhead catenary from being damaged by loose covers, or ropes, on the road vehicles. It is likely that the HGV drivers would have been segregated from their vehicles for the tunnel transit, if the design concept had been developed sufficiently to reach approval stage.

The Channel Fixed Link, selected by the British and French governments in early 1986, based on the Proposal to Governments submitted by the Channel Tunnel Group Ltd and France-Manche S.A., was founded, fundamentally, upon the concept of "non-segregation", whereby passengers on the Shuttle trains, including the drivers of HGVs, would remain with their vehicles for the entire duration of the journey between the two terminals.

The Concession Agreement (April 1986)

This agreement, between the two governments (France/UK) and the selected Concessionaires, (originally the Channel Tunnel Group Ltd/France-Manche S.A. but, in 1986, to be re-designated "Eurotunnel"), described the purpose of the concession and general rules for the construction and operation of the Fixed Link. Annex I "General Characteristics of the Fixed Link", of the document specified certain design features concerning the terminals, the Tunnel and the Shuttle Trains.

These design features were obligatory and could only be modified by agreement with the Inter-Governmental Commission (I.G.C.), a body created under Clause 10 of the Treaty of Canterbury. This Treaty was signed between the British and French governments on 12th February 1986, leading to the Concession Agreement and enabling the construction of the Channel Fixed Link to proceed.

Shuttle Wagon Design: The Concession Agreement, in addressing the Shuttles, made no distinction between Tourist and HGV Shuttles in terms of the basic design features of the wagons. The requirement was that the Shuttles would "consist of one or two rakes, each rake comprising a series of wagons, permitting embarkation at one end and disembarkation at the other". The overall width of the wagons would be "about 4 metres" and the maximum length of a Shuttle train would be "about 750 metres", (excluding locomotives)".

Three types of rake were projected:-

(i) rakes for tourists' low vehicles: having two decks, each with a minimum head-room of 1.95 metres, to accommodate vehicles up to 1.85 metres in height.

(ii) rakes for tourists' large vehicles: having a single deck and would accommodate larger passenger vehicles, mainly touring coaches and cars towing trailers/caravans, or mobile homes.

(iii) rakes for commercial vehicles: having a single deck and would accommodate vans and lorries.

The categories of vehicles which would be carried, together with their accompanying passengers, were defined:-

- motor cycles, larger than 49cc.
- tourist vehicles of all types, alone or pulling a trailer/caravan and coaches, which fall within dimension limits of not less than maximum length 12 metres maximum width 2.5 metres and maximum height 4 metres.
- vans and lorries with or without trailers and which fall within dimension limits of not less than maximum length 18 metres, maximum width 2.5 metres and maximum height 4 metres. Maximum weight 44 tonnes gross.

Fig. 1. Shuttle locomotive

Fig. 2. HGV Shuttle showing amenity carriage and loading wagon

Fig. 3. Interior of HGV Shuttle wagon

The rakes were to be designed:-

- to operate at a maximum speed of 160 kph;
- to have intermediate fire doors, or curtains, with fire resistance of at least 30 minutes, to prevent the spread of smoke along the train, in the event of a fire occurring on board;
- "as far as is practicable" to be capable, "in appropriate circumstances", to continue the journey, to clear the tunnel in the event of a fire.

Though this was not specifically stated, it could be inferred that the carrying wagons were to be fully enclosed.

Locomotive design: The Concession Agreement specified that there should be a locomotive at the head of the Shuttle train and another at the rear, "enabling the train to be split and to reverse direction". With a maximum speed of 160 kph, the transit time from terminal to terminal should be "of the order of 35 minutes". These two requirements, together with a specification that a single locomotive must be capable of starting a Shuttle on the most severe gradient in the tunnel, 1 in 90, and hauling the train out of the tunnel, determined the power rating necessary in the design of the locomotives and the axle configuration, as we shall see later.

Parliamentary Select Committees (1987)

In giving evidence before a House of Commons Select Committee, the Chief Inspecting Officer, Railways, on behalf of the Secretary of State for Transport, recognised that fire was the most serious risk, but that the basic design concept could be made acceptable if, for instance, fire doors or curtains, with a 30 minutes fire resistance, could be installed in the wagons.

During the course of subsequent evidence before the House of Lords Select Committee, in May 1987, the concept of a 30 minutes duration of resistance to fire for the entire Shuttle was developed. It was agreed that, in addition to the Concession Agreement requirement, whereby intermediate fire doors or curtains would be fire/smoke resistant for 30 minutes, each wagon would be fully enclosed. The body and under-frame would be fire and smoke resistant for 30 minutes. This was the first major enhancement of design requirement. No distinction was made between Tourist Shuttles and HGV Shuttles, despite a decision to segregate HGV drivers from their vehicles.

The Safety Authority

Clause 11 of the Treaty of Canterbury determined that a Safety Authority, comprising equal numbers of members from the U.K. and France and with Co-Chairmen, who would alternate annually in undertaking the role of Chairman, would represent and report to the I.G.C. on all matters concerning safety in the creation and operation of the Fixed Link.

Discussions started between Eurotunnel and the newly formed Safety Authority in the second half of 1986. Prompted by the deliberations of the Houses of Parliament, attention focused upon the safety of travel in Shuttles and, particularly, whether or not the proposed "non-segregation" of passengers and vehicles in transit would be acceptably safe. In turn this reflected itself in the Safety Authority's approach to the design of the Shuttles.

TOURIST SHUTTLES

The more detailed design of the Tourist Shuttles developed during an on-going dialogue with the Safety Authority in a cycle of discussions, presentations, submissions and seminars on issues related to "non-segregation". The first enhancements to the design, however, were introduced during the Parliamentary discussions when it became clear that a fire barrier would be requested at each end of each wagon. This barrier would need to be closed during transit and, therefore, should incorporate a means of allowing passengers to pass through whilst the barrier was in the closed position.

Having established that the wagons would be modules of fire resistance, the Safety Authority's next step was to determine that the Shuttles would have a capability to detect the presence of smoke or fire; that the staff could be alerted to that presence and its origin and that the cause could be suppressed quickly, either manually or automatically. This saw the start of design for a very sophisticated, computer-based, fire detection and suppression system for both the Tourist and the HGV Shuttles.

In March 1988 the Safety Authority laid down 7 issues on which they required to be satisfied:-

- the sequence of procedures from the detection of a fire to complete evacuation of passengers to a place of safety, (with particular reference to handicapped persons) ;
- fire, smoke, high temperature and toxic gas detection capability;

Fig. 4. HGV Shuttle loading wagon

Fig. 5. Single-deck Shuttle showing loading wagon with telescopic doors

- the procedure for alerting, informing and instructing passengers in the event of an accident;
- the speed and effectiveness of fire extinction apparatus, (including proof that levels of toxic gases which might result from the activation of the automatic extinction system would be acceptably low);
- the design of the rolling stock, with particular reference to the fire curtains at the ends of wagons;
- the number and roles of Eurotunnel personnel likely to be available in the event of an accident or incident;
- the securing of vehicles within the Shuttles.

In order to respond to these requirements, further studies and tests were commissioned.

Eurotunnel could now see "what winning looked like". They knew what must be achieved in order that the Safety Authority might give "non-objection" status to the design concept.

A custom-designed test facility, capable of simulating the characteristics of a single-deck Tourist carrier wagon, was constructed at a specialist test site some 60 kms to the north of Paris. Here, rigorous tests were conducted to demonstrate:-

- the potential risk of fire occurring on a touring coach, whilst on board a Shuttle train;
- the speed with which fire or smoke could be detected;
- the behaviour of fire if it developed, undetected,
  - in a baggage compartment,
  - in a toilet,
  - in a kitchenette,
  - on a passenger seat,
  - in the engine compartment,
- the speed with which a fire could be suppressed, after detection, in any of the identified main risk locations and regardless of the degree of development of the fire;
- the capability of evacuating coach passengers to the safety of adjacent wagons without risk to life or of serious injury.

The tests and studies were completed in May 1989 and a comprehensive report was submitted to the Safety Authority in July of that year. The Safety Authority expressed satisfaction with regard to diesel-engine coaches, but to allow further consideration to be given to petrol-engined coaches and motor cars, they requested further tests and clarification on a number of issues.

It was evident that the Safety Authority's requirements were, gradually, being fulfilled and that acceptance of the developing design concept for the Tourist Shuttle would be achieved. The final phase took the form of a number of "Binding Requirements", specified by the Safety Authority and agreed to by Eurotunnel, some of which concerned operational methods, whilst others required complex design changes:-

- fire barriers at each end of every carrier wagon, must have 30 minutes resistance to fire and smoke. They must be closed during transit. Each fire barrier must incorporate 2 passenger pass-doors, (one to the left and one to the right of the central vehicle gangway door). The pass-doors must be capable of being pushed, from either side, to allow easy access between adjacent wagons, but they must remain closed and fire-sealed when not in use, (resisting the pressure of air which exists when the train is travelling at speed in the Tunnel). Vision panels, to the required standard of fire resistance must be incorporated within the door panel. The overall width of the door aperture must not be less than 0.7 metres and the height, not less than 1.9 metres. There must be no sill, which might hinder evacuation. The whole of the fire-barriers, as well as the pass-doors incorporated within them should be able "as far as is reasonably practicable" to maintain their function, in the event of derailment or collision;
- fire detection/warning/extinction system: this must be an integrated system, incorporating the following features:-

detection -	capable of detecting flammable gases, vapours and liquids, before they reach dangerous quantities; capable of detecting smoke, flame and heat sources, likely to represent a danger;
warning -	a fire warning system would be capable of notifying passengers of actions to be taken in the event of an emergency;

extinction - the system must fulfil the following functions:-
inhibit and render inert the atmosphere of a wagon in the event of the escape of flammable or explosive substances;
contain a fire during the evacuation of a wagon;
extinguish any fire.

To achieve these requirements, each wagon must carry:-

- portable extinguishers;
- an extinguishing system, (other than Halon), capable of extinguishing a spillage fire;
- a Halon 1301 system, (or other agent with the same extinguishing capabilities). Halon would be used only as a last resort, if the lives of passengers would, otherwise, be endangered.

This specification demanded a more complex, more sophisticated, integrated system than had been proposed. In-built redundancy of components in a computer-based voting system was developed in order to increase reliability. A fail-safe capability was also developed. The whole system had to meet the stringent safety parameters which had evolved from the iterative process between Eurotunnel and the Safety Authority, over the 22 months or so between the first design proposal and December 1989.

Eurotunnel agreed to meet the Safety Authority's "Binding Requirements" and the Safety Authority signalled its future "non-objection" to the basic design concept, subject to the formal submission by Eurotunnel of required documentation, giving details of Tourist Shuttle design which would incorporate all of the "Binding Requirements", - those already described and others, including:-

- 30 minutes fire resistance in the intermediate floor of double-deck Tourist Carrier Wagons;
- video surveillance inside every wagon on a Shuttle, monitored by the Train Captain;
- the video system to be linked to the fire detection system so that it addressed, automatically, any wagon where fire was detected;
- lateral and longitudinal movement constraint mechanisms for vehicles on board Tourist Shuttles;
- fume extraction capability in the event of fire/smoke occurrence. This system was required to be additional

to and independent of the normal purging system used for the extraction of vehicle exhaust fumes during loading/unloading operations. The proposal was later dropped, in the face of reasoning that it would be unwise to expel smoke into the Tunnel.

The Rolling Stock design specifications and invitations for tenders, for the manufacture of the Tourist Shuttles were issued to prospective bidders in early 1989 and the contract for the manufacture and supply of 9 Tourist Shuttle Trains, (9x rakes of 12 single-deck wagons plus 2 loading wagons per rake and 9x rakes of twelve double-deck carrier wagons plus 2 loading wagons per rake), was awarded to the Euroshuttle Wagon Consortium, (E.S.C.W.), by Letter of Intent, in July 1989. The "Binding Requirements" and many other design changes, which evolved from discussions between Eurotunnel and the Safety Authority in the course of establishing acceptably safe conditions for the non-segregation of tourists and their vehicles, were agreed after the award of contract. Very significant design changes, at such an advanced stage of the Project, were costly both in time and money. The resulting complexity of the Tourist Shuttles has been calculated to be some 3 times greater than that of the T.M.S.T., (Eurostar) and more akin to a space shuttle than to a train.

HGV Shuttles

The development of the design of HGV Shuttles from the original concept of being, visually, similar to the Tourist Shuttle took a course which was, in many respects, the opposite to that of the Tourist Shuttles - simplification of the specification. The early decision to segregate vehicle drivers from their vehicles had only a small impact on design, - the need to create seating accommodation with 30 minutes fire resistance in which the lorry drivers might travel. This was achieved by introducing an Amenity Coach into the train formation for each Shuttle.

Mutually Exclusive Design Parameters: The principle design features required by the Concession Agreement made provision for road vehicles up to 18 metres in length and for vehicles with a gross laden weight of up to 44 tonnes. The Shuttle Trains were to be capable of a maximum operational speed of 160 kph. Eurotunnel added a load maximum of 22 tonnes per axle to the specification.

Fig. 6. Double-deck Shuttle showing loading wagon with sliding door

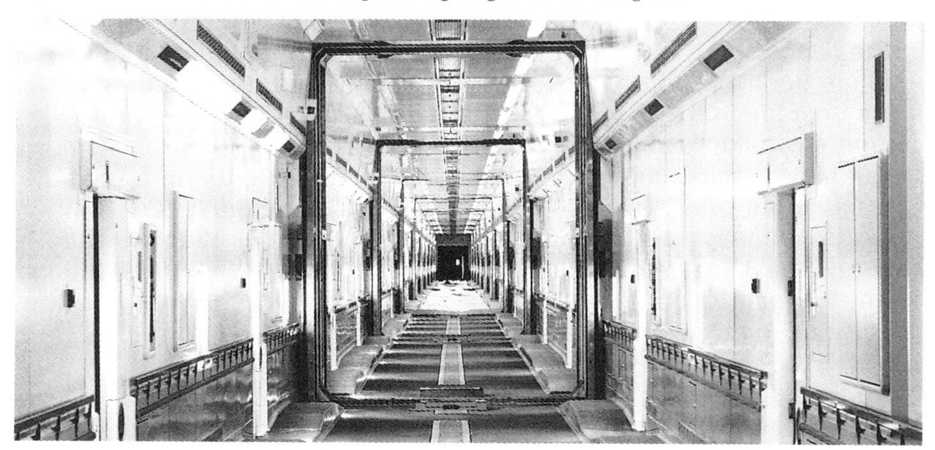

Fig. 7. Interior of single-deck Shuttle wagon

Fig. 8. Interior of double-deck Shuttle wagon

By mid-1988, T.M.L. was facing design parameters for the HGV Shuttles, which were mutually exclusive:-

- maximum speed - 160 kph
- wagon payload - 44 tonnes g.l.w. and
  - 18 metres length
- safety features - fully enclosed wagons
  - 30 minutes fire containment
  - fire detection on every wagon
  - fire suppression on every wagon
- maximum axle load - 22 tonnes

The first three items in the above list could only be modified by agreement with the I.G.C.. Eurotunnel had specified the fourth item, for operational reasons, and therefore had the power to modify it. At this stage Eurotunnel would not accept that the gross laden weight of 44 tonnes and an overall length of 18 metres were most unlikely to occur together in one HGV, although evidence to that effect was available in the E.C. regulations for the construction and use of road vehicles. The response to the design dilemma was to instruct that the wagons be designed to the lightest possible tare weight, - a course of action which would impinge upon the fire resistance integrity. Light-weight wagons were designed with 5 minutes of fire resistance but requiring stringent demarcation of the on-board marshalling positions for the vehicles to be carried, according to the length, weight and axle configuration of each HGV. This would have imposed severe operational constraints upon Eurotunnel and would have entailed careful initial assessment and subsequent segregated marshalling at the loading terminal, as well as sufficient staff to supervise the precise on-board positioning of each HGV.

The Semi-open HGV Concept

It was recognised that further tare weight reduction on the carrier wagons, if achievable, could overcome the marshalling problem and Eurotunnel requested that further design studies should be performed by T.M.L., dispensing with the totally enclosed wagon concept. There was concern, however, with regard to a proposal for open or semi-open HGV Shuttles at such a critical time in the Safety Authority's consideration of the "non-segregation" case for Tourist Shuttles:-

- because such a proposal might prejudice the chances of persuading the Safety Authority on the safety case for "non-segregation";

- the aerodynamic effects on open or semi-open Shuttles and their payloads had not been assessed. At speeds up to 160 kph, the side pressures upon trains from the "jet effect" of the piston relief ducts in the Tunnel could be unacceptably high;
- performance studies developed by T.M.L. indicated that suitably profiled, enclosed, wagons would be essential to achieving the contractually required transit times through the Tunnel. The different aerodynamic effect, with open Shuttles might prevent the achievement of those transit times.

Early in 1989, tenders were invited for the manufacture and supply of 9x HGV Shuttles, (18 rakes, each consisting of 12 carrier wagons plus two loading wagons). The specification to tenderers reflected the same safety features as for the Tourist Shuttles. The only easement was that of an increase in the permitted length of the carrier wagons, in order to facilitate on-board marshalling, whilst retaining 22 tonnes maximum axle loading. It was expected that the selected manufacturer would develop definitive design to meet the complete specification or would make a convincing case for some design concession in order to overcome "mutually exclusive parameters".

The bid of the Breda/Fiat Consortium was accepted in July 1989, with the signing of a Letter of Intent. It was intended that the actual contract would be finalised and signed in October of that year.

A Major Design Review

Before the T.M.L. - Breda/Fiat Contract was ready for signature, Eurotunnel instructed that all aspects of the Project should be reviewed in order to achieve significant cost reduction. The signing of all rolling stock contracts was deferred, to allow reconsideration of shuttle design:-

- There was little scope for reducing the costs of the locomotives, which were already tightly specified to meet performance and reliability criteria; furthermore, the enhanced design requirements for the Tourist Shuttles was impacting upon the design of the locomotives.
- The Tourist Shuttles were increasing in complexity as a consequence of Safety Authority requirements - there could be little scope there for rationalisation or simplification of design.

- The only opportunity for significant cost saving lay in radical redesign of the HGV Shuttles, and moving towards the simplicity of the 1974 Channel Tunnel Project Proposal.

On 8th December 1989, a joint team of rolling stock design engineers from both T.M.L. and Eurotunnel went to Italy to work with Breda/Fiat engineers on a total redesign of the HGV Shuttle. The specification in their working brief was considerably different from that which had existed until that time:-

- the wagons would not be fully enclosed;
- no fire detection or suppression facilities;
- maximum speed 130kph, (later increased to 140kph);
- maximum axle load increased to 22.5 tonnes;
- payload to include HGVs - up to 44 tonnes g.l.w.
- up to 18 metres long,
(but not both together);
- optimise wagon length;
- simplify bogie design.

By early January 1990 a revised outline design had been produced, which would half the cost of the Breda/Fiat contract. Eight Shuttles, each comprising 2 rakes, of 14 open carrier wagons per rake, would provide a total 224 carrier wagons, compared with the 216 carrier wagons in the 9 Shuttles originally proposed. There would be 2 flat-bed loading wagons per rake.

Eurotunnel presented the revised design proposal to the Safety Authority on 8th January 1990. In response, the Safety Authority requested proposals for detecting and dealing with fires on the proposed open HGV Shuttles. They also requested details of Eurotunnel's Freight Policy before they would give full consideration to the radical changes proposed.

Eurotunnel was faced with a most difficult judgemental decision. Breda/Fiat were very unhappy at the turn of events, with the prospect of the halving of the contract value and were threatening to withdraw completely from the Project unless they had an acceptable contract, duly signed, before the end of January 1990. On the other hand, there was a serious risk that the revised design for the HGV Shuttles might receive a formal objection from the Safety Authority. Rather than face the risk of having to re-tender for the manufacture of the HGV Shuttles, Eurotunnel instructed T.M.L. to negotiate a contract with Breda/Fiat for the simplified design.

Fig. 9. Fire barrier with pass doors in double-deck Shuttle wagon

Fig. 10. Driving cab of Shuttle locomotive

A process of discussion between Eurotunnel and the Safety Authority began and continued for 20 months before the Safety Authority signified "non-objection" to the revised design. The Safety Authority required the installation of a fire detection system in the two running tunnels and smoke detectors to be installed on each of the 4 loading wagons on every HGV Shuttle. The signals from the smoke detectors were required to feed to the Train Captain; the tunnel fixed installations were required to register in the Control Centre. On this basis, the Safety Authority declared its "non-objection" to the HGV Shuttle design, provided:-

- the detection systems were demonstrated and performed satisfactorily;
- the Amenity Coaches carrying the HGV drivers were fire resistant for 30 minutes;
- the distance between an HGV Shuttle and any following train could be maintained at a minimum of 4 kms.

LOCOMOTIVES

Performance Parameters: Prospective manufacturers for the Shuttle Locomotive Fleet were invited, in early 1989, to tender for the supply of 40 locomotives which would meet the following performance criteria:-

- journey time, platform to platform, for a train of 2100 trailing tonnes - 33 minutes;
- maximum axle load - 22.5 tonnes;
- maximum operating speed - 160kph;
- stopping distance from 160kph - 1090 metres;
- installed traction power - 5.6 MW;
- loading gauge - U.I.C. 505-1;
- minimum track radius - 100 metres;
- power supply, nominal - 25Kv;
- maximum gradient - 1 in 90;
- ambient temperature range - minus10°C to plus 45°C

The locomotives must also be capable of meeting the following stated emergency conditions:-

- in the event of the axle-drives on one bogie being inoperative, the locomotives on the train must be capable of restarting the train on the maximum rising gradient with an acceleration rate of 0.13m/sec.;
- if a locomotive fails completely, the remaining locomotive must be able to restart the train on the most severe rising gradient and proceed to the terminal.

<u>The Choice of Locomotives:</u> It was widely assumed that existing locomotives of proven design and capability would, perhaps with some modification, meet the performance specified for Tunnel operation. This assumption, whilst desirable and expressly stated in the Contract (ET/TML), proved to be wide of the mark.

The power rating was established at 5.6 MW as a consequence of outline design studies. This was higher than had been foreseen in the Contract.

Wheel adhesion became the focus of much attention, not only to meet the specified restarting criteria in emergency mode, but also to minimise the occurrence of conditions of wheel slip in the Tunnel, in meeting the designated 33 minutes platform to platform transit time. Two Bo-Bo locomotives per train could not be relied upon to provide the required adhesion. Three Bo-Bos would do so, but at greater cost and with no greater efficiency than could be achieved with 2 locos each of which had 6 driven axles. The Suppliers' bids, received early in 1989, proposed locomotives with various bogie and axle configuration options:-

- BB;
- Bo-Bo;
- Co-Co;
- Bo-Bo-Bo.

The latter two proposals would provide the 12 driven axles per Shuttle which would satisfy the adhesion requirements, but the Bo-Bo lobby was very active and saw an opportunity to increase the number of locomotives required, by having 3 Bo-Bo locos per train, if a competitive price per unit could be offered.

The bogie for the Bo-Bo-Bo proposal would need to be developed to standard gauge, from an existing narrow gauge bogie, supplied by Brush Traction Ltd to the New Zealand Railways.

Co-Co bogies, whilst well know in the U.K., were not favoured on the Continent.

With only two and a half years to go to the Contract Completion Date for the Project, a decision had to be made between the short term risks of delay, which might result from developing the Bo-Bo-Bo concept, compared with longer term risks, associated with performance/reliability and operational costs, of 3 Bo-Bo locos per train and likely increased track maintenance costs if Co-Co bogies were adopted.

The decision was made in favour of the Bo-Bo-Bo configuration and a contract was awarded to the proposers, the Eurotunnel Locomotive Consortium, (E.S.C.L.). It is pleasing to note that despite the early misgivings, the design, development, manufacture and testing of the bogies never strayed onto the critical path of the locomotive production programme.

Key Locomotive Design Features: Some key features of the locomotive design are:-

- fire detection and suppression in each of 4 zones;
- communication links to Rail Control Centre and on the train;
- on-board signalling, incorporating Automatic Train Control;
- main driving cab, pressurised and with air-conditioning;
- secondary driving position at rear end of the locomotive;
- communicating door, giving gangway access to the train.

The traction power system is based on 3-phase ac drive technology. 25 kv ac current is collected from the catenary and is converted into dc current for feeding to the intermediate dc link. Invertors re-instate ac current, at 950v to drive each of the 6 traction motors. Auxiliary windings in the main transformer provide power to convertors for the loco auxiliary equipment and for the dc current to the wagons.

The Impact of Wagons Design on the Locos: Enhanced safety specifications for the wagons had significant impact upon locomotive design. Additional train lines, to feed the extra equipment, took up all the available capacity in the coupler heads. However, the most demanding change started as an economy measure when, in 1989, it was decided that costs could be reduced by locating the position for the Train Captain in the driving cab of each of 40 locomotives, rather than in each of 72 loading wagons as had been intended. This meant that the Train Captain would operate from the driving cab of the locomotive at the extreme rear of the train. A change which appeared to be relatively straight forward at its inception became enormously difficult to achieve as more and more safety equipment, controls and monitoring apparatus, were added in order to comply with the requirements of the Safety Authority. The design task of incorporating closed-circuit video monitoring screens and an array of controls, alarms and communication links within a limited space to the right of the driving position in the locomotive cab without detrimental encroachment upon the Driver's equipment was extremely demanding. Additionally, Experts of various kinds required to be satisfied, not only that the systems would function reliably but that all equipment was appropriately accessible and ergonomically acceptable.

THE SHUTTLE FLEET-CONCLUSION

Eurotunnel have acquired and have commenced commercial service with, arguably, the most sophisticated, safety orientated fleet of trains in the World. 9x Tourist Shuttle Trains, each capable of carrying 12 Tourist Coaches, (up to 1100 passengers) and 120 cars, (up to some 480 to 500 passengers); plus 8x HGV Shuttle Trains, each with a carrying capacity for 28 HGV vehicles. These trains are controlled by a signalling system which provides Automatic Train Protection and allows 3 minutes operational headways between trains. This fleet of Shuttles will enable Eurotunnel to offer a service frequency, ease of access and short journey duration, unparalleled on any link between the U.K. and mainland Europe, with conditions of safety and comfort at the highest levels of design and technology capability.

Eurostar rolling stock

M. W. J. Etwell, BSc MSc CEng FIMechE, Director, Traction and Rolling Stock, European Passenger Services Limited

The Franco-British Treaty to construct the Channel Tunnel was signed in 1973 but agreement to finally proceed was not finalised until July 29th, 1987, between Margaret Thatcher, British Prime Minister at the time, and President Mitterrand of France. B.R. and SNCF co-operation had started in 1985 with open discussions with potential bidders for a Fixed Link.

The Rail Usage Agreement between Eurotunnel, British Rail and SNCF was also signed on 29 July 1987 and allocates 50% of the capacity of the Channel Tunnel from Eurotunnel to operate through international freight and passenger services.

The challenge of linking into the European high speed rail network is not a simple challenge, but a mix of many and varied challenges associated with the hardware of infrastructure and rolling stock, the integration of different cultures and technical standards and the recruitment and training of staff.

The British track gauge is the same as most continental railways but its structure gauge affecting the size of load carried under bridges through tunnels and past lineside structures is slightly smaller. B.R. developed a cost effective solution to overcome this by a large programme of work undertaken on bridges and tunnels on the main routes for Channel Tunnel traffic. 94 bridges between London and the Tunnel have been repaired, modified or replaced. The programme also involved re-signalling, installing new junctions and increasing power supplies.

The political and economic integration will put greater demands upon the Rail transport system for ever increasing mobility, and the EEC, whilst creating many barriers with red tape, does appear to be trying to play a key role to improve overall transport efficiency and quality of life, and remove barriers to industrial competition between the community manufacturers, and ensure competition within the European industry. The example of the Eurostar trains, Nightstock and Class 92 projects is how this challenge is being met, as the Railways manufacturers have had to consider differing standards and practices during both design, maintenance and commissioning of these trains into service.

It is certain that the transport market and Europe will change dramatically with new demands for growth of both passenger and freight, with forecasts of increases in passengers crossing the English Channel from 50 million to more than double this figure by 2003 and even 160 million in 2013. The number of Heavy Goods Vehicles is also forecast to grow rapidly with railfreight quadrupling within ten years.

European Passenger Services Limited in conjunction with its European partner railways will run international day and night train services linking major centres in Britain with mainland Europe through the Channel Tunnel. A new age of international high-speed rail travel has been born - EUROSTAR. The logo reflects the high ambitions for the new daytime services with the star pointing the way forward; the high quality and wavy lines - ease and enjoyment for customers. The stylised E of the logo represents the three European railways working together.

2. EUROSTAR ROLLING STOCK PROCUREMENT

For the Railways, the project for procurement of Eurostar rolling stock is unique and controlled through a Project Group based in Paris, called the International Project Group, which involves members on a permanent basis from the three partner Railways; SNCF, SNCB and B.R. Each Railway has a Project Engineer and various other engineers, administration and technical staff drawn largely from B.R. and SNCF. A series of working groups provides technical expertise to the I.P.G. through specialist engineers from the 3 Railways.

These groups have co-ordinated activities since 1988 for technical specification, design scrutiny, tests and now commissioning, including Quality Assurance at manufacturing locations. Current activities obviously are concentrating on ensuring the trains are fully tested and commissioned for service in Summer 1994, and establishing stocks of spares, maintenance documentation and training to support the servicing and maintenance at the depots in London (North Pole International), Paris (Le Landy) and Brussels (Forest).

Major achievements have been made through working in close co-operation with partner railways to ensure common standards have been developed and understood as applicable to the T.M.S.T. in areas where U.I.C. Working Groups have been considering debate for many years.

All documentation on the project is translated into both English and French.

For political reasons the supply of equipment and trains involves the supply industry from France, Belgium and U.K. with an initial split of work at approx. 40%, 20% and 40% to be representative of the respective investments in trainset ownership.

Basically the electrical design responsibility was given to the British consortium and the mechanical design responsibility to the French consortium. A group was formed in 1987 as a joint venture to bid for the supply of trains and this group named T.M.S.T.G. manages all aspects of the design, manufacture and supply of trains with the Project Management based in Paris, which ensures effective communication between the I.P.G. and T.M.S.T.G.

teams.

There are 17 main locations for manufacture and supply of equipment which are obviously supported by the many other equipment suppliers for components and sub-systems. This highlights the need for effective project control and the I.P.G. applies agreed technical and commercial standards with the contractors through the T.M.S.T.G.

Even with the best planning and control the complex systems will have initial problems particularly with respect to the integration of component parts of systems and sub-systems. A specialist task force has been established and working for over 12 months to address such teething problems and ensure start of service reliability is maximised.

3. EUROSTAR TRAINS

Each Eurostar train consists of two half train sets.

A total of 38 high speed trains are being supplied by an international consortium of manufacturers, led by GEC-Alsthom, at a cost of £25m each. 31 of the trains will operate the London-Paris and London-Brussels routes. These trains are 394mm long, consisting of a power car (locomotive) at each end and 18 coaches. There will be 584 seats in standard class and 210 seats in first class. On existing lines between London and the Channel Tunnel the trains will travel at speeds of up to 160.kph (100 mph). Speeds of up to 300kpm (186 mph) will be possible on new high speed lines in mainland Europe. Each train-set is expected to complete four single journeys daily between London-Paris or London-Brussels. Seven trains will operate trains on Beyond London services between Manchester and Glasgow to Paris and Brussels in late 1995. These trains have 14 coaches, for 578 passengers, reflecting limits of platform lengths at U.K. destinations, and are 320 metres long.

The fleet of 31 is allocated on the basis of EPS - 11, SNCF - 16, SNCB - 4, with all 7 North of London train-sets owned by E.P.S. Operation and maintenance of all sets is on a common fleet basis.

Eurostar trainsets are developments from previous generations of T.G.V.'s but reflect the necessary changes for operation through the Channel Tunnel and in the U.K. and Belgium. They will work on three different power supplies and four different signalling systems.

Mechanically the design is based on the TGV Atlantique but narrower - 2.8 m compared with 2.904 m - and the power cars do not have the raised roof as on TGV trains. The axle-loads throughout the trains are limited to 17 tonnes to satisfy the requirements of 300 km/h operation in France. The bogies have also been modified to reduce the overhang of air springs and dampers.

The main characteristics are given for the 18 coach and 2 Power Car formation :-

Length overall	394m
Maximum width	2.8m
Power car bogie centres	14m
Trailer car bogie centres	18.7m
Bogie wheelbase	3m
Wheel diameter	0.9m
Weight in working order	750t
Weight when laden	815t
Adhesion weight	200t
Maximum speed in service	300km/h
Continuous rating at 25kV	12.2MW
Continuous rating at 3kV	5.7MW
Continuous rating at 675kV	3.4MW

Different platform heights are catered for in revised door-step arrangements.

In the Tunnel the train interfaces with the walkway for emergency evacuation which is further from the track than a normal platform. B.R. platforms are higher than SNCF and SNCB platforms and far closer to the track centre line. Two mobile steps are provided which are both used when the train is running in the Tunnel or on SNCF and SNCB with the upper step only used on B.R. This requires a complex door control arrangement to ensure that lower steps are not deployed on BR as the lower steps naturally are far out of gauge for B.R. when deployed.

The electrical equipment is a new generation and very different from previous T.G.V.'s. Eurostar trains use 3-phase asynchronous motors fed by GTO inverters and has to operate on three different supply voltages. Current collection and power supply arrangements are automatically set by the driver when selecting one of the following positions on the driver selector switch :-

25kV A.C.	-	B.R.
25kV A.C.	-	B.R. High speed line
750V D.C.	-	B.R.
25kV A.C.	-	Eurotunnel
25kV A.C.	-	SNCF/SNCB High speed lines
3kV D.C.	-	SNCB conventional lines

The 750V 3rd rail current collection pick-up shoes presented a major design evaluation exercise and a B.R. loco was fitted with TMST bogies to prove current collection and a similar bogie was fitted to a T.G.V. to evaluate high speed performance and security of the bogie mounted equipment.

A proto-type of the 3-voltage power equipment was also installed in an SNCF loco, BB10003, and extensively tested in 1990/91. High power testing was also carried out at the test-bed facility in Preston.

To enable 300 km/h operation on the new line gradients of up to 2.5% on SNCF and SNCB each end of the train has three motor bogies - two at the power car and one at the adjacent trailer car. The twelve traction motors are capable of developing a tractive power of 12.2 MW on the new high speed lines, but are limited in other areas by the constraints of power supplies.

The philosophy of "keep going if it is safe to do so" has increased duplication and complexity and recognising this a mock-up of the complete network of more than 3° computers was set up and tested at the GEC-Alsthom Research Centre at Stafford to prove the communications system before it was installed on the trains.

The complexity of all the electrical equipment including auxiliary suppliers for heating/air conditioning, catering, communications, battery charging had also to recognise the intrinsically heavier and bulkier multi-voltage equipment, and although many functions are controlled by micro electronics and computers instead of traditional electro-mechanical relays the equipment is spread throughout all vehicles in the train. The power car body structure has been re-designed with a saving of 15% of TGV-A structural weight.

The traction system consists of six independent motor blocs, one for each power bogie. Two motor blocs are located at the rear of the power car and one in the equipment compartment of the adjacent trailer. Each controls traction and braking of the two traction motors on one power bogie.

Each power car has a 25kV and a 3kV pantograph and to improve reliability of train operation the 3kV D.C. pan can be used as an emergency back-up in Tunnel operation.

The incorporation of the various signalling displays and controls together with other cab equipment involved many representatives from partner railways with full involvement of driver representatives to develop an ergonomically acceptable solution. The driver can access on-board computers for information on the state of the train and how to correct possible equipment failures.

Eurostar trains have the following signalling equipment :-

TVM 430	:	Signalling in the Tunnel is based on the TVM 430
TVM 430	:	Cab signalling system installed on TGV Nord Europe (high speed line)
KVB	:	the SNCF system for conventional line automatic train protection

"Crocodile" : lineside signal repetition for France TBL for running in Belgium on conventional lines

AWS : used on B.R. lines

3.1 TESTING

Since January, 1993, a programme of testing has been underway. The first tests started with a seven coach and two power car formation (P.S.1) in France on the line between Strasbourg and Mulhouse. The second pre-series train P.S.2 (a full length formation) started tests from May 1993 with 300 km/h achieved between Paris and Lille in July 1993. P.S.1 was delivered to the U.K. through the Tunnel in June 1993 to start tests on the 750V D.C. system with static tests at N.P.I. and Dollands Moor and on-line between the Tunnel, Ashford and London. Tests in Belgium started in November 1993 with operation at 215 km/h on the Ghent-Bruges line on night of 19/20 March 1994.

Tests were successfully conducted in the Channel Tunnel in March 1994 with train-set F2 to validate in particular :

- the voltage changeover from the BR 750V network to the Tunnel 25kV network, and between the signalling systems (AWS (Automatic Warning System) and TVM 430)

- the operation of TVM 430 in the specific conditions of the Tunnel;

- current collection using each of the two types of pantograph (25kV and 3kV). It will be possible to use the 3kV pantographs, normally used in Belgium, in the Tunnel should the need arise;

- traction performance;

Various other tests related to passenger comfort have been conducted, including measurements of internal noise levels. The results of these tests were satisfactory.

It has been essential to ensure compatibility with signalling systems in all three railway networks.

The high values of traction/auxiliary currents flowing through the train with 3-phase traction drive equipment was identified as a serious problem for signalling equipment interference during specification and design stages. The problem is made more difficult with traction motor inverters operating at variable frequencies in the range 0-200 Hz which can interfere with the correct operation of reed relay track circuits. A programme of track circuit replacement and development of an on-board monitor system has been essential to ensure that critical harmonic levels of frequency signals are controlled and do not cause interference with correct operation of track circuits.

May 1994 saw the start of the series testing for each of the trains involving tests for each train on each of the three rail networks.

Successful completion of these tests and implementation of the necessary modifications will then allow the launch of services this Autum following a period of operation with invited passengers from 17 August, 1994.

4. CONCLUSION

The Channel Tunnel offers a unique challenge and opportunity for the railways and railway·industries of Britain and continental Europe. For the first time we are physically linked together and will be operating a fast frequent service.

As part of the Engineering support to a successful operation, North Pole International and its staff, along with its sister depots at Le Landy (Paris) and Forest (Brussels) will play a vital part in ensuring that customers are offered a high quality travel experience and a premier European Passenger Service with the build up of Eurostar services in 1994 and 1995.

European Passenger Services, together with continental railway partners are committed to taking full advantage of this opportunity now in 1994, with the introduction of services and the start of a new era, a revolution in transport between the U.K. and mainland Europe with Eurostar trains.

MAINTENANCE CYCLE

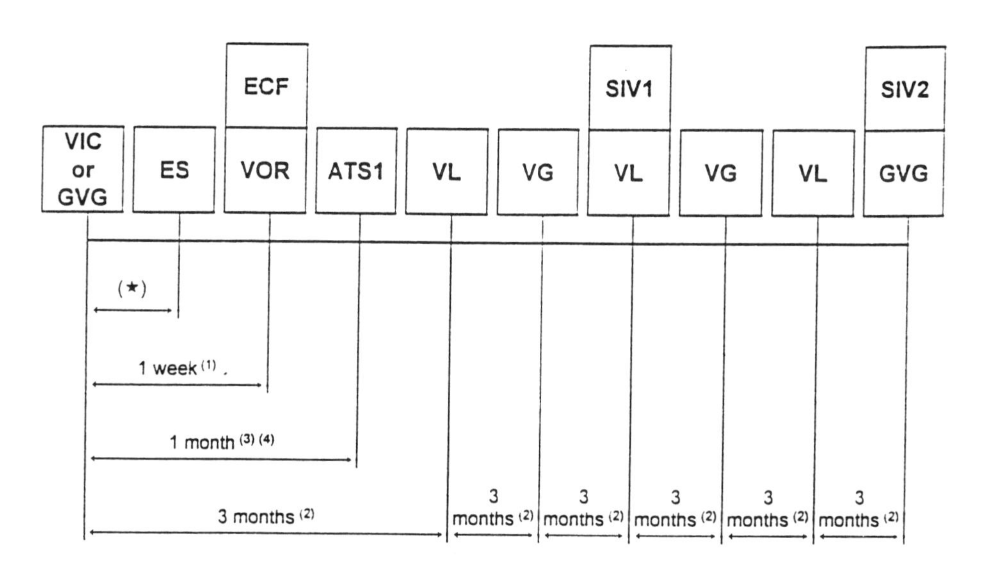

(★) **ES**: In service inspection every day, without exceeding 1500miles/2500km (or 1000miles/1600km on High Speed Lines).

For pre-series trainsets not exceeding 125mph (200km/h): ES every 2 days without exceeding 1500miles/2500km

(1) **Between two VORs**: the maximum interval is **9 days.**
Between two ECFs: the maximum interval is **9 days.**

(2) **Between two "Visite" exams (VL - VG - GVG)**: the maximum interval is **3 months + 2 weeks.**

(3) **Performed at the same time as a VOR.**

(4) **Between two ATS1s**: the maximum interval is **1 month + 1 week.**

OPCE: *Operation de Confort Esthetique* - Aesthetic Comfort Operation - is planned for a minimum frequency of **8 years.**

Discussion on session 3

R. Ford, *Modern Railways*

Is there any evidence of cars spontaneously catching fire?

M. Gellatley, *London Underground Limited*

Bearing in mind the significant number of design variables and parameters, could the authors please explain at what stage they considered the kinematic envelopes and how they addressed this to (*a*) Eurostar and (*b*) Le Shuttle?

T. Ridley, *University of London*

How would the authors have done the project differently?

N. Roth, *London Transport Planning*

Could the authors explain how the safety requirements are achieved to ensure that a train never comes nearer than 4 km behind an HGV shuttle train?

Could the authors explain why there has been a change in policy for the 'north of London' Eurostars? At one time these were to have been as long as London-Paris/Brussels Eurostars and would uncouple en route. Now they are to be shorter than the London-Paris/Brussels Eurostars without requiring to uncouple.

B. J. Hardy, *EPD Consultants Ltd*

It has been reported in the press that the Eurostar trains have experienced difficulties with supply trip-outs at the London end of the route. Would the authors comment on this, and, if there is truth in the reports, explain how the problems have been overcome?

B. Driver
Reply to R. Ford

Widespread research into the risk of spontaneous fire occurring on cars, during transit by rail or ferry, failed to bring any instances to light in Europe, or the USA, prior to commencement of Shuttle operations. However, during the 'marche blanc' period of trial running by Eurotunnel, before the commencement of commercial services, one such incident did occur. An electrical fault on a car caused a fire to break out during the loading operation at the UK terminal. The fire was confined to the one vehicle and was contained within the one wagon. The incident served to demonstrate the efficiency of the on-board systems for the detection and suppression of fire and the effectiveness of the procedures for the safe evacuation of passengers in the event of fire.

Reply to M. Gellatley

The kinematic envelopes were determined at an early stage of the project, during the design studies. The envelope for the Le Shuttle was, generally speaking, more than adequate for the much smaller dimensions of the Eurostar trains. However, in one respect Eurostar did condition the kinematic envelope of Le Shuttle. The running tunnels' walkways were designed to provide access from the Shuttle trains, for evacuation purposes. The smaller Eurostar trains needed a lower step to overcome the height and width differential between the doorway and the walkway. This lower step became a significant element in determining the kinematic envelope for the Shuttle trains, because of the limited clearance which resulted from its introduction into tunnel design.

Reply to T. Ridley

Seven years was allowed from the start to finish. In practical terms this timescale was too short. It demanded parallel progress, unhindered by change, on all fronts, namely

- tunnels
- terminals
- mechanical/electrical equipment
- rolling stock

and relied on them all coming together for a short period of successful testing, prior to the granting of an operating certificate to Eurotunnel, by the I.G.C. For any complex project and, in particular, for one which has so many unique aspects, it would be better to maintain a tight development and construction programme, but allow a more realistic duration for testing the equipment and generally 'starting up' the operation.

Secondly, the I. G. C., acting in the interests of the two Governments, to ensure that safety was adequately considered, had a major impact on the cost and programme of the project. Perhaps they should have been responsible to the two Governments for the effects of their requirements, with the Governments meeting the additional costs of equipment and delays, rather than these being borne by the concessionaire.

Reply to N. Roth

The Rail Traffic Management (RTM) system, in the Control Centres, is programmed to recognise the existence of an HGV shuttle and to block-off, or 'occupy', sufficient block sections to the rear of that train, to ensure no encroachment within 4 km by any other train.

Operational strategy — the intention of the design

D. F. Love, Lenihan, Germer and Associates, London, England, and
D. Maurin, TML, Folkestone, England

1. INTERRELATIONSHIP BETWEEN DESIGN PARAMETERS

The design of the railway system was led by key parameters which form the commercial base of the transport system:

Throughput, measured:	in road vehicles per hour by type, in number of national trains per hour. (Contractual input based on traffic forecasts carried out before the Contract was signed)
Transit and cycle times,	platform to platform and complete round trip times for the shuttle. Transit time is particularly sensitive to commercial competition by other transport modes.
Safety	degraded mode operation, fire and evacuation.
Continuous operation	no *"close down"* for maintenance.

1.1 Throughput

Obviously, the larger the shuttle capacity the less shuttles per hour need to be run to satisfy the throughput requirement, thereby maximising throughput within the limitation of signalling headway which is inevitably reached. Practical length and tonnage are limited by power, ruling gradient, drawgear and space for platforms. Platforms must be straight to facilitate loading and unloading, and the desired lengths in the limited UK site were only achieved by placing the first points of the layout inside the tunnel portal. The shuttle length also defined the distance between cross-passage doors in tunnel, and the gauge of the road vehicles (coaches, heavy goods vehicles) defined the diameter of the tunnel - early parameters to be unalterably fixed in the design process.

The accommodation of national trains running at faster or slower speeds than the shuttles without delay requires a suitable track alignment on the approaches to the tunnel, a minimum length of common standard gauge line used by both shuttles and national trains and a maximum entrance/exit speed onto that line by the shuttles. The differing speeds and performances makes use of more than one shuttle path.

The summation of these demands required a three minute signalling headway and a track capacity unencumbered by flat junctions and dead-end platforms. Thus the shuttle runs in a continuous circle.

1.2 Transit and cycle time
The shuttle transit time was a contractual input into the determination of the size and weight of the shuttle and is sufficiently critical to require the matching of the design speed of the curves in the termini to avoid impeding the shuttle performance. The minimisation of the loading/unloading time was essential to keep within the cycle time which defines the number of shuttles to be purchased, and of sidings and platforms to be constructed.

1.3 Safety
The shuttles needed to have the capability of exiting the tunnel in the event of locomotive failure or of splitting. This requirement led to one locomotive at each end and signalling capable of reversing anywhere in the tunnel. In addition terminals were required to have sufficient capacity to accommodate all shuttles exiting the tunnel which, on the UK side, was dealt with by constructing the British Rail yard at Dollands Moor to shuttle gauge and length.

The management of the effect of train movements on air flow and its integration with the air flow direction caused by fan settings has been dealt with by designing a large mimic panel in the Control Centre which gives the controller an overview of train positions, piston relief duct damper and door positions and fan direction for the whole tunnel complex.

This is in addition to the indications available on the workstation screen.

1.4 Continuous operation
This consideration led to the maximum of equipment being located with maintenance access from the service tunnel and the provision for working trains both ways in one running tunnel (single line working) over intermediate crossovers when the opposite tunnel is blocked for maintenance. Duplicate track layout facilities in the termini increases availability and the signalling system incorporates comprehensive track possession protection arrangements, including short (1.5 kilometres) possession sections in the tunnel which also allow speed restrictions to be imposed.

2. THE CONTRACT, BASIS OF THE DESIGN

2.1 Performance requirement
The Contract sets out the key performances which must be met by the Project.

2.1.1 Types of services
Two types of services are provided: the carriage of road vehicles by special rail wagons (the shuttles) and the transit of through trains between Great Britain and the continent.

The number of road vehicles to be carried in one direction during peak hour is defined at opening, in 2003 and at ultimate. Opening and 2003 are traffic forecasts while ultimate represents the maximum possible capacity of the system at 2 minute intervals between trains.

Two types of peak are considered, the Tourist peak and the Freight peak. The figures used for design are those corresponding to year 2003, and are as follows:

	Tourist peak	Freight peak
Cars less than 1.85m high	665	220
Cars 1.85m high and over	120	40
Coaches	74	25
Lorries	55	130

The first category are those vehicles to be carried in Double Deck rakes while the second and third are those for Single deck rakes. At the time of peak in one direction, traffic is assumed to be only half in the other direction.

When the road vehicle peak occurs, there will be five through trains per hour per direction. These through trains were considered as having compatible operational characteristics with shuttles, this being understood to include following the same speed profile as shuttles along the tunnel.

2.1.2 Extent of the work

As a general principle the work to be implemented should meet the traffic requirement of year 2003, but design should provide the possibility of expansion for ultimate capacity. There are however a few exceptions to that principle:

Rolling Stock: only that required to meet traffic forecast at Opening is to be supplied,

Fixed equipment:
- . cooling is not included,
- . signalling and control systems should allow 20 trains and shuttles per hour per direction and be expandable to 24,
- . works required after 2003 to achieve "ultimate" capacity, the subsequent implementation of which would significantly affect operation, should be provided at opening.

Among these exceptions, the only one affecting operation is signalling. Three minute headway was considered to be the best achievable, using the available technology, with 800 metre long trains travelling at 160km/h on 1.1% down gradients.

2.1.3 Performance requirement

Performance requirements are specified in the Contract in terms of throughput of the system, performance of the shuttles and environment.

Under the heading throughput of the system are specified a cycle time of 110 minutes for Tourist shuttles and 130 minutes for HGV shuttles, as well as a transit time of 33 minutes (with a 2 minute tolerance) for Tourist shuttles. Transit time had to be no longer than currently provided by the fastest cross-Channel carrier (35 minutes by hovercraft) in order to be attractive to the customer. Cycle time resulted from the addition of two dwell times to two transit times. The dwell time is the time spent in the terminal for unloading and loading operations. It is longer for lorries than for Tourist vehicles, hence their longer cycle time.

Performance of the shuttles encompass maximum speed and ride index, as well as the minimum headway already mentioned.

Maximum speed is specified as 160km/h (we shall see later that it had to be reduced).

The ride index reflects the high level of comfort which was looked for.

Environmental conditions, refer to temperature range in the shuttles and the tunnel, noise, carbon monoxide and smoke content and air pressure fluctuations. Only the two last items have an impact on rail operation.

Carbon monoxide and smoke limits have been set up as shown below:

	Smoke mg/m^3	Carbon monoxide ppm
Normal operating conditions		
during loading and unloading	5	200
during shuttle journey	2	30
Working environment for staff		
8 hour average	3	50
20 minute average	N/A	100
instantaneous maximum	N/A	200

Compliance with these limits has been achieved by providing a purging system on board Tourist shuttles in order to clear before entering the tunnel exhaust fumes produced during loading and unloading. Operation of this purging system had to be concurrent with the loading and unloading itself to avoid extending the dwell time. To minimise impact on dwell time, sequential closure of fire doors was necessary as loading progressed, which ruled out longitudinal purging from one end of the rake to the other.

Air pressure fluctuations are limited to a change of $3kN/m^2$ within a period of 3 seconds for individual pulses and a change of $0.45kN/m^2$ for frequently repeating pulses.

2.1.4 Safety and evacuation

The Proposal to Governments set the safety level identical to the most recently constructed (1986) public transport systems such as French TGV, Paris RER (Regional transit system) or Lille VAL (Automatic metro). In addition a specific requirement is to evacuate all the passengers out of the tunnels within 90 minutes in case of incident, taking into account the fact that one shuttle could carry up to 1500 passengers, some of them disabled.

2.2 Development of the design

Although the Preliminary Outline Design included in the Contract was recognised as representing a viable solution, the Contract required the Contractor to reappraise a number of points. Those linked with rail operation were:

- Train speed and traction power
- Running tunnel diameter and aerodynamic effects
- Wagon design
- Tunnel gradients
- System control and communications
- Number and location of tunnel crossovers
- Terminal layouts.

These various points will be examined later.

3. ADDITIONAL REQUIREMENTS OF THE CLIENT

A number of additional requirements were expressed by the Client. Either they resulted from their own initiative or had been imposed by external authorities such as the Inter-Governmental Commission.

3.1 Operational characteristics of through trains

The Contract specified that at shuttle peak, through trains should have compatible operational characteristics with shuttles, implying they followed the same speed profile. The requirement that even at shuttle peak slower freight trains could use the tunnel as well as faster passenger trains meant that both categories of through trains would use more than one shuttle signalling path.

As a result of differing braking characteristics of loco hauled through trains a different maximum speed must be imposed on them. A "line clear" indication in tunnel which is interpreted as 130km/h by a shuttle will mean 160km/h to a Eurostar and 100km/h for a freight train (MA100).

3.2 Acceptance of soft sided wagons

The possibility of through trains including soft sided wagons, as well a the semi-open design of HGV carriers, led to the necessity to reduce the strength of air flow from piston relief ducts. In order to keep it to an acceptable value even in worst case conditions, the maximum speed of shuttles having already been limited to 130km/h, restrictors had to be provided at the outlet of piston relief ducts.

3.3 4km separation behind a HGV shuttle

If a fire broke out in a HGV shuttle the semi-open design of the wagon could allow smoke to spread behind it in the tunnel. In order to prevent a following train or shuttle entering the smoky area a following movement should be kept at least 4 kilometres behind the HGV shuttle. This is achieved by a special link between the Rail Traffic Management and Signalling systems. When RTM recognises a movement as a HGV shuttle, it imposes behind it an additional length of protection of the required length. This uses the facility already provided for short possessions (generally 3 track circuits long).

3.4 Segregation of coaches

Whilst at the time of the contract and during the first stages of the design we planned other vehicles to be loaded together with a coach in the Single Deck carriers in order to occupy as much of the available space as possible, it was later required that one coach would not share a wagon with any other vehicle. This resulted in a reduction of the useable capacity of Single Deck rakes, but as far as design is concerned this led to a reconsideration of the principles for allocating road vehicles to shuttles.

3.5 Second fire barrier

Initially it had been considered that to provide a fire barrier at one end of each wagon would be sufficient to prevent smoke propagating along a rake. It was later requested that a fire barrier be provided at both ends of each wagon thus making each wagon an individual fire containing unit. Adding this second fire barrier reduced the useable length of the wagons and had a significant impact on the composition of shuttles.

3.6 Fixed shuttle formation
The original concept was for fixed formation shuttles, i.e. similar to TGV or HST. Variable formations were considered to be more effective in managing maintenance and maximising wagon and locomotive availability.

4. KEY FEATURES OF THE DESIGN

4.1 Cycle time
Cycle time is the sum of Transit times in each direction and Dwell times in each terminal. It is a key factor of the operating costs since, for a given number of departures per hour, the shorter the cycle time the lesser the fleet size required to achieve it. However in the present case it was given in the Contract to which we had to work, but we had to optimise its two components within the constraint of maximum transit time which was also given in the Contract.

Transit time: any attempt to reduce transit time involves a speed increase. Two distinct cases have to be considered: tunnel and terminal.

In tunnel, increasing speed becomes uneconomical. The attached graph shows the variation of running resistance R with speed. At 120 km/h R = 21205 daN while at 140km/h R = 27501, i.e. an increase of 30% of energy.

Ideally the 25 minute transit time in tunnel could be achieved at a constant speed of 120km/h, but maintaining this speed in the up gradient of 1.1% would require a power at wheel rim of 16MW per shuttle which would be very costly in terms of fixed equipment for power supply. Finally the power per shuttle was 11.2MW (5.6MW per locomotive) and the maximum speed has been limited to 130km/h by the choice of HGV bogies. This maximum speed also applies to Tourist shuttles since the same locomotives are used, receiving the same speed codes from the track, for both types of shuttles.

In the terminals, the radii of curves have been adjusted within the topographical constraints so that be the farther the curve is from the platforms the higher the allowed speed.

Dwell time had to be reduced as much as possible. It is the sum of four time elements : preparation for unloading, unloading, loading and preparation to depart. Loading and unloading times vary according to the number of vehicles entering the shuttle at each loading point. A way to reduce dwell time is to have more than one simultaneously used loading point in order to reduce the number of vehicles entering through each point.

A Tourist shuttle has three loading points: one for each deck of the Double Deck rake and one for the Single Deck rake.

HGV shuttles, which were initially planned as a single rake, have developed as two rakes, providing two loading points.

In addition, it is possible to start loading before the last vehicle has left the rake in the unloading process.

4.2 Shuttle composition
General principle: one shuttle is made up of 1 or 2 rakes. Two rakes is the normal composition for peak traffic. In order to keep a commercially attractive frequency of departure at low traffic periods without having

uneconomically low load factors, shuttles could then be reduced to one rake. In all cases there will be two locomotives, one at each end. This provides a back up should a locomotive break down (each locomotive is capable of hauling a full length shuttle although with reduced performance). This also makes it possible to split a disabled shuttle inside the tunnel and remove part in either direction, leaving the disabled portion behind to be dealt with later.

Tourist: the addition of the second fire barrier in each wagon led to an increase by one metre in the overall wagon length in order to keep road vehicle parking length to an acceptable value. As a consequence the number of carriers per rake was reduced from 13 to 12 in order to remain within the total shuttle length allowed by terminals. This also allowed rationalisation of rake composition by forming it of 4 identical sets of 3 wagons.

HGV: HGV shuttles are made up of two rakes, each rake having 14 carriers and two loaders. The semi-open lightweight structure does not match the requirements of noise insulation and fire containment and requires lorry drivers to be segregated to a special carriage at the front of the shuttle.

4.3 Tunnel cross-section

Maximum road vehicle size (2.50 metre wide and 4.20 metre high) led to the unusually large wagon cross-section of 4.10 metre width and 5.60 metre height. This defined the tunnel size as all national trains are of smaller cross-section.

The choice of single track tunnels relates to the safety case which depends for evacuation on an unaffected running tunnel during a fire incident and eliminating the risk of collision with a derailed train on the adjacent line.

4.4 Number and location of tunnel crossovers

Unlike urban underground rail systems which normally shut down at night, allowing maintenance to be performed after revenue service has stopped, the Channel Tunnel operates 24 hours a day. Therefore crossovers are required to allow traffic to move from one track to the other so that both directions of traffic use a section of single track when maintenance is performed on the other track. These crossovers could also be used in case of incident.

When operating in single track throughput varies as a function of the inverse of the length of single track, i.e. of the distance between crossovers. In addition there is a requirement to maintain at least an hourly shuttle frequency. When both tracks are on the same formation, crossovers may be installed at relatively low extra cost and are usually provided to match the demands of traffic. In the present case, with single track tunnels, major underground structures (156 metres long and 18 metres wide) with high cost and time implications are required for accommodating crossovers. The UK crossover was on the critical path for tunnel construction and an early start, nearer UK, had benefits to be taken into account.

Very detailed studies were carried out in view to optimise the number of crossovers. They took into account the various constraints of location, which are:

- transit times of each section of track between crossovers should ideally be identical, in order to have a similar capacity effect whichever section is blocked,
- ground conditions must allow the construction of the structure accommodating the crossover,
- adverse gradient must be limited to 0.7% on either side of the crossover in order to allow trains to resume speed as quickly as possible (in reality that adverse gradient did not exceed 0.3%).

As a result of these studies it was decided to provide two undersea crossovers, located respectively at 17.1km from the UK portal and 15.8km from the French portal, the distance between these crossovers being 17.6km.

The choice of scissors instead of following crossovers was a result of choice of tunnelling method.

4.5 Terminal layout

The usual layout of a railway terminal is a dead end. Trains reverse at the end of each line, and this is even easier when, as in the present case, trains are reversible, the locomotive not having to be provided to head the next journey.

The loop design of the terminal track layout makes it possible to load and unload simultaneously with passengers facing the direction of travel in normal operation. Arrival tracks are as long as possible in order to allow an incoming shuttle to clear the tunnel and the national train route if no loading track is available when it arrives.

Radii on the main curve of the loop, on the arrival track, decrease toward the platform.

It should also be mentioned that in the French terminal, arrival and departure tracks cross by a flyover. In the UK terminal shuttles turn clockwise, and anti-clockwise in the French terminal. This arrangement has been chosen in order to even out wheel wear on either side of the shuttle.

As a result of the optimisation of shuttle composition, both Tourist and HGV shuttles have similar lengths and layout, allowing the same type of platform to be used and permitting the number of platform tracks to be reduced from 10 to 8 at opening, any track being capable of being used by both types of shuttles.

4.6 Train movements in the tunnel

As already mentioned, signalling allows 20 trains and shuttles per hour provided they proceed at the same speed, i.e. provides one path every 3 minutes, including operating margin. As through trains may be slower or faster than shuttles, they are allocated more than one shuttle path. At shuttle peak there could be ten shuttles and five through trains per hour per direction. Two shuttles will be sent at three minute headway and the next shuttle nine minutes after, leaving two paths for one through train. If this train is a fast train, it will enter the tunnel six minutes behind the shuttle which it will catch up, exiting three minutes behind. On the other hand a slow train will enter the tunnel three minutes behind the shuttle and exit six minutes behind.

This operating pattern also allows a better spacing of trains and shuttles keeping power requirements at an acceptable level. It must be noted that should a train or shuttle become delayed in the tunnel the following ones would bunch behind it, thus increasing power requirement per unit length of tunnel. This will be developed in paper 15 and we shall only mention here that a special provision has been introduced in the design by requiring from shuttle locomotives a special power curve dropping sharply with the voltage in order to limit the overload of the traction power supply in such a configuration.

In order to manage the integration of trains and shuttles without causing delays, the Rail Traffic Management system forecasts the possible path of approaching national trains based on their actual running after Tonbridge, Maidstone and Lille and thereby assisting the controller's decision.

5. SUMMARY

The resultant system in railway terms departs from what could be considered as "normal" as found on SNCF, BR, LT or RER. Here is a summary of the major differences:

Power: about double per train

Weight: 2300 tonnes per shuttle against 800t (Eurostar) to 1800 (heavy freight)

Annual tonnage carried: 125 million tonnes

Reversible signalling, ability to split and reverse anywhere in the tunn

Track possession: extensive and comprehensive facility

Aerodynamics

Doors at crossovers

Mixed traffic in a cab signalled system

Shuttle loading gauge

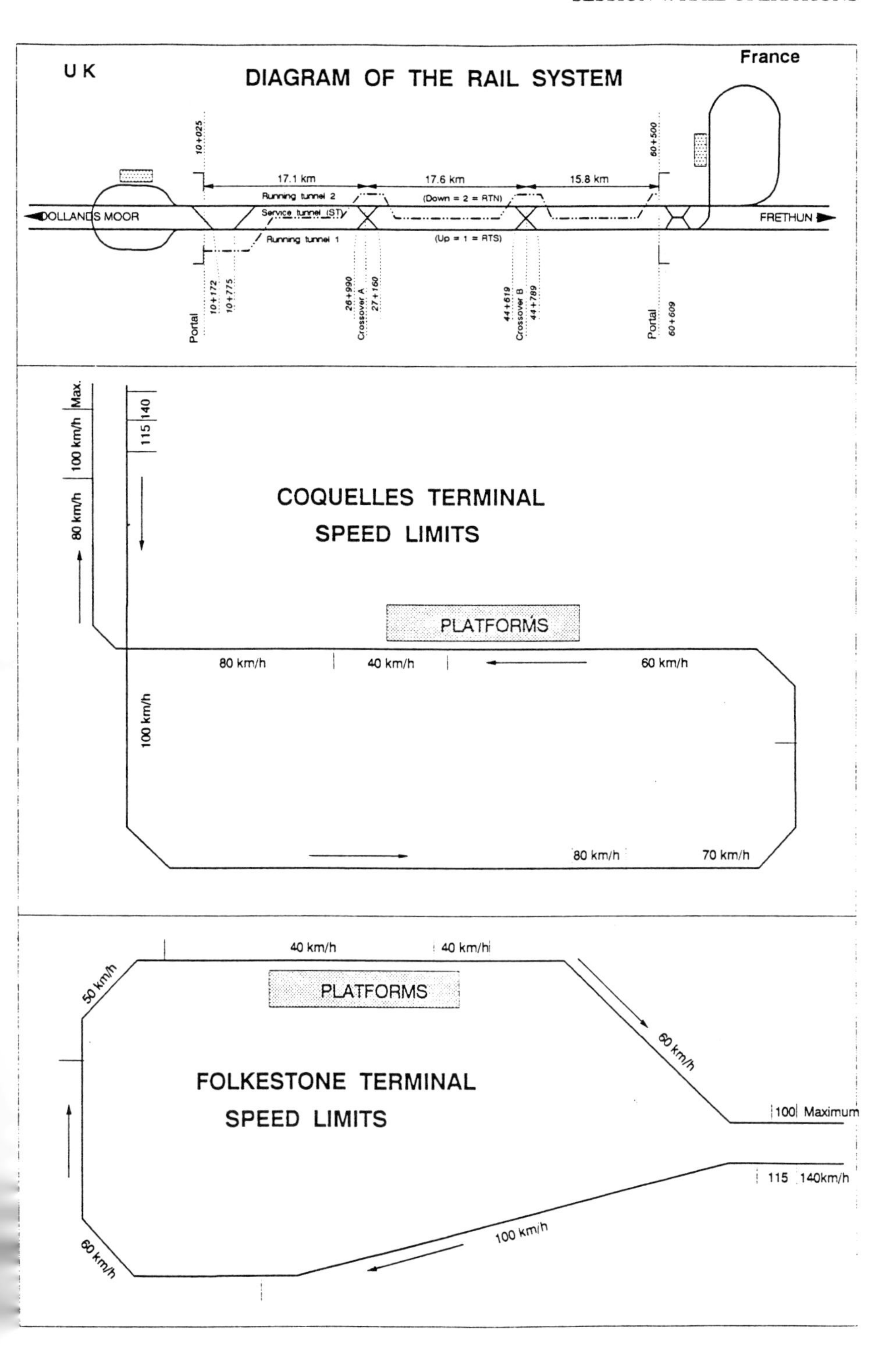
UK
DIAGRAM OF THE RAIL SYSTEM
France
10+025
60+500
17.1 km
17.6 km
15.8 km
Running tunnel 2
(Down = 2 = RTN)
Service tunnel (ST)
DOLLANDS MOOR
FRETHUN
Running tunnel 1
(Up = 1 = RTS)
Portal
10+172
10+775
26+990
Crossover A
27+160
44+619
Crossover B
44+789
Portal
60+609
COQUELLES TERMINAL
SPEED LIMITS
Max.
100 km/h
80 km/h
115
140
PLATFORMS
80 km/h
40 km/h
60 km/h
100 km/h
80 km/h
70 km/h
FOLKESTONE TERMINAL
SPEED LIMITS
40 km/h
40 km/h
50 km/h
PLATFORMS
60 km/h
100 Maximum
115 140km/h
100 km/h
60 km/h

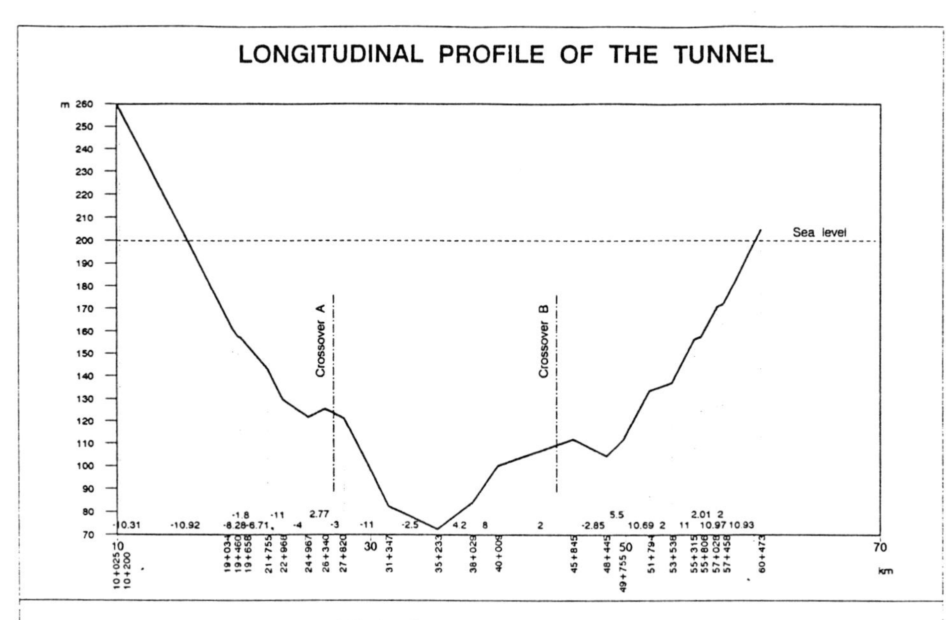

LONGITUDINAL PROFILE OF THE TUNNEL
Sea level
Crossover A
Crossover B
km

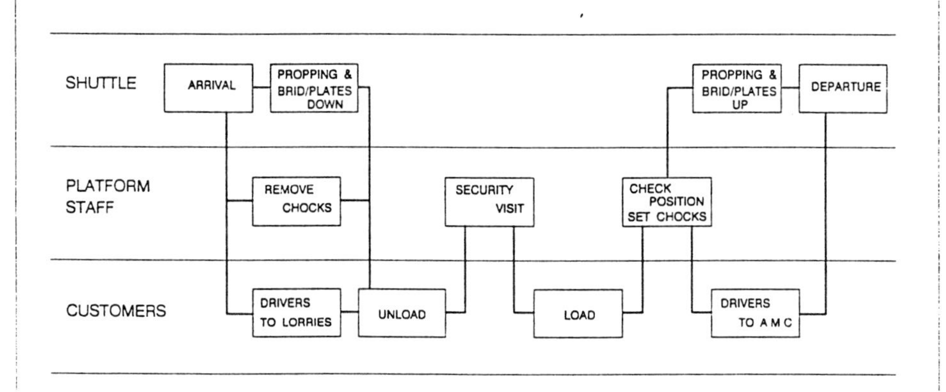

MAKE-UP OF H G V SHUTTLE DWELL TIME
SHUTTLE
PLATFORM STAFF
CUSTOMERS
ARRIVAL
PROPPING & BRID/PLATES DOWN
PROPPING & BRID/PLATES UP
DEPARTURE
REMOVE CHOCKS
SECURITY VISIT
CHECK POSITION SET CHOCKS
DRIVERS TO LORRIES
UNLOAD
LOAD
DRIVERS TO A M C

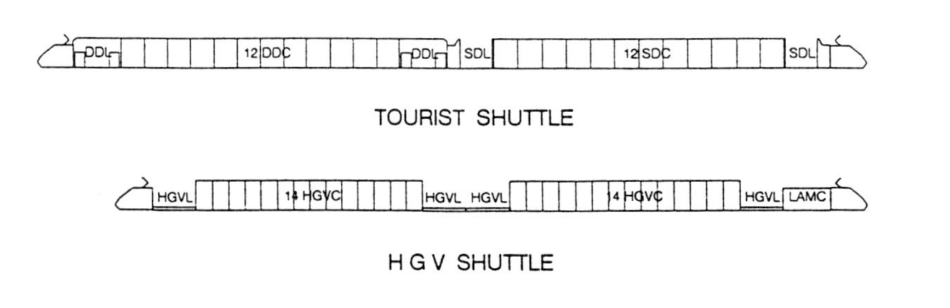

SHUTTLE COMPOSITION
DDL
12 DDC
SDL
12 SDC
TOURIST SHUTTLE
HGVL
14 HGVC
LAMC
H G V SHUTTLE

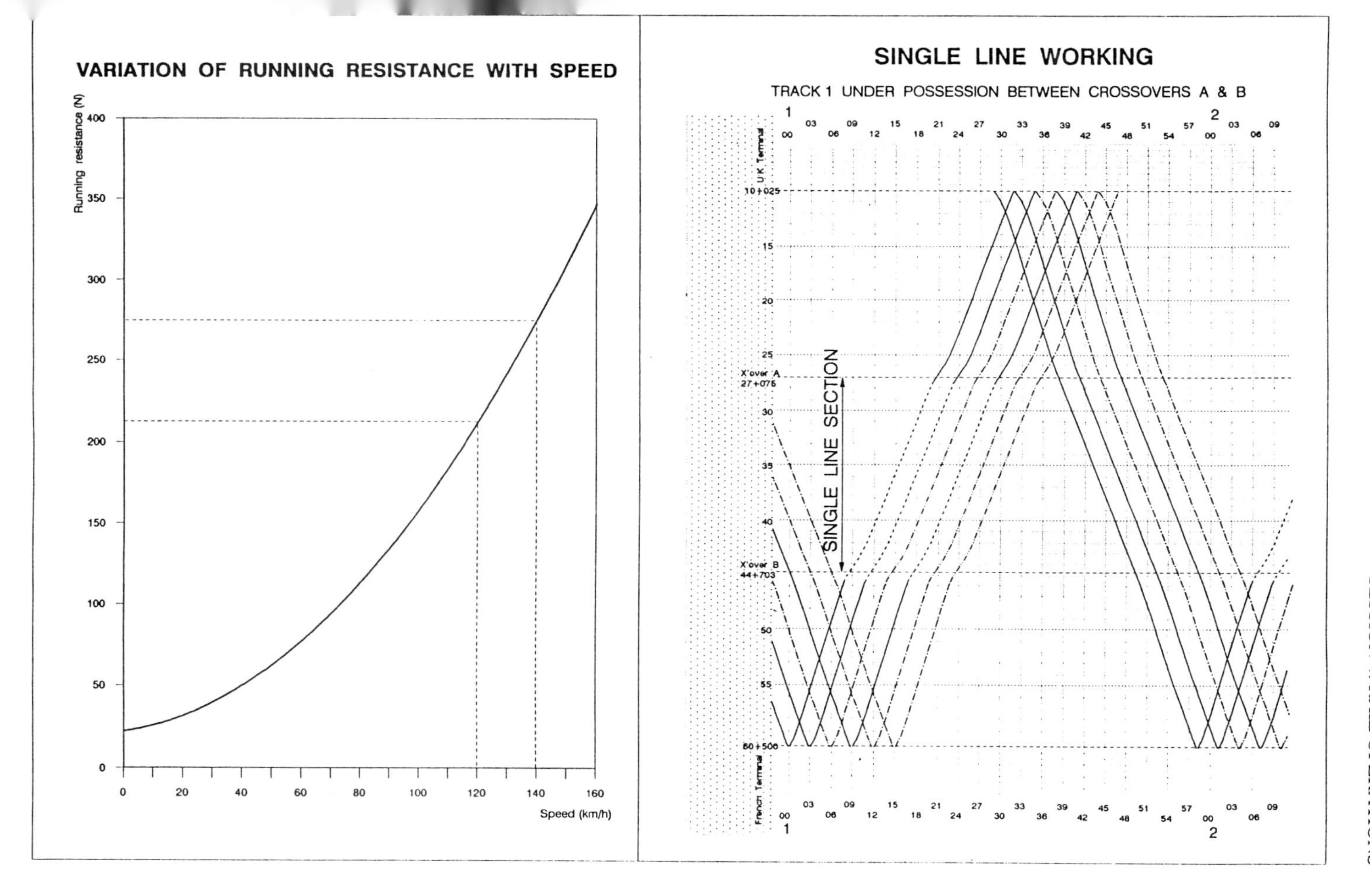
VARIATION OF RUNNING RESISTANCE WITH SPEED
Running resistance (N)
0
50
100
150
200
250
300
350
400
0
20
40
60
80
100
120
140
160
Speed (km/h)
SINGLE LINE WORKING
TRACK 1 UNDER POSSESSION BETWEEN CROSSOVERS A & B
U.K. Terminal
10+025
15
20
25
X'over A
27+075
30
35
40
X'over B
44+703
50
55
60+500
French Terminal
SINGLE LINE SECTION
1
2
00 03 06 09 12 15 18 21 24 27 30 33 36 39 42 45 48 51 54 57 00 03 06 09

COMMISSIONING

MARC CHATELARD
TRANSMANCHE LINK
Folkestone
Kent

INTRODUCTION

Three tunnels of 50 kms each
250 submarine technical rooms
40000 (Input/Outputs) from sites to be treated of which 15000 were signalling
A data transmission network of 700 Mbytes /s
1 000 000 lines of software programme to debug

Figures like those above show the magnitude of the tasks to be achieved to commission the Channel Tunnel.

12 months to Commission it as per the original contract.

This time scale gives the level of challenge that the Commissioning team had to face to bring to its satisfactory conclusion the project of the Century.

In 1990 a thorough study of the Commissioning programme highlighted that there was an urgent necessity to organise the Commissioning in a flexible way that could accommodate any slippage of upstream activity.

To provide this flexibility a strategy in two parts was decided.

First: Test any equipment as soon as it is installed: As lot of parts of the systems were prototype, this would allow early discovery of any technical problem and give hopefully sufficient time to bring adequate solution before opening.

Second: Organise an overlap between the installation and test phase. This would avoid to cumulate installation and commissioning durations.

But overlapping installation and commissioning is basically unsafe unless one sets up stringent methods to cope with the disruptions brought in. A proper organisation was then put in place and described in a Commissioning Manual issued project wide. The Commissioning Manual was based on five principles:

a) Clearly identify elements of the Channel Tunnel that could be turned over to the Commissioning team for the purpose of testing even though installation was not complete. This has led to the creation of **Commissioning Lots.** ie: to define very precise parts of the installation with well identified boundaries.

b) Clearly define a formal transfer between Installation and Commissioning in order to enable work forces to know precisely and at any moment whether the system was under an installation or under a commissioning custody. The formal transfer was called "**The**

Installation Release Notice" and became a major element in the life of the Project during years 1992 and 1993.

c) In order to gain flexibility, Commissioning teams had to accept to take over uncomplete Installation Works provided the outstanding items were not hindering the process of Commissioning - But of course a good knowledge of the outstanding items was an absolute necessity.

A project wide management system of outstanding items was set up tracking the remaining works on each part of the installation during the commissioning phase.

This has been called the **Punch List data base** permanently updated during three years.

d) Working on a system under testing is basically unsafe - A proper system to allow the installation teams clear their outstanding works safely during the commissioning phase was then established.

This has led to the creation of a unique project wide **Permit to Work** Procedure harmonising French and British practices in this area.

e) Finally a system of certification of tests (Partial Acceptance Certificate Acceptance Certificates) allowed the Commissioning Management through an adhoc committee (the **Commissioning Working Committee)** to endorse on a timely basis the results of tests and to avoid any doubt about the progress and the quality of the tests. This was proven essential vis a vis external monitoring agencies such as the Maitre d'Oeuvre, Safety Authority and the Inter-governmental Commission.

The results obtained from this organisation in term of Safety are self explanatory when you note that for a total of more than 1.000 000 man hours spent in a very difficult environment for Commissioning, the total reportable incident is nil.

In its late phase the organisation of the fast track project has also been greatly helped by the re-negotiation of the initial contract between TML and EUROTUNNEL allowing through a "Protocol" signed on July.1993, to carry out a phased opening, a process that was not foreseen in the original contract.

THE COMMISSIONING LOGIC (see attachment 1)
The Commissioning of the Channel Tunnel starts with Power Supply and mainly with the two main intake substations (132/225 kV) immediately followed by the commissioning of terminal and tunnel power supply (21 kV, 3.3kV, 400V).

The logic then is to test the users:

- in terminals
  - Radio, paging and telephones
  - Access control, lighting, workshops, utilities
  - Terminal Traffic Management/Access Control
  - Lighting

- at both ends of the tunnel
  - Emergency diesel generators
  - Fire fighting plants
  - Cooling plants
  - Ventilation plants

- in tunnel
  - Drainage
  - Fire detection and fire protection

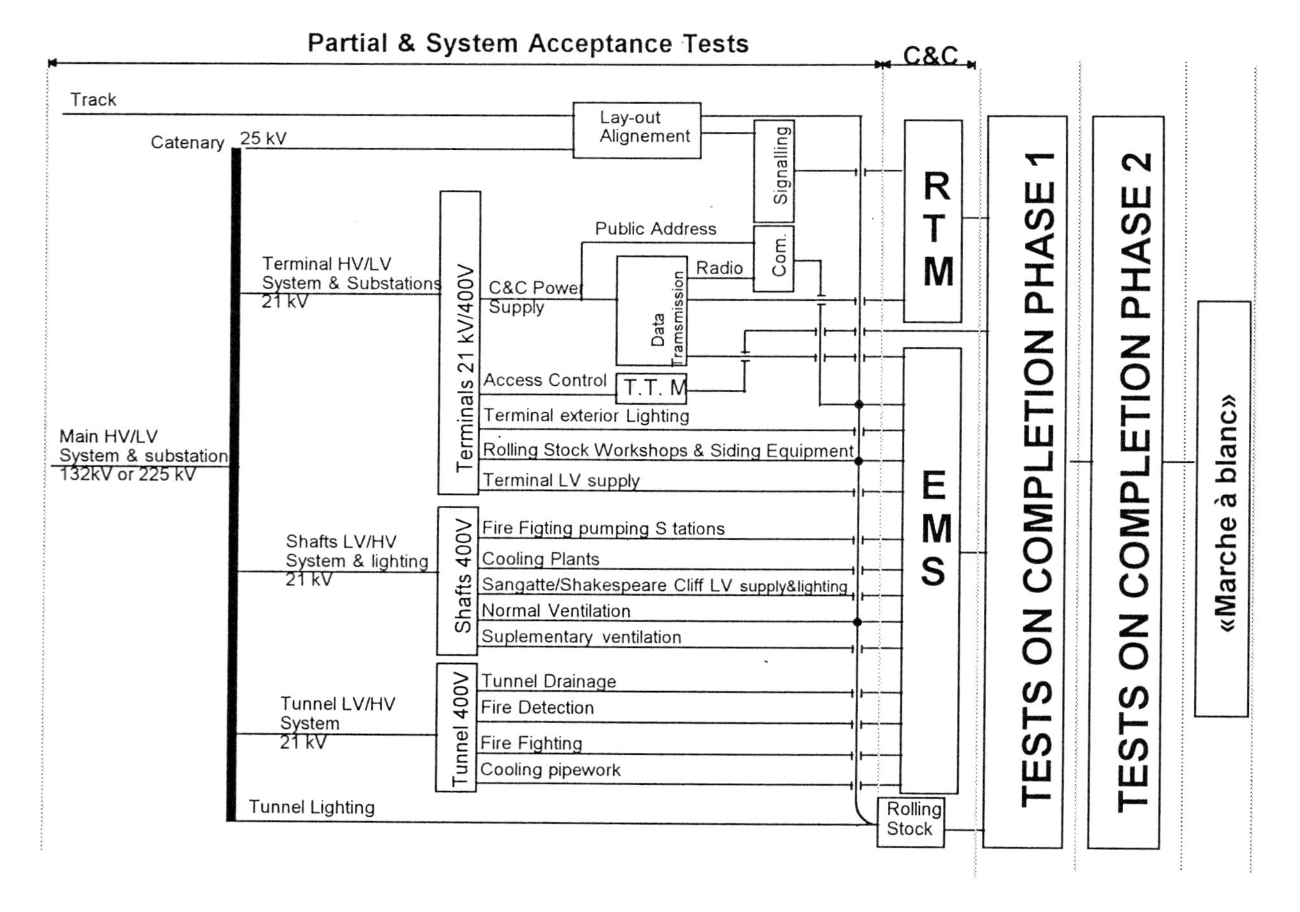

Attachment 1. Simplified test logic

- Doors, dampers, Pressure Relief Ducts
- Lighting

All these systems are tested locally and then linked to data transmission to be operated from the Control Centre (remote operation) from the EMS (Engineering Management Software).

In parallel with the activity above, the railway systems are tested:

- Track
- Catenary

and

- Signalling

linked to the Railway Traffic Management System (RTM).

All these systems are tested independently and then starts the integration of all the systems together during Tests on Completion .

The logic of **Tests onCompletion** is based on a gradual build up of operation while checking interfaces between fixed equipments and Rolling Stock:

a) check availability of track and catenary; check structure gauge all around the concession.

This allows the safe operation of one single train on one single track at low speed.

b) check aerodynamic and ventilation effects in the tunnels at steady ramp speed.

This allows the safe operation of one single train on one single track at any speed from zero to nominal speed.

It also allows the normal opertion of the ventilation and the creation of the safe haven in the service tunnel

The aerodynamic tests have also allowed the validation of the aerodynamic simulation.

c) check signalling dynamically, (level of capture of TVM 430 signal, satisfactory operation at normal speed, protected points).

This allows the safe operation of several trains on the same track.

d) Once these three important phases have been complete several trains may run simultaneously on the concession with no speed restriction while relying only on signalling and aerodynamic protection. It is then possible to run tests involving numerous trains. Seven categories of tests have been identified.

. Twin train oepration: rescues

. Control centre tests Railway Traffic Management Software integration control centre failure.

. Full load tests: catenary,....

. Downgraded power supply: load sheddings,....

. Transit times, cycle times, through put measurements

. Evacuation tests

Tests involving fleets of cars and lorries.

Once these tests have been carried out a phased opening process was entered led by Rolling Stock availability.

- freight service
- HGV service
- TMST service
- Tourist service

Each service has been preceeded by a proper "Marche a Blanc" period.

THE COURSE OF EVENTS
Chronologically the Pre-Commissioning Phase actually started on January 1991 by testing small pumps on the French Terminal and gradually increased during summer 1991.

Main Intake Substations
The first major equipment tested were then the two main intake substations 132/21 kV in UK and 225 /21kV in France which covers the period from May 1991 to October 1992.

When questionned, the commissioning engineers involved in this task remembered a Commissioning with no real technical surprises, although late delivery of equipment made the programme very tight.

The smooth commissioning of these two main intake substations is the result of the use of standard equipment and a good level of design.

Power Supply in Tunnels and Terminals - Utilities
Then followed the Commissioning of power supply substations (21kV/3.3kV/400V) in the tunnel and in parallel on the two terminals of Coquelles and Folkestone.

If the process of Commissioning of the terminal substations have been smooth (with the exception of an early defect of transformers) Commissioning of tunnel substations has been more difficult. As a matter of fact, the latter process started on June 1991 on both French and UK Side and lasted up to June 1993.

The original logic was to energise according to a very progressive sequence, starting from both tunnel ends and progressing towards mid point; the tunnel being divided into 4km sections, to be energised one by one. Each user would be energised with a simple logic sequence.(Attachment 2).

The actual course of event has unfortunately not been that simple.

Installation did not progress on a unique front. Different tests zones had then to be set up to commission the substations either simultaneously or even in a different order.

But, the strategy was kept of following closely the installation progress and it brought its part of success.

- on a programme point of view. It has surely been the shortest way of commissioning such works in such circumstances.

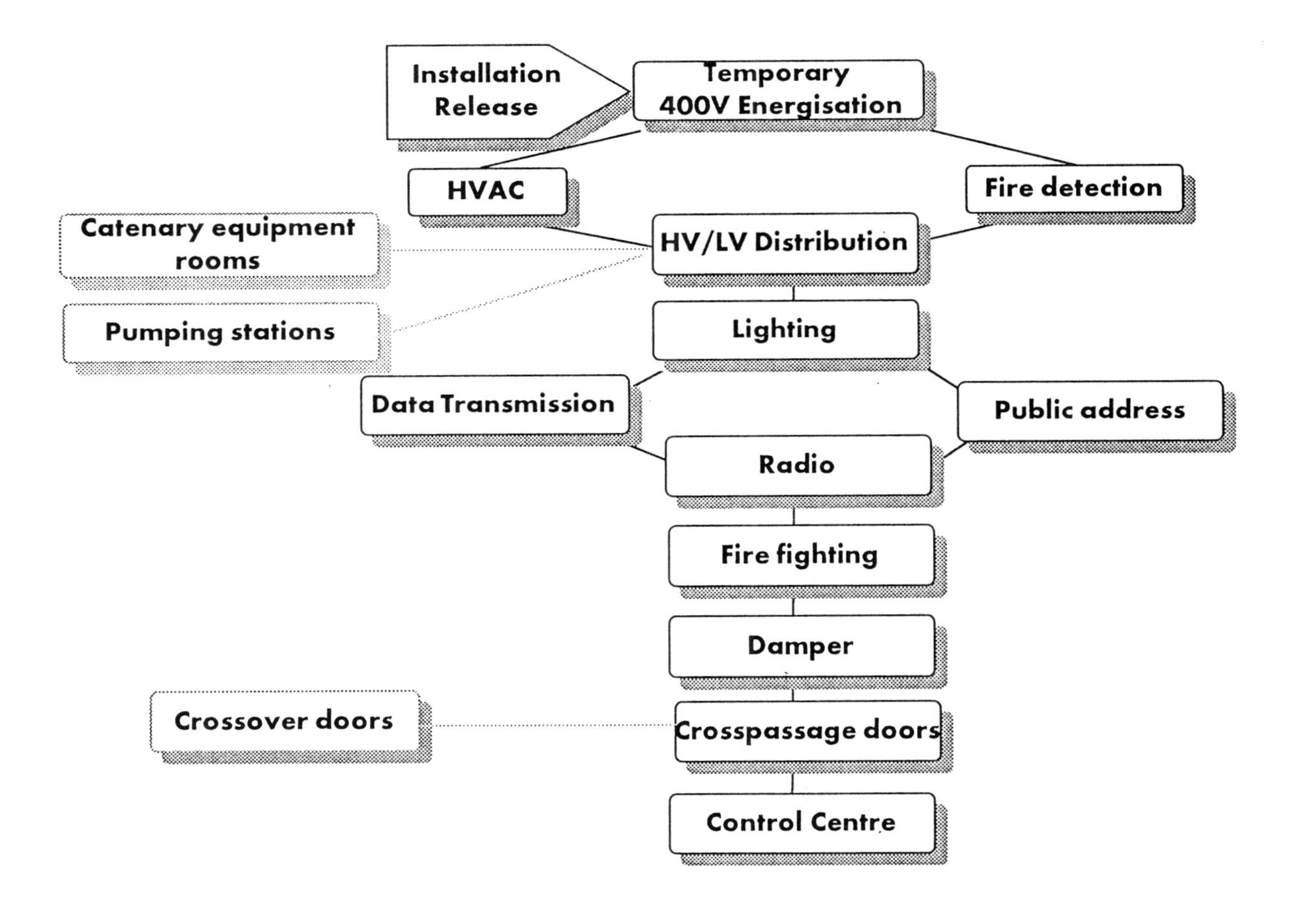

Attachment 2. Tunnel utilities commissioning sequence

- As expected, design and interface problems were discovered early, this gave opportunity for the engineering to bring solutions to the problems raised as they occurred without accumulating all problems to the end. It has finally been very beneficial to the project as no huge modification batch has been necessary in the late phase.

Such a strategy nevertheless has:

- increased the logistic problems (Commissioning teams had to enter the tunnel for very little amount of works, and in parallel with installation activities).

- increased the amount of outstanding installation works to be cleared during the commissioning phase. This has been highly demonstrated by the number of punch list items raised as an average during that phase and also the number of Permit to Work delivered every day to clear those punch lists items (up to 2000 a week). (Attachment 3).

Data Transmission System
Inside the tunnel another difficulty arose during this early phase of Commissioning, i.e the data transmission system.

In the good old days, data transmission between M&E Equipment on site and Control Centre was made of electrical connections between the equipment itself and a control cabinet, and then from the Control cabinet to the Control Centre.

At least, the process of Commissioning was rather simple.

- Check the equipment locally.

- Check the control cabinet and its connection with the Control Centre and the equipment.

- Start operation from the Control Centre.

On the Channel Tunnel the data transmission system is a complex, resilient, computer controlled fibre optic network.

Equipment have been checked locally but when came the time to link the equipment to the Control Centre the entire data transmission system had to be commissioned as a whole; and the commissioning of the data transmission only ended by October 1993 more than two years after the first equipment on site was commissioned.

The consequence of it is that during more than two years (mid 91 to mid 93), local operation has taken place with hundreds of operators working on shift (manual mode) instead of remote operation from the control centre with a few operators.

For sure, the late availability of the data transmission system on this project has been an important factor for increasing the manpower during the Commissioning Phase while maintaining the safety standards at their highest level.

Plants and Mechanical Equipment
In parallel with this data transmission testing campaign in the tunnel, Commissioning had to progress on the plants at both ends of the tunnel and on the mechanical equipment inside the tunnels.

Plants were mainly the following:

- Ventilation plants
- Fire fighting plants
- Cooling plants
- the pumping stations

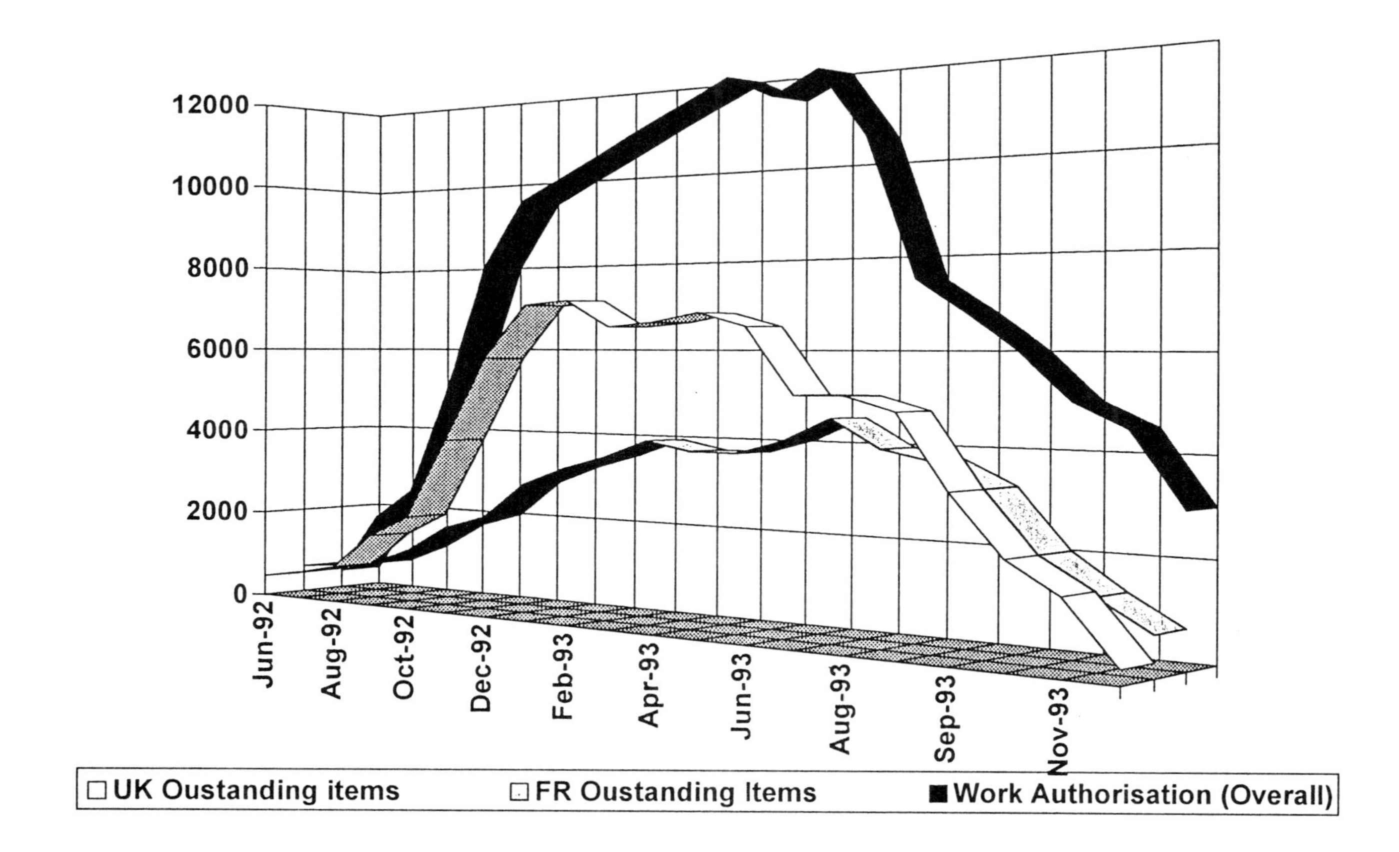

Attachment 3. Punch list and work authorisations

- the emergency diesel generators
- the waste treatment plants

these activities were performed from March 92 to February 1994.

Except for some vibration problems encountered on Ventilation plants and pumping stations, the commissioning of the plants went efficiently again reflecting a good level of design.

Inside the tunnel the commissioning of doors, dampers, safety valves and pipe work have been more delicate. Difficulties happened due to the late completion of installation, interfaces between disciplines, and even problems with the original design that can be understood when you consider the magnitude of the Works.

Distance to the work face increased the difficulties encountered. As a matter of fact, it may take 5 min to change a limit switch at the surface, it is an other job for a trouble shooter to spend a full day to go back and forth inside the tunnel and change a limit switch at km say 29 from the tunnel entry. Test engineers have to be highly motivated to do so. Commissioning had to introduce the use of bicycles at one stage, in order to move faster in the tunnels.

Track

When compared to the other system, the **track** commissioning process in itself is very simple (points checking and MAUZIN Coach running, measurements on bolts torques, cleaning and insulation measurement). This has not been really a subject of concern and lasted from July 92 to December 1993 as installation works were progressing.

Track problems are more Installation than Commissioning problems.

Catenary

The **catenary** testing process is very different from track and leads to energisation with its highly hazardous aspects. (25kV).

Energisation of a catenary must be associated with safety arrangements and training.

In order to support the catenary energisation a Commissioning Rule Book and an Orange Training Card were put in place.:

Those two aspects are dealt with separately by other speakers during this conference but their importance has been paramount during the late phase of the Project.

Nobody has been injured during the first 18 months of energisation thanks to those precautions - They are fundamental.

With regard to the testing itself of the catenary, the process went smoothly but is necessary nevertheless to mention an incident encountered on 13 November 1993 not because of its magnitude but more because of the publicity made at the time by the newspapers.

This incident (resulting in a damage and melting of a limited section of catenary) was of a very limited magnitude during a commissioning process, and it was treated as such by all involved bodies around (ET, TML, H&SE). The unfortunate is the report made by the newspapers at the time. This could be called the "Channel Tunnel effect!"

Signalling

The third track side system is of course the **signalling** (i.e. TVM 430).

The programme for testing the signalling was made of several phases

- Campagnes fictives (test interlocking cabinets and computers using a simulator for field equipment)

- Liaisons poste campagne (field to technical room links)
- Sequences d'annonce (from room to next room on train progression)

The programme announced on November 1992 was with a target of 1.11.93.

The completion of signalling tests occurred on 4.11.93. This highlights how closely the programme has been followed.

A special section of this conference deals with signalling, nevertheless the commissioning of it has been of a high standard.

Softwares (EMS - RTM)
Both of these systems have been treated with a lot of care and subject to highly developed Factory Acceptance Tests in Platforms.

The EMS testing on site lasted from August 1993 to November 1993 on site and went remarkably well.

The test campaign has been made in three phases.

- First local tests were to ensure that Remote Telemetering Units (RTU) were working properly.

- Then tests link between EMS (Central) and RTU.

- And then a sample check to clarify the final stage.

This method, decided in Spring 1993, anticipated difficulties with the data transmission and has allowed work to occur around a logic difficulty that would have impacted the whole project for several months if not counter-acted.

The first release of RTM has been installed in December 1993. The tests itself of RTM has then been included in Tests on Completion Phase.

TESTS ON COMPLETION

During the period leading to the freight service, problems were encountered - with regard to the performance of Tests on Completion themselves - essentially in the following area:

- difficulties encountered with regard to air tighness from Running Tunnels to Running tunnels to Service Tunnels.

Important sealing campaigns have been necessary to reach asatisfactory level of leakage and re-calculations have been necessary to allow a satisfactory ventilation operation with the existing level of leakages.

- difficulties encountered with regard to Railway Traffic Management software availability. As a matter of fact a number of anomalies were found when installing the first RTM release. This has led afterward to the installation of successive releases each one being subject to non regression tests.

Thanks to the software management group that had been set up at the beginning of the project, the software changes have always been under control but they have been with regard to RTM more numerous than one could have reasonably expected.

- difficulties to prove the adequacy of Fire Detection in the running tunnels by running a 5MW fire in the tunnel itself.

The problems above were important but in terms of time scale the main problems have been related to logistics, and organisation linked to Rolling Stock availability.

CONCLUSION

The critical path for pre-commissioning phase have been mainly signalling and data transmission progress

The Tests on Completion have been highly disrupted by lack of reliability of Rolling Stock leading to numerous day to day cancellation reprogrammation of tests - This has been highly counter productive and has increased substantially the man hours spent for Tests on Completion and gave a feeling of frustration to the operators.

The main lesson for the future would be that as far as practicable such Tests on Completion phase should only be carried out with a minimum quantity of Rolling Stock of proven reliability. However, on this project the sophisticated design of the Rolling Stock prolonged their delivery and testing with consequent knock on effect for the final stages of Commissioning.

Generally speaking far from lasting 1 year in total as originally forecasted, the commissioning of the Channel Tunnel has been spread over a period of three years and a half. But most of it has been carried out in parallel to installation.

The main difficulty during all the phase has been co-ordination and logistics.

The TML Commissioning Team during the Pre-Commissioning Phase was mainly a co-ordination team, the tests themselves being carried out by TML's subcontractors.

At peak time this team of co-ordination totalled 650 engineers and technicians based either in FOLKESTONE or CALAIS. This has allowed in the very active phase to run the commissioning at twice the speed anticipated by programme and meet important milestones such as the anticipated date of hand over of the Works from TML to EUROTUNNEL (10 December 1993).

The result of it in general terms has been an achievement of 1 year between the end of installation and the first opening (see attachment 4). Contract fulfilled thanks to the methods chosen and the organisation in place.

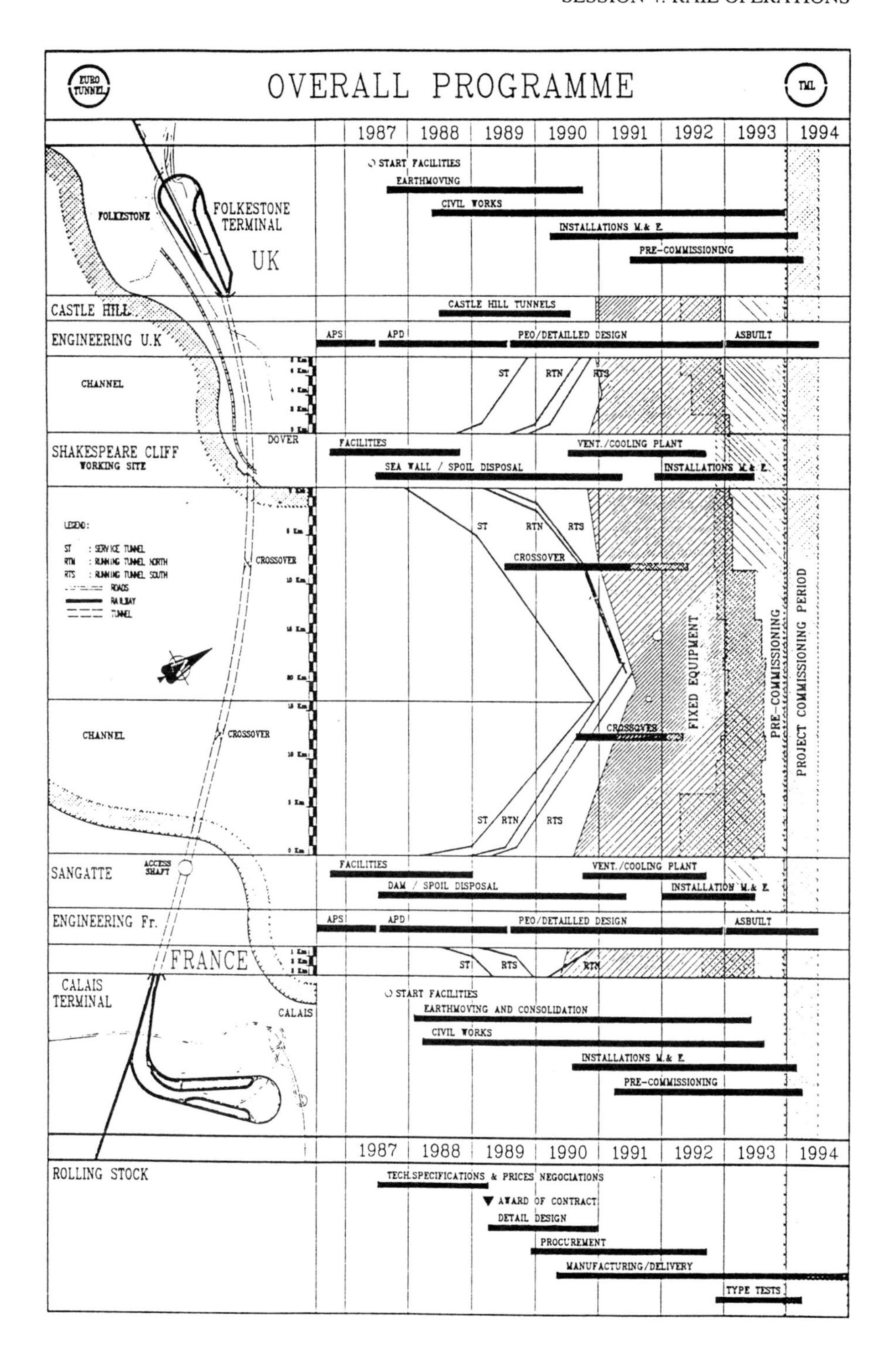

OVERALL PROGRAMME
EURO TUNNEL
TML
1987
1988
1989
1990
1991
1992
1993
1994
FOLKESTONE
FOLKESTONE TERMINAL
UK
START FACILITIES
EARTHMOVING
CIVIL WORKS
INSTALLATIONS M.& E.
PRE-COMMISSIONING
CASTLE HILL
CASTLE HILL TUNNELS
ENGINEERING U.K
APS
APD
PEO/DETAILLED DESIGN
ASBUILT
CHANNEL
ST
RTN
RTS
SHAKESPEARE CLIFF
WORKING SITE
DOVER
FACILITIES
VENT./COOLING PLANT
SEA WALL / SPOIL DISPOSAL
INSTALLATIONS M.& E.
LEGEND:
ST : SERVICE TUNNEL
RTN : RUNNING TUNNEL NORTH
RTS : RUNNING TUNNEL SOUTH
ROADS
RAILWAY
TUNNEL
CROSSOVER
FIXED EQUIPMENT
PRE-COMMISSIONING
PROJECT COMMISSIONING PERIOD
SANGATTE
ACCESS SHAFT
DAM / SPOIL DISPOSAL
INSTALLATION M.& E.
ENGINEERING Fr.
FRANCE
CALAIS TERMINAL
CALAIS
START FACILITIES
EARTHMOVING AND CONSOLIDATION
CIVIL WORKS
INSTALLATIONS M.& E.
PRE-COMMISSIONING
ROLLING STOCK
TECH.SPECIFICATIONS & PRICES NEGOCIATIONS
AWARD OF CONTRACT
DETAIL DESIGN
PROCUREMENT
MANUFACTURING/DELIVERY
TYPE TESTS

CHANNEL TUNNEL OPERATIONAL STRATEGY THE OPERATOR'S INTENTIONS

P T Dyke, FCIT. **Director of Operations, Terminals and Security - Eurotunnel Coquelles, Calais. France**

1. DEVELOPMENT OF THE OPERATING STRATEGY

1.1 Introduction

The Operational Strategy was born out of a mixture of competition, commercial viability (i.e. what the market would accept) practicality and feasibility and a good deal of emotion.

The dream was always to connect the UK and France but the methodology sèlected was developed only after the competition in late 1985 when four final schemes, out of a total of nine, were short listed. Even then in late 1985, Mrs Thatcher was believed to have been a supporter of a combined bridge tunnel scheme.

However, operational strategy depended on getting enough traffic to finance the whole project and it was realised that the successful scheme had to take road and rail traffic to survive. Therefore the project was driven commercially both taking into account the market and the financing institutions.

Thus it was that the successful bid for the concession was won by the Channel Tunnel Group and the Governments in giving their reasons for their choice indicated that they centred largely on the financing proposals, the practicality of the scheme, the safety and security aspects and the lack of potential maritime problems.

So in early 1986 it was clear that the Eurotunnel system as it became known would cater for rail traffic on services run by the respective National Railways, both passenger and freight and road traffic between the two countries carried on shuttle trains that would circulate through specially constructed terminals at each end of the tunnels.

The strategy would be to negotiate revenues from the railways in exchange for use of the tunnels and infrastructure and to operate directly shuttle services for road freight and tourist traffic. The word tourist incidentally is used extensively but includes business and leisure traffic. The railways had long seen the potential for international traffic and for the French in particular this venture coincided with the development of the TGV services and therefore came at a perfect time. Indeed, with the benefit of hindsight we might speculate that there could not have been a successful cross channel fixed link before the development of proven high speed rail connections either in France or the UK. It is hard to imagine a successful challenge to the airline dominance on the London/Paris/Brussels routes without a high speed train.

For road borne traffic the challenge was a straight competition with the ferries but acknowledging at that time the highly successful, albeit ageing Hovercraft and their possible derivatives or successors. That the Eurotunnel scheme strategy was developed at that time in mature and well-established markets is of immense significance because it has enabled the original concept to remain largely unchanged.

Airlines, Shipping lines, airports and ports have all had to adapt to very substantial technical changes, significantly in the size, speed and turnaround capability of the vehicle. Eurotunnel was entering a reasonably stable marketplace. The Cross Channel Ferry operators had already identified their large vessels and the crossing times and service levels were well established. Dover/Calais had become the prime route and with the possible exception of the hovercraft and introduction of catamarans no radical new developments were envisaged. In this context the significance of the TGV network in France can be seen and the vision of the integration of the UK into the high speed train network would be a critical piece in the jigsaw.

The final factor in the strategy package; crossing time is fascinating. By amazing coincidence the target crossing time platform to platform was set at 35 minutes, the same as for the existing fastest routine crossing by hovercraft. Sets of forecasts were produced which resulted in capacity projections for the design of the system. Reference has already been made in this conference to the design capacity of the terminals and the trains. From the operators point of view, these are driven by the market demands as set out in the commercial part of the operating strategy and were set at a level that would permit the forecast levels of traffic to be carried without queuing at all but the peak period. With hourly capacity forecasts by vehicle type it is then possible to calculate train size and profile, taking into account weight, train technology, speed, headway and the number of paths available for the railways and the shuttles.

So the foundation was set in 1986 and the beginning of 1987 for an operating strategy to provide a tunnel system for rail transport that would provide fast and simple means of travelling by international railways, freight and passengers, by road freight or by car or coach and in all cases competitively.

1.2 The impact of the IGC

The basic strategy was, therefore, in place. It was an inherently safe and secure design with three tunnels providing all the best possible combinations of safety and security in the unlikely event of an incident, a sophisticated ventilation system, and producing always the principle of the central service tunnel as the safe haven as well as a means for maintenance and incident access.

The two Governments had appointed a Commission to supervise construction and operation of the Fixed Link and inter alia approve the designs, plans and safety arrangements, and the Intergovernmental Commission (IGC) was set up. The Governments also appointed a Safety Authority to advise the IGC and carry out the detailed work of studying the scheme, with the intention that the Safety Authority would, when it was satisfied, recommend to the IGC that an operating certificate could be issued at the appropriate time. The Maître d'Oeuvre (MDO) appointed with a wider technical brief found itself expected to offer considerable and detailed advice to the Safety Authority on some matters with substantial operational implications. The next stage of the operational strategy, the details, can best be described as a series of very tough negotiations as Eurotunnel sought to convince the IGC and its advisors that the system would work safely and securely.

Eurotunnel's strategy during this period, from 1987 to the present has been to preserve the key elements set out in its original submission to Governments, speed and simplicity, on which basis the mandate was awarded. An integral part of this proposal was the need to keep passengers and vehicles together at all times. The segregation of passengers would produce, in effect, a service little different from the existing ferry services. It would considerably increase the overall journey time, reduce capacity and frustrate the objectives of speed and simplicity, and in consequence would not offer the traveller a viable alternative to the existing services. The proposals set out in the submission to the Goverments were reflected with, however, some additional safety requirements of the two Goverments. In reviewing the design of the HGV wagons in the light of these it became apparent that it would be impractical, on weight grounds, to provide a wagon design that would enable HGV drivers to remain with their vehicles, in the same way as tourist drivers and passengers would with their vehicles. Eurotunnel therefore decided to carry HGV drivers in a separate amenity carriage (club car) at the front of each shuttle. This requires platform buses to transfer lorry drivers from their lorries, once loaded onto the shuttle, to the club car, and at the end of the journey to be returned by bus along the platform. In addition very significant restrictions on the carriage of certain materials means that Eurotunnel is not able to carry, under any circumstances, hazardous goods. Both these processes are developed a little further later in this paper.

For tourist traffic (i.e. cars and coaches), the IGC on the advice of the Safety Authority conceded that non-segregation could be pursued provided that a number of physical and operational measures were taken. The requirements would need to be, as they were required for HGVs, fire resistant wagons, independently protected from each other by two sets of fire barrier doors, several separate fire detection and suppression systems, closed circuit television cameras and patrolling by on board train crew. At the time of writing, approval has been given for freight services, both railway and HGV shuttle and approval to operate services for invited passengers on the Eurostar through passenger trains and tourist shuttles. When these have been satisfactorily developed the operating strategy will have incorporated the segregation of lorry drivers and the measures necessary to secure non-segregation of tourist vehicle drivers.

There were a number of other detailed requirements of course, and where these are of significance they are explained in the descriptive text that follows.

1.3 Security and Frontier Controls

In parallel with the development of safety arrangements to meet the IGC's demands the two Governments' security requirements had to be incorporated into Eurotunnel's security plan. The two Governments appointed teams of experts and advisors to consider Eurotunnel's proposals with the intention of implementing an approved system to secure the fixed link from both ends. This produced an immensely complex set of international discussions, lasting over 3 years that has resulted in a clear understanding of procedures and responsibilities in both terminals.

Security needs to be seen in the context of the agreed system of frontier controls that formed part of Eurotunnel's operational strategy with the two Governments for "juxtaposed" controls. This strategy provides for and permits all controls to be exercised at the terminal of departure; Customs, Immigration, Police and Security. The point of this is to facilitate free flow onto the motorway system in the country of arrival and is absolutely integral to the design and operating principals of the system. Thus the French Authorities work alongside their British counterparts carrying out their obligations at the start of the passengers' journey and both inbound and outbound checks are completed sequentially in one location; extremely efficient on space and critical for the UK in particular with its small terminal site.

The work with the Frontier Authorities has been extremely successful and Eurotunnel found the French and British Authorities constructive and interested in this new and innovative approach.

The agreed security arrangements require checks to be carried out on vehicles, passengers and staff. Eurotunnel cannot discuss the details but the measures will require some vehicles to undergo examinations. This process will be carried out both manually and using the latest technology equipment and the implications are relatively small as the traffic flow plans have incorporated discrete routes and search areas that should not cause significant delay.

For HGVs a state of the art scanning facility has been installed in each terminal that permits entire lorries to be conveyed remotely into a building whilst the driver waits in a separate waiting area. The process provides trained operators with detailed information with which to clear the entire vehicle and contents quickly, safely and efficiently. This particular facility, which is part of a package of security measures is known as Euroscan.

The progressive relaxation of frontier controls has not moved as fast as Eurotunnel would have liked and passports are still essential for travel in each direction.

1.4 Commercial Aspects - The Market Place

At the beginning of this paper, reference was made to the Governments' comments on the selection of a successful bidder for the concession. They had to be sure of the financial arrangements. Throughout the development of Eurotunnels plans, bankers have taken a hands-on role and monitored each step of our progress. Their greatest concern has been of course to ensure the repayment of their loans and interest and they have focused on the development of the customer side of the business. They want to be able to assess what the product is, how good is it, when will it be ready, will it work and will it attract the level of business forecast.

Therefore, Eurotunnel's operating strategy has had to be developed since early 1987 to ensure that these needs can be met (and of course because any private company's main raison d'être is to make money).

Happily, it can be said that the commercial and operating philosophies are complementary in almost all areas and the respective teams have worked harmoniously towards the original objectives as previously set out. The one exception to this relates to ticketing and tariffs. The original intention (and still remains) was to create a system that permits travellers to simply arrive at the toll barrier, pay and depart, exactly as one would at a motorway toll, operated so smoothly in France. However, Eurotunnel is entering an established market where passengers currently expect to make prior arrangements and where the distance and cost, involving a frontier crossing for people less used to it are not conducive to spontaneous travel.

Accordingly provision has been made for passengers to prepay and order and obtain a ticket in advance. It does not constitute a booking or reservation however, but does provide a "halfway house" between a motorway toll and a ferry.

2. The Operation of the System

2.1 How traffic will be scheduled

Having set a policy that is driven by forecasts, types and volumes of traffic and expectations, developed an operating philosophy to handle customers, arrangements are then put in hand to receive the traffic and handle it effectively. It has been explained that Eurotunnel has entered an established market with little short term changes in types or patterns of traffic and the system has been designed accordingly. There is limited scope for short term changes to the rolling stock. In particular the decision to dedicate three departures per hour exclusively to heavy goods vehicle carrying shuttles, and four departures per hour exclusively to tourist shuttles is fixed, and only extensive changes to rolling stock and some significant modifications to terminals would be necessary to change that.

The next step is to prepare a timetable to match, as closely as practicable the forecast daily and hourly demand. This is a customer driven process that identifies through the commercial part of Eurotunnel the needs of the market.

At this point it is appropriate to describe briefly how Eurotunnel has chosen to organise the operation of its system. Fig. 1 shows that there are two main operating units; Railways and Terminals. Railways are organised into Control Centre, Train Crew, Fixed Equipment and Rolling Stock. Terminals are organised into Road Traffic, Tolls, Security and Maintenance. Commercial and Marketing interfaces, as necessary with most of these departments.

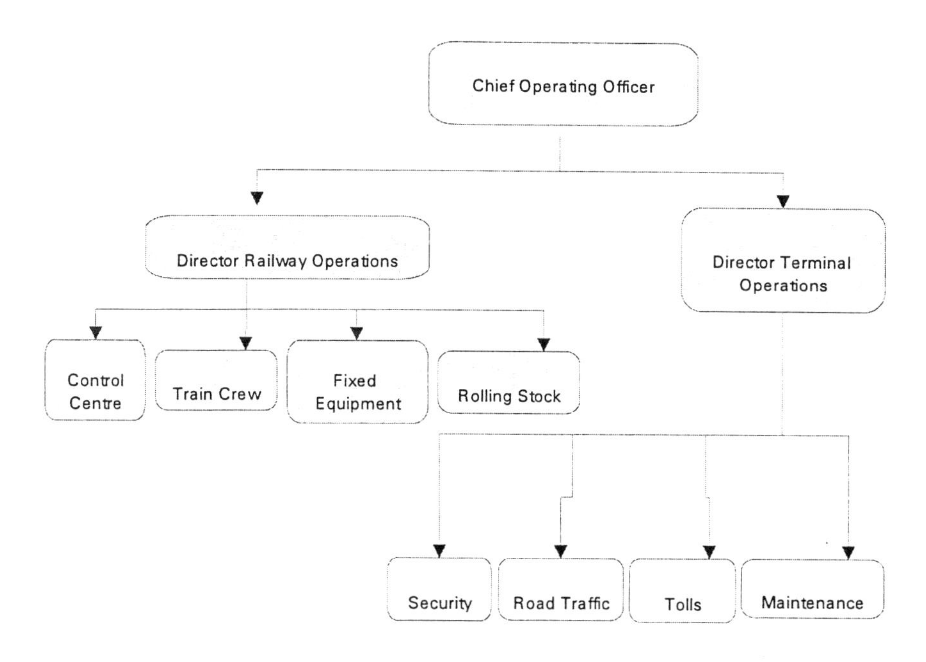

Fig. 1. Terminal and Railway Directorates - Organisation

A timetable is constructed by the Planning Unit within the Control Centre Team, taking into account the traffic flow needs provided by Commercial Department, shuttle availability, maintenance requirements within the Fixed Equipment areas and Rolling Stock. Available shuttle paths are utilised taking into account the requirements of the National Railways.
Full consultation takes place before the timetable is agreed. Following this each department can calculate how it will meet its role and deliver an agreed level of service, organising staff rosters, liaising with concessionaires, sub-contractors, frontier authorities and maintenance teams to produce a cohesive traffic flow.

The day-to-day operation is handled through four 24-hour, seven days per week Control Centres. The main rail Control Centre in the UK organises and runs all train movements and has a standby Control Centre in France that can take over in the event of an incident. Two Terminal Control Centres, one in France and one in the UK, organise the flow of vehicle traffic and sort, allocate and load it. Constant liaison between the controllers in each location ensures a smooth operation.

2.2 Description of the Transport System

2.2.1 *The Shuttles*

All shuttles comprise two rakes and two locomotives, a locomotive is located at each end of the shuttle. There are three types of shuttle wagon: HGV wagons and single and twin deck Tourist wagons. The twin deck wagons will take cars and other vehicles less than 1.85m in height, the single deck wagons will accept coaches and other high sided vehicles. The HGV wagons will accept Freight vehicles with a maximum height of 4.2m, width of 2.6m, length of 18.35m and a maximum weight of 44 tonnes.

There is one type of shuttle locomotive. These are all electric, using an overhead power supply system - the catenary. Diesel locomotives are used for marshalling, maintenance and emergency purposes.

2.2.2 *Handling and receiving traffic through the system*

From the Terminal approach, road customer vehicles pass through the toll plaza and continue through the frontier control zone, where security checks may be performed. Vehicles proceed to a designated area for allocation to a shuttle train, from where they are directed to the shuttle loading platform according to the safety rules.

The principal access to the UK Terminal is along a slip road off the M20 motorway. Principal egress from the Folkestone site is via a three lane exit road direct from the unloading overbridges. At the French terminal the primary access is from a dedicated grade-separated junction off the RN1 dual carriageway at Fort Nieulay. Main egress route from the site is separate for tourist and freight traffic. The two traffic systems will converge on the slip-road to the A16 at the Fort Nieulay interchange. Both road traffic systems are designed to allow free exit from the shuttles directly onto both national road network systems.

Freight and tourist vehicles are segregated for allocation to the appropriate shuttle. In the UK, directions are given on the Terminal approach roads by signs using vehicle symbols that will allow the driver to select the appropriate lane. On the French site there are separate freight and tourist terminals with traffic being segregated at the main interchange.

Approach to French Tolls

The principle means of vehicle control will be by road signs and markings, control signals and barriers. Signs are either static panels or variable message displays giving information about lane changes or routes to follow. Signs for users of the system will be bilingual, with the "home" language first followed by the other language, but operational signs will only be in the "home" language. An initial policy considered in the operational strategy was for traffic to be led by a pilot car. However, concerns about the labour intensive nature of this solution and the unanimous desire for an automatic system with a high capacity, led to the use of automatically controlled barriers and lights.

2.2.3 *Entrance into the Eurotunnel system*
The main entrance into the Eurotunnel system is through the toll plaza that fulfils the role of acting as a gateway for vehicles approaching the terminals.

The design and layout of the toll booths are influenced by the operators' intention of a rapid transaction time for a variety of payment methods. They have been assembled to serve both left and right handed drive vehicles consequently reducing queues and increasing throughput. After passing through the tolls, tourist traffic at both Terminals proceeds either to the amenity building or directly to the frontier controls.

UK TouristTolls

HGV Tolls at the French Terminal

2.2.4 *Operations at Frontier Controls and Security Areas*
At frontier controls vehicles may be stopped as necessary by Frontier Control Authorities or Eurotunnel Security.

2.2.5 *Tourist Vehicles*
At this point vehicle flow is picked up and becomes the responsibility of the terminal Traffic Control Centre. Road Traffic Controllers, operating with remote control and mimic display panels, direct traffic as described in the following sections. They liaise closely with Rail Traffic Controllers to ensure the smooth interface between the vehicles and the trains. Each shuttle is given a mission number by the railway department and the progress of this shuttle train is monitored constantly by the control centre.

Should further checks be necessary, vehicles will be taken out of line to a separate area so as not to impede the traffic flow from continuing to the next checks beyond.

2.2.6 *Freight Vehicles*
On the UK site, after tolls, freight vehicles proceed to the left of the main route into a freight amenity parking area. Here, there are six inspection lay-bys and a freight inspection booth. This allows processing of vehicles that may be transporting dangerous goods and confirmation, or otherwise, that they may travel. Those vehicles selected for further security inspection will be directed to the Euroscan facility. On clearance, these vehicles rejoin the through traffic to advance to the French Frontier Control.

At Freight Terminal France, after tolls, freight traffic will flow directly to the French Frontier

Control or can diverge to the left to make use of an "airside" parking area. On passing through directly to the frontier controls, vehicles are switched selectively into either an approach road to the French Frontier Controls or Freight Inspection/Security Area. Vehicles selected into the frontier controls area may be subject to checks of their documents. Should further checks be required, vehicles will undergo a security check in the Freight Inspection Facility that is similar to the Facility on the Folkestone site.

2.2.7 *Allocation of vehicles to trains*

After passing through the frontier controls, vehicles then proceed to the allocation area where they are allocated to shuttles that depart according to the scheduled timetable. To achieve this, the allocation zone is split into two areas:

(i) Pre-ordering zone. Tourist vehicles arriving from the frontier controls areas are sorted by type and size. At the front of each stream are barriers and lights that are controlled by the Terminal Traffic Management system and are regulated at intervals allowing the drivers at the front of the queues to proceed to the allocation reservoir in the correct order.

(ii) Handling reservoir. The handling zone is divided into two parts for vehicles that will load at the rear rake of the shuttle and those that will load at the centre for the front rakes. When ready for loading, barriers at the head of each lane of the stream will open to allow vehicles to proceed to the appropriate platforms.

The principle of the allocation operation is basically identical for both the British and French terminals and for both tourist and freight traffic.

Unloading at the UK Terminal

2.2.8 *Loading and unloading shuttles*
Vehicles are released from the holding reservoirs and are directed to the appropriate platforms along a route selected to avoid conflict with other traffic. Vehicles reach the relevant platforms by means of overbridges crossing the platform tracks and ramps from the bridges leading down to the platforms. On each terminal there are four overbridges and loading takes place from the rear two overbridges and ramps, and unloading on the front two. The management of traffic is the responsibility of the Road Traffic Department until the shuttle crew take over guidance and direction of traffic on its entry into the shuttle loader wagon.

2.2.9 *Loading Tourist Shuttles*
On the platforms, vehicles are directed by Customer Service Agents who are present at each loading door to guide vehicles into the shuttle. When on the shuttle, direction and care of customers and their vehicles lies with the shuttle crew. Tourist vehicles, unlike freight vehicles, will not be chocked. At the end of each wagon, there are full height and width fire barriers that are closed before the shuttle departs together with a vehicle stop barrier that is raised during transit and which prevents tourist vehicles moving forward to damage the fire doors. The fire barriers include pass doors enabling passengers to move between wagons.

2.2.10 *Handling Dangerous Goods through the System*
On arrival at the Terminal, the driver must declare the type and quantity of dangerous goods being carried. Eurotunnel then checks that the goods conform to the rules, register the vehicle and the goods under an internal reference number. A visual inspection of the exterior of the vehicle, by the Customer Service Agent Dangerous Goods, is carried out. If the vehicle is accepted, it must be recorded and identified by a dangerous goods sticker attached to the windscreen. Information regarding the vehicle's location on the shuttle is recorded against the shuttle's mission number. If the consignment described in the declaration does not comply with Eurotunnel's requirements, the vehicle with its load is refused entry to the system. The grounds for refusal are noted. It is also possible to use the security scanning facilities to ensure that no dangerous goods are concealed on freight vehicles.

3. Reason for a phased opening

The operators did not originally intend to implement a phased opening strategy. Eurotunnel had planned to introduce a full-running programme but for various reasons accepted a gradual build-up of services.

Due to the well publicised dispute with the manufacturers of the rolling stock, deliveries of the shuttle wagons were considerably delayed. This not only delayed acceptance testing and commissioning of the wagons, but also delayed commissioning of aspects of the tunnel system and training of staff.

The various types of rolling stock coming from different suppliers and of different complexity were being delivered, tested and commissioned to different timescales.

The very sophisticated safety measures incorporated into the rolling stock and tunnel system itself led to the commissioning taking longer than anticipated.

There was a natural preference of the Safety Authority for a gradual build up of services rather than a full launch of then to summer traffic.

Eurotunnel naturally wanted to open to revenue earning traffic as soon as the various elements of the project were ready and authorisation to commence commercial operation was granted.

These points combined to lead to a phased opening strategy.

The philosophy of a phased opening did have certain attractions for the operating departments. The opportunity to start with HGV services and through freight trains has enabled the operators to build up a vast knowledge of operating expertise during the summer of 1994. The operators will therefore be able to rectify any difficulties that may arise during the build-up of services. Specifically, the opportunity could be taken to commission the tunnel system including signalling, the response of emergency services and systems, the locomotives and all the operating staff under a lower level of traffic and therefore without the pressure of peak summer traffic. Adding all tourist traffic (shuttle and through trains) to the system would present an incremental increase that would be much easier and smoother for the staff given their experience gained from a phased opening.

4. Maintenance

4.1 *Tunnels and Fixed Equipment*

The necessity to run 24 hours, 7 days a week was always an operational necessity and the design of the system had to accommodate this. Accordingly a capability to transfer trains between tunnels to enable maintenance to be carried out was built in. The simple solution was to construct the tunnel system in sections, connected by rail crossovers that would enable single line working in either tunnel whilst maintaining the other. This was achieved by the construction of two crossovers that divide the tunnel system into three sections of approximately the same size. With three sections in each running tunnel there is the capability to maintain within one sixth of the system at one time.

This is done at night from works trains that enter from bases in both terminals. Tunnel maintenance is handled by bi-national teams of maintenance engineers split into four principal areas of activity: control and communications, track and catenary, power supplies and stores and planning and logistics. Work is scheduled according to planned maintenance programmes and conventional railway possessions organised through the Rail Control Centre. Eurotunnel has a sub-contracting policy that makes use of specialist companies whilst maintaining a core expertise in each discipline within the company.

Thus works trains are planned to provide a variety of activity simultaneously to make use of track possessions at night. Trains are made up and led by Eurotunnel technical staff.

Complementary to these is a multi-purpose fleet of service tunnel transport vehicles, known as STTSs. These purpose designed bi-directional vehicles carry works teams and equipment through the service tunnel whilst trains operate normally in the running tunnels. To supplement these rapid response teams, a fleet of small, highly mobile more flexible LADOG, engineering support and quick response vehicles provide a total maintenance response capability from either terminal.

4.2 *Rolling Stock*

Rolling Stock Maintenance is the subject of a separate paper and for the purposes of this paper it needs only be explained that a comprehensive rolling stock maintenance facility operates in the Calais terminal with a small support unit in the UK. The workshops are well-equipped and are similar to those provided by the SNCF for the TGV service. The principle feature is the ability to work on groups of wagons or triplets, groups of triplets or rakes (half a full train) without the need to uncouple and separate.

4.3 *Terminals*

Maintenance in the terminal areas on critical electronic and control systems handling traffic management, toll equipment and security equipment is handled by technicians on 24 hour roster whilst comprehensive sub-contracting is used for civil and E & M Maintenance, cleaning, waste disposal, fire detection and alarm systems, weigh bridges, catering equipment and lifts.

5. Conclusion

At the time of writing the first HGV and National Railways Freight Trains have started commercial service and Eurotunnel is hopeful that full Operating Certificates will be granted shortly for passenger services.

The strategies and operating methodologies described in this paper are being tested and Eurotunnel is feeling confident that the system is being made to work extremely well by a very highly motivated and competent operational work force.

The product is superb; the trains are powerful, fast and silent and the feedback from the first customers is extremely positive. The operational strategy is surviving contact with reality.

EPS Operations

A. Bath, Operations Director, European Passenger Services, Waterloo Station, London

BACKGROUND

The title of this session is EPS Operations. Perhaps I should first explain what is EPS and how it fits in to the total picture.

European Passenger Services came into being, formally, some four years ago as the British Rail subsidiary Company specifically formed to work with our European National Railway partners, principally SNCF and SNCB, in capitalizing upon the exciting opportunities for through rail journies between the U.K. and continental Europe opened up by the creation of the Channel Tunnel. Today, EPS is already a substantial Company with very significant assets, over a billion pounds of investment providing state-of-the-art rolling stock, stations and maintenance depots, with a highly motivated and skilled work force, EPS was transferred to Government ownership on the 09 May this year as a prelude to eventual privatization. This separation from British Rail has created the need for back-to-back contracts to be negotiated to assign previously existing contractural rights, the negotiation of a new Access Contract with Railtrack, and certain other new contracts for services supplied. Originally, BR and SNCF teams had negotiated jointly with Eurotunnel a contract called the "Usage Contract" which covered all the payment of tolls and costs by the Railways, the 50% right to capacity through the Tunnel and the obligations of the parties.

THE MARKET

Travel by UK residents to near European countries has exhibited strong growth over the last decade, with growth in air travel outstripping sea growth by over 3 to 1. Across the Channel, the picture is similar although the market is only about half the size. Altogether, growth in travel between the UK and these countries has averaged 4.5% per annum over the last 10 years. Travel from the UK is dominated by holiday traffic - 60% of total travel compared with 45% in the reverse direction - and by travel to France which accounts for 65% of the total.

Taking the European Union as a whole, the total number of single journeys between Britain and other continental countries amounts to some 68 million. Rail is unlikely to be able to compete in all of this market, either because the journeys are over longer distances, and more likely to be captured by air, or because journeys are made by car, with the decision to use a car often being based on touring needs and luggage convenience in the case of families.

The key targets for rail are short haul air journeys and non-car-based sea journeys - a market roughly equating to 38 million single journeys. The economics of passenger rail services compared with those of competitor modes - air, coach and car - favour journeys in the 2-4 hour time band. This factor, coupled with the distribution of cross-Channel passenger demand which is concentrated on the capital cities, means that the core passenger services will be concentrated on London to Paris and London to Brussels flows.

THE TIMETABLING OPPORTUNITIES

Before considering what detailed train services were necessary to service this market, it was first necessary to establish what capacity was available not only for EPS but also for Railfreight Distribution, the B.R. freight Division that was similarly working with our continental partners to develop the international freight rail market. Capacity in the Tunnel was relatively easily established; the National Railways expecting, by contract, to have available to them 50% of the total pathways. Initially, and other than at nights and weekends, three minute headways were expected to ideally produce 20 paths each hour. Fast National Railway passenger trains would, of course, potentially use more than 1 "standard" path (defined as the time taken by a Eurotunnel Shuttle train) as would slower moving freight trains. The mix of, trains was, therefore, of considerable importance in planning terms if tunnel capacity was to be maximised. Needless to say, it was accepted that at some future date the capacity of the Tunnel could only be maximised if all trains ran at a constant speed. The implications of this will obviously have to be addressed in the years to come.

In terms of complexity, however, the Tunnel and indeed the problems of timetabling in France and Belgium were as nothing compared with those faced by the planners in creating sufficient capacity over British Rail - now Railtrack - metals.

Not only was the problem complex, but regard also had to be paid to the additional limitations imposed by the Channel Tunnel Act which, amongst other constraints, provided certain protections to existing commuters and required all stations on the lines of route to remain open. This effectively placed a limit on the number of peak hour international services. Additionally, there were the financial parameters which constrained route infrastructure improvements and the physical constraints which limited the size of Waterloo International terminal to five platforms. Differing national "cultures" had also to be reconciled with the British planners preferring a regular interval frequency of services compared to the traditional French style of gaps in service mid morning and mid afternoon.

After much work in darkened rooms, a simple, yet exciting and original solution emerged with provision made for two flights of two international passenger trains each hour running four minutes apart. The opportunity was therefore created for an hourly service to and from Paris and Brussels with the potential to supplement this to a half-hourly service when the market required it.

Figure 1

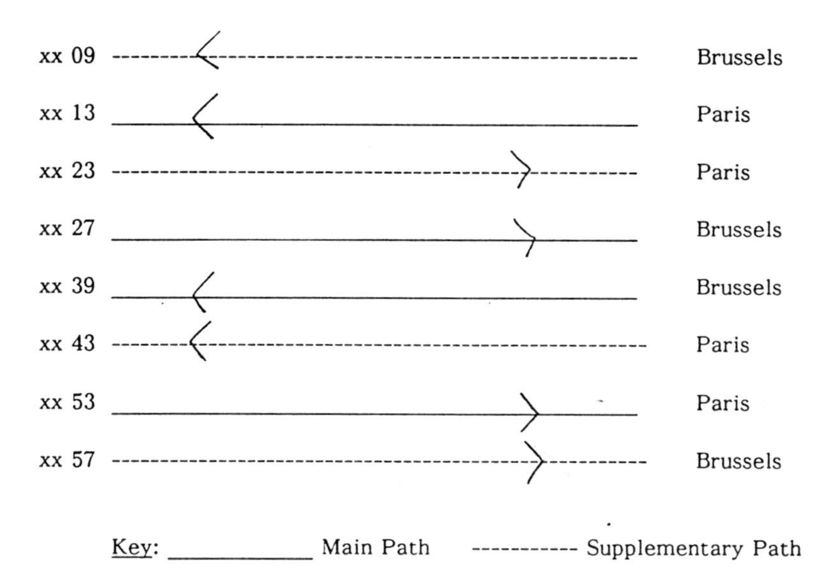

Unfortunately, the imposed constraints meant that this solution could not apply in the two-hour London commuter peak periods, the most serious problem being in the outwards evening peak from London when capacity only exists for 6 pathways. It is hoped that this can be overcome in due course thus enabling a regular pattern of services to apply throughout the whole day.

The timetable planners also found a good solution for the international freight trains with, other than during peak periods, one path per hour via Maidstone East (Boat Train Route 2; since retitled Channel Tunnel Route - CTR - 2), and one path per hour via Tonbridge and Redhill (CTR3). A total of 35 freight paths each weekday were identified using these two routes. International passenger trains use the routes via Orpington (CTR1) and Maidstone East (CTR2) with additional sections available via the Catford Loop and via Bat and Ball.

The complete planning process is as illustrated in Figure 2.

Figure 2.

THE PLANNING CYCLE

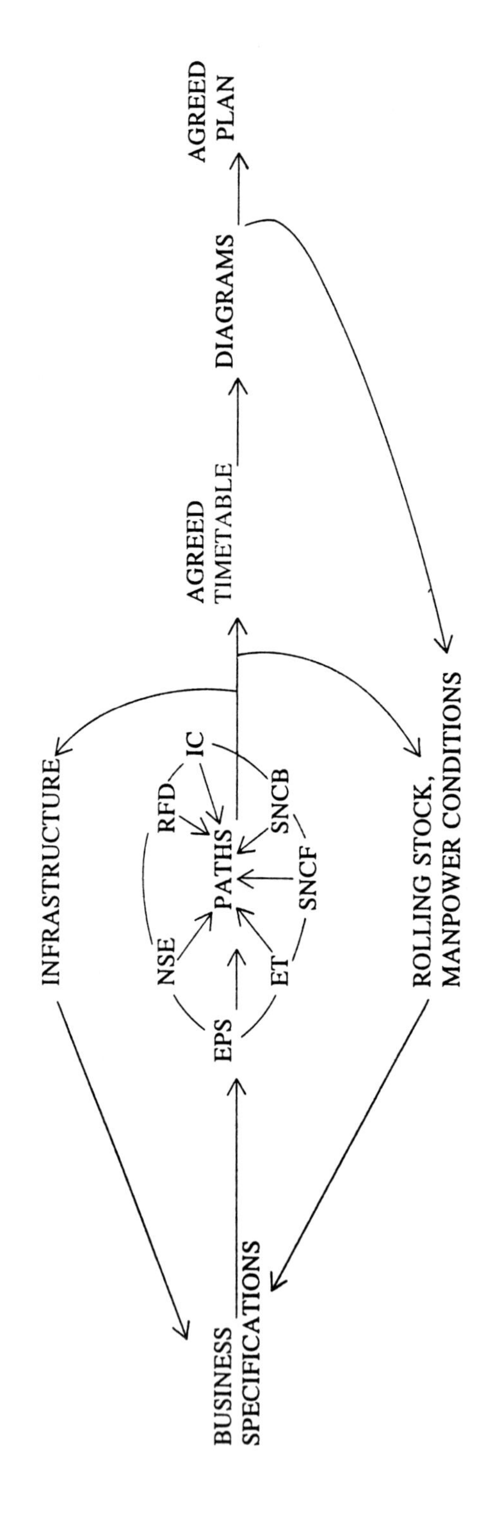

INTERNATIONAL PASSENGER TRAIN SERVICES

The train services fall into 3 groups:-

(1) London-Paris and London-Brussels ("Inter Capital" services)

(2) North of London to both Paris and Brussels ("Beyond London" services)

(3) Overnight services

The Inter Capitals services will be operated in collaboration with French and Belgian Railways and the three railways have collectively purchased 31 new trains to provide services on an hourly pattern between both London-Paris and London-Brussels - supplemented at peak times to half-hourly. The new services will be marketed under the brand name Eurostar with its very distinctive logo.

3 hour London-Paris journey times will be achieved by Eurostar trains. London-Brussels times will initially be 15 minutes longer but when the high speed line from the French border to Brussels is completed in 1997, Brussels journeys will be shortened by half an hour. Intermediate stations at Lille and Calais Frethun will be served by selected trains, as will the new International Station at Ashford scheduled to be open at the end of 1995.

Much of the market lies outside the 3 capitals and this can be served in the following ways:-

in the case of Antwerp, Liege, Holland and Germany by interchange at Brussels Midi Station. The addition of traffic from beyond Brussels will strengthen demand on the Brussels route and result in a more dense pattern of services on this route than could be justified by the Brussels market alone.

in France, by interchange at Lille from London-Lille Eurostar services to French inter-regional TGV services to the South and West of France.

and in Britain, by a limited range of direct services provided by a subfleet of 7 modified Eurostar trains operating 1 return service per day on 5 routes:-

Manchester to Brussels

Manchester to Paris

Birmingham to Paris

Glasgow to Paris

Glasgow to Brussels

These latter services are designed principally for the leisure market, leisure passengers tending to be both interchange averse and having a lower value of time than business customers. A wider range of journey opportunities will be provided by interchange in London between domestic and Eurostar services. Due to capacity constraints on the routes between London and the Channel Tunnel, each beyond London service must use one of the 4 paths per hour earmarked for Eurostar on routes between London and the Channel Tunnel.

EPS is also a shareholder in European Night Services Ltd - a company established with French, German and Dutch Railways to provide over-night services through the Channel Tunnel. These services are designed to extend rail market penetration by combining a night's sleep with travel. A fleet of 139 vehicles has been ordered consisting of:-

sleeping cars

coaches containing reclining seats

service vehicles containing buffet bar and lounge.

These vehicles will be marshalled into trains which it is, anticipated will operate between:-

London to Dortmund, Frankfurt and Amsterdam

Glasgow to Paris and Brussels

Swansea to Paris

Plymouth to Brussels

All our products are aiming to be highly competitive, providing our customers not just with an excellent journey but giving them what we call "quality time" plus added value packages such as meals and business lounges in stations.

OUR STATIONS

Purpose designed stations have been built in Paris (Gare du Nord), Brussels (Midi), and Waterloo. Mike Etwell has described the trains and maintenance facilities already but, within EPS, we are also extremely proud of our new terminal at Waterloo.

The station has high quality facilities for passengers and comprises 5 dedicated platforms, a departure level, an arrival level and a car park (140 spaces) together with back up servicing facilities located in the undercroft of Waterloo Station. It has been designed to handle a maximum of 4 trains and 3000 passengers per hour, both arriving and departing.

Considerable effort has been devoted in the design of the terminal to maximise convenience for both departing and arriving passengers, particularly in terms of minimising walking distances. Professional consultant advice, based on considerable experience in designing modern airports, was obtained in respect of the passenger flows and road access design. It is these elements that have led to the 4 level design of the terminal.

The terminal has also been designed to meet the requirements of Government Border Control Authorities and agreed security standards. A Station Operators Licence has already been obtained following the submission of a Safety Case to the Health and Safety Executive earlier this year.

Ashford International Station is currently under construction. The work provides for an additional island platform (two platform faces) to be provided for NSE services and one of the existing NSE island platforms to be lengthened to accommodate the Eurostar Trains. New, but separate Passenger reception buildings are being provided for Domestic and International Passengers with new bridge and subway connections to/from the platforms. The International building is specified to similar quality standards as Waterloo International with provision for Border and Security control facilities. There will be a large car parking facility adjacent. For the passenger building and Car Park EPS has concluded a contractual arrangement with Laings, by which the latter build and own the facility. EPS will operate it and pay tolls per passenger to Laings.

Appropriate Track and Signalling alterations are included in the authorised work to provide flexible and reliable operation of all services. The work is currently on target and is expected to be complete and the facilities ready for use in late 1995.

OUR STAFF

The Eurostar service will be provided jointly by EPS, SNCF and SNCB but based upon an agreement that each partner would employ its own part of the contributing workforce. So far as EPS is concerned, these requirements were built up from a zero base with analysis of tasks and resources needed being first undertaken. EPS staff currently number some 930 with final numbers estimated to be between 1400 and 1500. The build up of staff has been quite dramatic with numbers doubling this year alone. Recruitment, however, continues to go well. It is also interesting to note that a number of important activities are being contracted out, including security, train cleaning, and on-board service provision.

A new Company and a new workforce has consequently been created and with this has come new employment contracts and conditions with the objective of attracting and retaining quality staff to deliver a quality service. A brand new set of arrangements, very different from those existing on BR, have been put in place with a single Contract of Employment for all full time staff (Appendices cover variations in work patterns, etc.). Inclusive salaries - all paid four-weekly by bank transfer - are applicable with no enhancements or allowances of any kind. We have been determined to move away from a traditional "overtime culture". All staff have salary ranges rather than fixed point salaries, and all increases are performance related. Annualised hours provide maximum flexibility with many staff having both "contract" and "rostered" hours. In the case of International Train Drivers, for example, a 1900 hours Annual Contract exists with Drivers being rostered for 1700 of these hours. The remaining 200 are available to cover sickness, short notice absences, etc. and provide considerable flexibility.

Recruitment has been by means of structured competitive selection with, at present, less than 40% of the workforce having come from BR. 60% have come from other sources including airlines, airports, travel companies, armed forces, etc. and as recruitment continues increasing numbers are coming from outwith the industry. High standards, freedom of choice and an attractive image have created a strikingly young Company with an average age already below 35.

On train staffing is one Driver, two Train Managers plus up to 10 on-board services staff (two of whom are essential for safety duties whilst the train is in the Tunnel).

Finally, mention must be made of our Company's relations with the Trade Unions. At present, we are a non-unionised Company. Nevertheless, constructive discussions have taken place with the four major railway Trade Unions and staff will be given the opportunity to decide for themselves, in due course, whether, and which, Trade Unions should be considered for formal recognition. The whole thrust of EPS's approach is to deal with people on an individual basis, hopefully thereby creating a very limited agenda of collective issues.

TRAINING

Five particular peculiarities exist so far as training of staff is concerned. The sets are both new and complex, catering as they do for four different railway systems, whilst at the same time introducing many original and innovative design features. Eurotunnel Rules and Procedures have, in conjunction with them, had to be agreed and published in a form acceptable to all concerned. Again, many features are totally new to all staff concerned. Foreign Rules, Regulations, procedures and routes have all had to be learnt for the first time, not just once but twice as the practices in France and Belgium do vary very significantly. Above all, foreign languages have had to be learnt.

A few words on the latter may well be appropriate as it was originally considered to be the biggest risk area to our whole operation. When the original decision was made that driving a train to and from Paris or Brussels in a turn of duty (and vice versa of course) represented a fair day's work, the challenge was thrown down that our Train Crew would need to learn adequate French (the language of the Inter-Capitals Services being English and French) to enable them to operate safely on the continent. In the absence of a suitable language training package for land transportation, four London Universities were contracted to construct one. The course duration was, for Drivers, agreed as 20 weeks with 30 hours training per week minimum. The course was constructed in a series of modules, the actual delivery of which could be put out to tender to any language provider able and willing to undertake this work. The final six weeks of the 20 week course was arranged to be undertaken in France in two separate spells with staff living continuously for 18 days with a French family instructed to speak only in French. At the same time, 30 hours of classroom tuition was also provided each week - a case of "total immersion".

Examinations have to be undertaken at the end of each module and the whole was rounded off by an independent examination and certification. We thought it a quite daunting task (Mike Etwell and myself having been two of the four "guinea pigs" who had test marketed one of the 3 week foreign modules), especially when it is remembered that most of our Drivers left school at an early age with relatively few qualifications. I am very pleased to report, however, that at this stage we have had a 100% success level and we now have 47 of our existing 61 Drivers fully competent to the level of French we aspired. A real success story.

Operationally, new features specific to the Eurostar trains had to be trained in, and perhaps it is relevant to mention a few of the most important. The Eurostar Driver's position is equipped with a screen and a keyboard by which the Driver can access an on-board computer for information on the condition of the train set, how to correct possible equipment failures, and what restrictions might apply to its operation in a given condition. This information may also be sent by radio directly to the Control Office; each Network having its own Control but co-ordinated by a central office in Lille. The Control Office can thus inform any maintenance centre if there has been an incident or if work is required to be undertaken enabling the repair staff to begin to prepare for such work even before the train set arrives. The on-board signalling system - TVM430 - was also new to British crews. This system features a cab display indicating the speed limits to be observed by the driver and operates through the picking up and de-coding of data sent to the train through trackside beacons and the running rails. Not only does it plot a speed control curve but applies braking to the train if the prescribed speed is not observed. The train is also equipped with an ATESS system, a sophisticated "black box" recording everything that the Driver demands and the train delivers (other than voice exchanges with signal boxes which are themselves recorded at the boxes).

Finally, from an operational point of view, the trains are equipped with an "ET NO GO" indication which informs the Driver should the train be in an unsound condition - for whatever reason - which will prohibit it from entering the Channel Tunnel. We all trust this will be a very rare occurrence! It will, in fact, only apply if one or more of the following conditions have not been met:

a) the main circuit breakers in both power cars are closed

b) the computers in both power cars are in liaison with each other

c) at least one air compressor is available on each half-set

d) at least two battery chargers are available on each half-set

e) at least 50% transformer output is available to supply 1 motor bloc (2 traction motors) and the essential auxilliary supply for passenger comfort on a half-set

f) there is sufficient traction power available to one motor block to move a half-set out of the Tunnel from the steepest gradient.

Particular attention is being given to ensuring that trains will not be stopped in the Tunnel due to equipment defect or malfunction due to fire. This is achieved by protection of critical components, careful selection of materials and duplication of control systems. Special care has been taken in the selection of cable insulation materials and finishing used on the trains to minimise the generation of toxic fumes should a fire occur. Carriage floors will be capable of resisting the spread of fire for 30 minutes as will fire doors at either end of each vehicle. In the event of a fire, passengers can be evacuated to an adjacent coach.

There will be automatic fire extinguishers in the traction power units. All carriages will be air conditioned with sealed windows. If there is smoke in the Tunnel, the driver can switch the air conditioning to full recirculation mode to prevent smoke from being drawn into the coaches. External door blocking will be under the remote control of the driver. In an emergency, doors may, however, be opened locally.

Each international train can be split in the centre creating two halves, each with its own power car and also behind each power car. If necessary, part of the train can be used to evacuate passengers from the Tunnel. In the event of a power car failure, the other is able to move the whole train out of the Tunnel.

COMMISSIONING

Commissioning Tests with Eurostar trains were conducted in the Channel Tunnel in March and April this year.

These tests allowed verification of proper operation of the trainsets in the Tunnel, in particular:

* the voltage changeover from the BR 750V network to the Tunnel 25kV network, and between the signalling systems (AWS [Automatic Warning System] and TVM 430);

* the operation of TVM 430 in the specific conditions of the Tunnel;

* current collection using each of the two types of pantograph (25kV and 3kV). It will be possible to use the 3kV pantographs, normally used in Belgium, in the Tunnel should the need arise;

* traction performance;

* the operation of the fire detection and fire-fighting devices.

Various other tests related to passenger comfort have been conducted, including measurements of internal noise levels. All tests were satisfactorily concluded.

In conclusion, therefore, this Conference is taking place at a time when, for the Inter-Capitals service, EPS, with its partner railways, is moving from a planning to an operational phase. Our immediate requirements are obviously to build revenue and to deliver quality.

At the same time, planning continues on the "Beyond London" and night services, while presentations are currently being made to those short-listed consortia hoping to gain the contract to build the new Channel Tunnel Rail Link (CTRL). That link will not only release capacity to allow continued growth, but will generate more traffic as a result of better journey times for both domestic and international services. For the latter, half an hour or so will be taken off the journey time from St Pancras to the Tunnel with a 16 minute reduction from Waterloo. CTRL is likely to provide 20 passenger train paths per hour, half of which are likely to be used by international passenger services. The impact of that on the Tunnel may well for the subject of a separate Conference in the years to come.

Discussion on session 4

B. North, *North Transport Consultants*

How are the types and numbers of vehicles allocated, firstly, to the trains and, secondly, to the wagons to maximize the capacity of the trains?

D. Love
Reply to B. North

Road vehicles must be allocated and directed to the following types of shuttles.

- HGV Shuttle (train). A unique shuttle only suitable for HGVs (because of segregation of drivers) and never combined with another type of shuttle. It may comprise 2 rakes (sets). One HGV is the load of one wagon.
- Single Deck Rake. Suitable for coaches and cars. Normally one coach per wagon.
- Double Deck Rake. Only suitable for cars with limited height.

Single and Double Deck rakes can be in combination, two rakes per shuttle.
The outline terminal traffic sequence is as follows.

- Identification — by self (e.g. coach or HGV driver) or by measurement of height and length at toll payment area. HGVs are separately streamed before this point.
- Ordering — by proceeding into lanes appropriate to each type and capacity of shuttle rake.
- Release — when shuttle is ready to load, the ordering lanes are released to the correct shuttle loading point.

The process is controlled from a Road Control Centre for each terminal by means of signs, lights, lifting barriers and ground personnel. The controllers are computer aided and have a visual overview of the terminal, either directly from the control tower or by CCTV. Means of communication are available to coordinate with all parties, especially the Rail Control.
The object is to achieve 100% load factor if sufficient traffic is on offer for a given frequency of service, the avoidance of misdirection or misallocation which could be inconvenient to the customer and a minimum time between vehicle arrival at Eurotunnel and safe dispatch on the shuttle.
This answer is a highly simplified summary on what developed into a unique and complex operation. The subject is explained in the paper *Terminal traffic flows* by R. Napthine and D. Meredith.

The Channel Tunnel Signalling System

P.M. Robins BSc CEng MIEE MIRSE
Eurotunnel, Calais, France

Introduction

Railway signalling is the primary safety system of the channel tunnel transport system. Its role is to maintain a safe separation between following trains and to prevent conflicts at junctions. The signalling thus imposes a minimum separation between trains, and hence determines the maximum capacity in trains per hour of the tunnel.

In order to obtain a return on the massive investment involved in the construction of the tunnel, the operator obviously wishes to maximise the number of trains using it, and hence the traffic capacity of the tunnel must not be unduly constrained by the signalling. In other words, the trains must be allowed to run as close together as possible.

Trains with relatively high speeds and great length and weight have correspondingly long braking distances. This conflicts with the aim of running them close together. The problem is further exacerbated by the mixture of different train types running at different speeds. The signalling design can only be optimum for any one class of train.

The challenge for the signalling engineer has been to design a system that resolves this conflict whilst assuring absolute safety of operation.

The service frequency specified for the start of operations is a minimum interval between trains in each direction of 3 minutes. This is minimum interval is only meaningful for signalling design purposes in association with a specific maximum speed and minimum braking distance. For the purposes of the Channel Tunnel, the maximum speed has been taken as 160 km/h and the minimum braking distance as that of a fully loaded shuttle train. The train path, i.e. the time interval occupied by a single train, is thus specified around the shuttle train performance.

The 3 minute service frequency performance target for the signalling system is equivalent to a capacity of 20 shuttle train paths per hour in each direction. This can be expanded to 24 paths per hour with the current system but the ultimate target of 30 paths an hour will probably only be achieved by a new system.

These paths are divided equally between the railways and ET. However, since the performance of the railways trains is not the same as that of the ET shuttles (the speed is higher or lower than that of the shuttle), each train may require two or more shuttle paths. Thus in practice the likely initial maximum service is 15 trains per hour, 10 shuttles and 5 from the railways.

Choice of Signalling System

The Act of Concession, under which Eurotunnel operate, lays down certain technical constraints for the railway signalling. these are essentially that a cab signalling system with automatic train protection (ATP) should be used. A cab signalling system is one in which all indications are normally be given to the train driver on a display in the driving cab rather than by conventional coloured light signals by the track. ATP is a system on the locomotive which will stop the train automatically if the driver makes an error such as driving too fast or too close to the train in front.

Cab signalling and ATP are relatively new technologies, particularly in conventional railway, as opposed to metro, applications. The need to install and test the system quickly ruled out the development of a new system, or extensive modification to any existing one. This restricted the choice to three or four systems; a choice which was further restricted by the desire on the part of British and French Railways (BR and SNCF) to minimise the number of different systems carried by their trains. This desire is understandable, given that the BR and SNCF trains would in any case have to be equipped to cope with the British, two French and the Belgian conventional signalling systems and the system installed on the high speed line from Paris to the tunnel.

The obvious solution, therefore, was to use this latter system in the tunnel. It is known as TVM430 and was developed by SNCF from the TVM300 used first on the high speed line from Paris to Lyons. Drivers of trains from Paris to London have therefore to be familiar with only three types of signalling (French lineside, TVM430, UK lineside), rather than four.

TVM430 will be implemented in the Tunnel using the same philosophy as on TGV Nord; that is, as a speed code system. The line is divided into block sections, in each of which normally only one train may be present, the end of one section and the start of the next is indicated by a sign beside the track called a "block marker". The presence of a train in a block section causes a series of indications to be transmitted in preceding sections instructing any following train to slow down and stop. (Figure 1).

The block section immediately preceding an occupied section is known as the "overlap section" and no train may normally enter it. The next four sections form the stopping distance, in each of which the driver receives instructions to reduce speed. The first section in which an indication other than "line clear" is received is the warning block, in which the driver is alerted to the need to commence a speed reduction in the next block.

The indication to the driver takes the form of a 3 digit, fail-safe display. If the line is clear for at least six block sections ahead this indicates the current safe maximum speed. In the braking section the target speed is shown - this being the speed which the driver must achieve at the next block marker. If a speed restriction is in force the display gives a speed reduction sequence followed by the new safe maximum speed.

The distinction between these different indications is made by the colour of the digits - black on green for line clear, black on white for warning of a speed reduction, white on black to instruct execution of a speed restriction, black on red for a stop. In the case of the speed reduction, if it must continue in the next block, the display will flash.

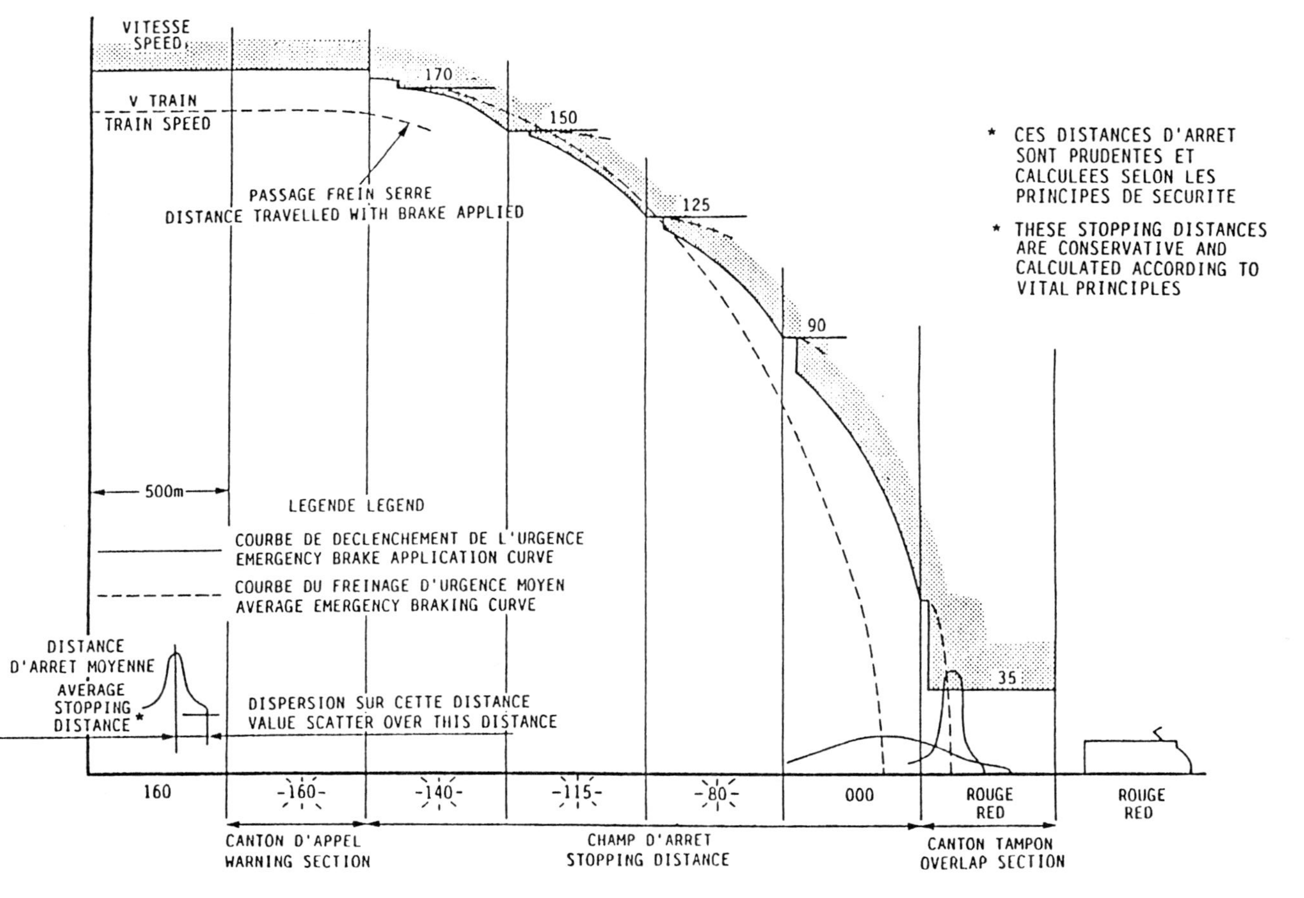

Fig. 1. TVM 430 design principle

Should the driver enter the overlap block section, an occupied block, or one where the ground equipment has failed the display shows red.

The driver is backed by a fail-safe Automatic Train Protection system. If the train exceeds the maximum safe speed at any time by more than 10 km/h (5 km/h below 80 km/h), an emergency brake application is enforced to bring the train to a stand.

The principal difference in philosophy between TGV Nord and the Tunnel concerns the use of permissive blocks. On the TGV Nord line the blocks are normally permissive, unless there are points within the block section. Thus after bringing the train to a stand at the block marker denoting the end of the block section, the driver may proceed into the following section under "proceed on sight" rules without further authorisation. The ATP system will restrict speed under these conditions to 35 km/h.

All blocks in the Tunnel are absolute, and may not be passed by the driver until he is authorised to do so. In the terminals where such authorisations may have to be given regularly in the course of shunting operations, the authorisation is given by a white light mounted on the block marker, which is illuminated when it is safe to allow the train to proceed on sight. Elsewhere the authorisation is given verbally by radio. If the driver attempts to proceed without authorisation an emergency brake application is enforced by the ATP system.

Trackside Equipment

The TVM430 uses the running rails both to detect the presence of trains and to transmit information to them. Audio frequency jointless track circuits are used for both purposes. Each track circuit consists of a transmitter and a receiver connected across the rails, one at each end of the track circuit. A signal is transmitted from transmitter to receiver through the rails. When a train is present, its axles shunt the signal so that it does not reach the receiver. The absence of the signal is interpreted by the receiver as meaning that the circuit is "occupied".

The signal is audio frequency, modulated with the information to be transmitted to the train. It is detected by antennae mounted before the front axle of the locomotive and decoded by the on-train equipment.

There are four carrier frequencies, two of which are used on each running line, alternating from track circuit to track circuit i.e. f1,f2,f1 ... on line 1, f3,f4,f3 ... on line 2. This maintains separation between adjacent track circuits on the same line and prevents interference between track circuits on parallel lines. The on-train equipment is switched from one frequency pair to the other by a "track change loop" - described later.

The carrier frequency is modulated with one or more from a total of 27 possible low modulation frequencies. Since any combination of these frequencies may be present at one time, the code transmitted from the track circuit may be thought of as a 27 bit digital word, the absence of any frequency representing a "0" in that bit position, the presence representing a "1".

This word is divided up into fields, each of which represents an element of information required by the on-train equipment. These are speed code, gradient, block section length, gradient, network code, error checking.

The speed code represents in a coded form the current maximum safe speed for the train, the speed it should be doing at the end of the current block (the "target speed") and the target speed for the end of the next block. The code transmitted will depend, therefore, on the civil engineering speed limit in force, and the state of track circuits ahead. The gradient is the average over the current block, the length of which is specified by the next field.

The network code allows the same track to train transmission system to be used on lines with different characteristics. Depending on the network code, the same speed code will be interpreted in different ways by the on board equipment. For example, on the high speed line the maximum speed is 300 km/h, requiring a particular interpretation of the speed codes. In the tunnel, where the speeds are much lower, a completely different interpretation is required. Thus the high speed line and Tunnel TVM430 systems will transmit different network codes.

The error checking field is a checksum of the previous fields, allowing the on-train equipment to verify correct reception of the codes.

In order to provide the capacities given in the Introduction, track circuit lengths in the tunnel are around 450 m, considerably less in the terminals.

Track circuit transmitters and receivers are located with the processors which calculate the codes to be transmitted. These are housed in the Tunnel in equipment rooms at intervals of about 14 km, determined by the 7 km maximum feeding distance for the track circuits.

Processing is carried by the "monoprocesseur codé" (coded single processor). This device uses a single industry standard microprocessor (Motorola 68000 series) to perform processing to a vital standard (mean time between wrong side outputs $< 10^{-9}$). This is achieved by the coding of the data and the checking of the codes generated from these codes during processing. The monoprocesseur codé was developed for use in the SACEM signalling system now in service on RER line A in Paris.

In addition to transmission by track circuit, a non-vital means of transmitting supplementary information is available. This is a cable loop placed in the track where required, which transmits a phase-shift modulated digital signal. This is used in for several functions, including automatic control of loco power through neutral sections, track change instructions (see above) and to enforce the emergency stop after unauthorised passing of a block marker (see above).

All temporary and permanent speed limits are imposed through the TVM 430 system. Temporary restrictions may be imposed either locally, by switches located at each equipment cross passage (each 750 m), or remotely, through the Rail Traffic Management system at the control centre. In the tunnel, speed limits of 100, 60 or 30 km/h are available. A 0 km/h speed limit may also be imposed as protection for engineering works.

On-Train Equipment (Figure 2)

The signal from the track circuit is detected by two pairs of antennas, one antenna from each pair over each running rail. These are mounted on the loco body, about a metre ahead of the leading axle. The signal from each pair of antennas is decoded by a digital signal processor, one per pair. The function of these processors is to demodulate the signal frequencies to produce the 27 bit data word.

The data is fed to a monoprocesseur codé forming the display processor, which performs the main decoding functions. If the data received from the two digital signal processors differs, the monoprocesseur signals an error, causing the system to shut down. This guards against hardware faults in the signal processors.

The display processor decodes the speed code field and drives the cab display, through relays whose position is monitored by the processor. It also passes the speed, together with the gradient and block length information to a separate processor which carries out the ATP functions.

This processor uses this data to calculate a deceleration curve which the train should follow. The real speed is continuously monitored against this curve, and the emergency brakes are called if the safe speed is exceeded.

The real train speed is obtained from a fail-safe tachometer, which obtains three readings from two independently driven axles. It has inputs from the braking and slip/slide protection systems and uses these to produce a speed measurement accurate to 2%.

The ATP processor is not a monoprocesseur codé, but guards against hardware error by a different mechanism. Each program cycle is executed twice, using different memory areas and driving separate outputs. A hardware self-test routine is also executed every program cycle. Each output drives a separate relay, whose contacts are monitored by the processor. Contacts of these relays are in the emergency brake circuit, such that if either drops, the brakes are applied.

All on board equipment is monitored by a fail safe monitoring device, which cuts the power supply if a fault is detected. The on board system is completely duplicated for availability, so an emergency brake application is not made unless both equipments fail. This is because it is highly undesirable for safety reasons to stop trains unnecessarily in the tunnel, and this duplication minimises emergency stops caused solely by equipment failure.

Interlocking

Interlocking is the function which prevents conflicting routes being set and hence prevents conflicts between trains at junctions.

Interlocking functions are performed by standard SNCF PRCI (Poste à relais à commande informatique) equipment. All vital functions are performed by fail-safe relays, whilst non-vital control functions are performed by a series of dedicated microprocessors.

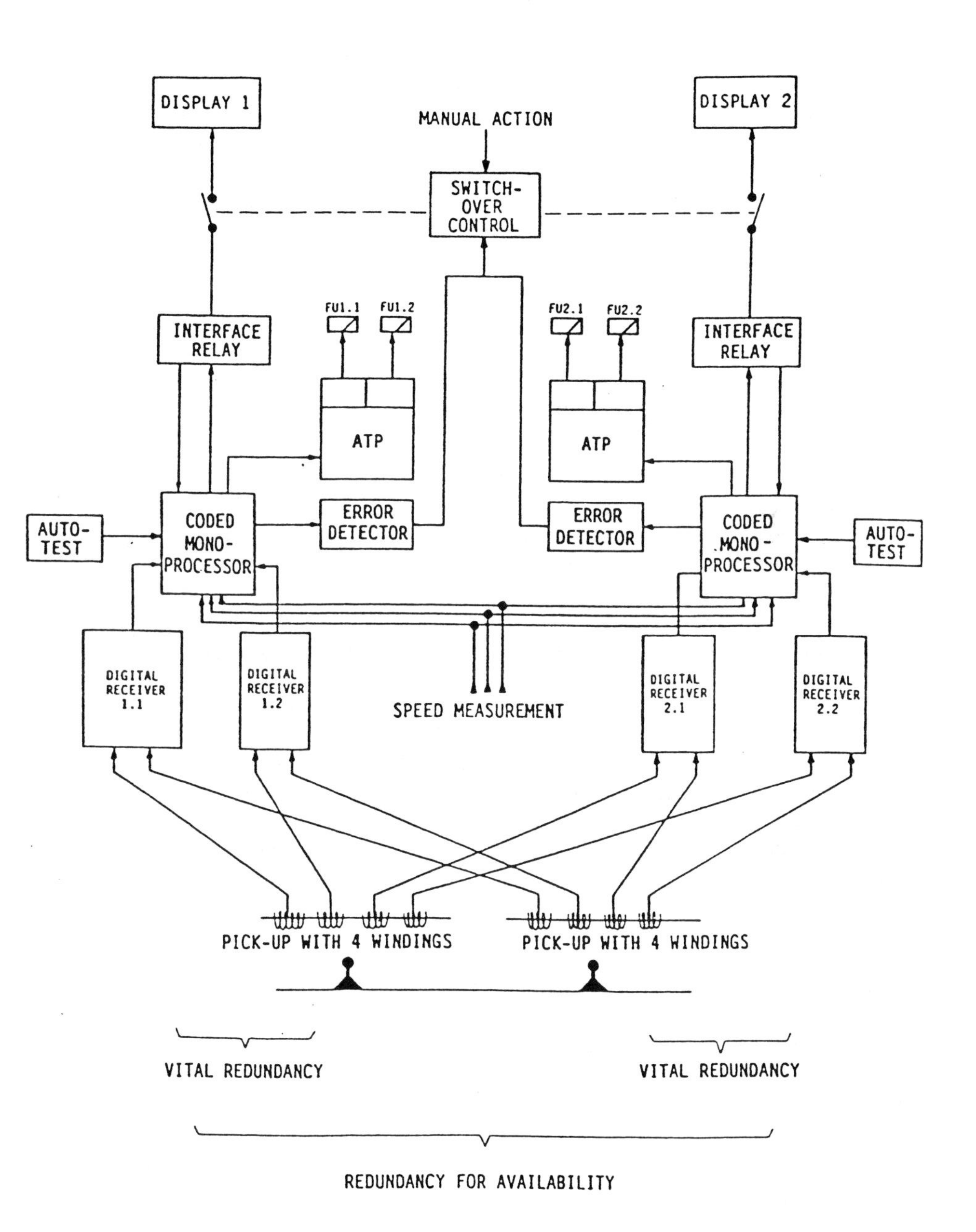

Fig. 2. Principle of signalling data processing on the train

The PRCI has been described on several occasions in the past, and will not be covered in more detail here.

Four PRCIs are installed at each terminal and two at each undersea crossover. The division of their control areas is such that the failure of any one PRCI does not completely block operation of the tunnel.

It may appear strange that given the availability of a proven solid state interlocking system (British Rail's SSI) the decision was made to use relay technology. However, the TVM430 is designed to work with the PRCI, and vice-versa. Use of the PRCI therefore minimises the development risk - an important consideration in a privately funded project with a tight construction schedule.

Furthermore, in a tunnel environment, where it is not desirable to distribute active equipment along the trackside, the cabling economies normally offered by SSI are not obtainable.

Development and Testing

The body responsible for monitoring the safety of the Channel Tunnel is the Safety Authority of the Inter-Governmental Commission (the IGC SA). Day-to-day monitoring of activity is carried on on their behalf by the Maitre d'Oeuvre (MdO), who also provide an independent report on any submission made by Eurotunnel to the IGC SA.

In view of the direct safety implications of the signalling system, the IGC SA and MdO decided, in co-operation with Eurotunnel and the constructors, TML, to create a committee of experts to follow and report on the development of the signalling system. This committee is known as the External Monitoring Group (EMG).

This group has examined in detail the development methods used by all suppliers of safety-critical software and verified that the appropriate precautions have been taken. Where existing hardware or software has been used, the EMG have assured themselves that its use on this project does not differ significantly from previous applications.

The TVM 430 has been subjected to an extensive series of tests by the laboratories of the SNCF on the test track at Glaignes. In particular, extensive testing has been performed to demonstrate the immunity of the system to electro-magnetic interference. The system has been approved by the SNCF and the French department of transport. In spite of this, the EMG has investigated the development process in detail, so as to provide an independent guarantee of its safety.

Following installation on site, the signalling was subjected to a complete static functional test by Sofrérail using standard SNCF methods and procedures. Tests are carried out by a specialised team, completely independent of the system designers. This team produces a test specification working from first principles, that is from the signalling layout and their understanding of the signalling principles. Thus the tests provide an independent check not only of the manufacturing and installation work, but also of the entire design process as well.

Following completion of these tests, which have also been monitored by the EMG, a series of tests using the various types of rolling stock have been performed to prove the correct dynamic operation of the system. These tests demonstrate electromagnetic compatibility between the rolling stock and the signalling and that the braking performance of the trains is within the specification assumed by the signalling designers. This dynamic testing is again carried out by an independent team and monitored by the EMG.

The combination of these independent static and dynamic tests gives complete confidence in the safety of the signalling system.

Discussion on session 5

G. Peacock, *Channel Tunnel Safety Authority*

One of my interests, in relation to the safety case, is the validity of reliability figures. Signal engineers have been, in my experience, reluctant to quote such figures. It is known that figures have been prepared for the LUL Central Line refurbishment. Does the author have any comment about the reliability of figures for the Eurotunnel signalling system used in the QRA as part of the safety case?

R. Spoors, *Railtrack (Major Projects Division)*

Eurotunnel will provide 50% of its train path capacity to SNCF/SNCB and BR. With regard to the commissioning and staffing issues within the main Railway Control Centre, that have arisen since 20 January 1994, when a Eurotunnel train operation was started, could the author describe the management system interface with SNCF, with particular reference to the acceptance of BR trains into and through the Eurotunnel complex?

A. R. Thomas, *Mott Ewbank Preece*

Was the procedural approach to control a culturally influenced response, i.e. UK/French inexperience of operators in a railway, electrical, or process industry?

A number of questions arise regarding the management of the design process, could the authors provide answers to these based on their experience of the project over six years?

N. Roth, *London Transport Planning*

How many times has the Eurotunnel railway timetable been changed this year, how easy was it to do and how often does Eurotunnel expect to be changing its timetable in the long term?

P. Powell, *Capitol Projects*

How confident are the authors that the new software, which is shortly to be introduced, will have the level of functionality and robustness required to meet future peak train movement demands (170–250 per day) and how have they acquired this level of confidence?

B. Briggs, *AEA Technology*

Given the promise that 'the client/user can only expect to receive what he has asked for', please tell us how the authors decided what to act for and what experience they have had of Systems Assurance Planning?

M. Donnelly
Reply to G. Peacock

We need to validate the assumptions and see if the results lead to the possibility of relaxation (or otherwise) of the parameters set out in the 'S' case. Eurotunnel intend to maintain the 'S' case as a living document and use it as a management tool.

P. Robins
Reply to G. Peacock

We have started to collect figures with the objective of comparing the results with the assumptions made in the 'S' case. We will be willing to release these in due course.

With regard to control of software development, TML put in progress supplier checks including static and dynamic procedures. Eurotunnel have taken over these procedures from TML. The RTM software was the most difficult to apply an 'in factory' type of client. It had to be developed in situ.

An overall description of the operation of fixed equipment power supplies and electrical systems

Dr C. Bayliss, Engineering Director, Transmanche-Link

CHANNEL TUNNEL

The power system is unusual in that it normally has two independent sources of supply. One from the French and one from the British Grid Systems which must never be paralleled. The total load of the system is shared approximately 50/50 between the two sources of supply. (FIG 1).

The nature of the load can also be split into two categories traction load and auxiliary load. The loads on each side ar made up of approximately 120 MVA of traction load and 40 MVA o auxiliary load for the year 2003, developing to 180 MVA o traction load and 45 MVA of auxiliary load at the ultimat capacity of the fixed-link transportation system.

Whereas the power system is designed to ensure that the tw sources of supply are never paralleled, the earthing system i connected solidly throughout. As with all 25 kV AC overhea traction systems, the return current is through earth and care i taken to ensure that the steady-state touch and step potential do not exceed 25V. For fault conditions, the relationship c touch voltage with regard to fault clearance times has been base on the most recent work published in IEC 479-1 (1984). Thi approach was necessary in order to provide a common basis for tt touch and step potential design criteria since standarc currently differ both Nationally and between differer engineering disciplines.

To develop the design of the power system and also to sub-contract the work in logical manageable packages, the system has been divided into a number of primary sub-systems as follows:-

- grid connections
- main intake sub-stations
- tunnel access shafts and standby generators
- terminal distribution systems
- exterior lighting of the Terminals
- tunnels' HV distribution system
- tunnels' LV distribution system and lighting

hese primary sub-systems exist independently in France and the 'K, except for the last two dealing with the tunnels themselves, here their system has to be completely integrated throughout.

RID CONNECTIONS

K Side

he load has a large traction content with its inherent unbalance nd high harmonic content. Consequently, it is essential that ne connection is made to an electrically "strong" network to educe the effect of these disturbances on other consumers. This ecessitated a connection at 400 kV and the nearest existing ub-station was at Sellindge approximately 14 Km to the West.

ne grid connection on the UK side consists effectively of uplicate connections, each rated at 240 MVA. These connections re effected in practice by extending the existing 400 kV double usbar SF_6 GIS sub-station at Sellindge to accommodate an dditional 400 kV switchgear bay at each end of the busbars. nese switchgear bays are connected to 400/132 kV utotransformers.

the two transformers are connected by 132 kV oil-filled cabl into a single busbar 132 kV SF_6 switchboard housed in a extension of the existing 132 kV switchroom and making use of th same cranage facilities. This switchboard increases th availability of the supply by permitting the simultaneous outag of either transformer with either of the main cable connectior to Folkestone.

The connection to Folkestone is by two 132 kV 100 mm^2 oil-fille cable circuits, each capable of 240 MVA continuous rating unde summer ambient conditions. The circuits follow the same basi route but are sufficiently separated to prevent a mechanica digger from causing damage to both circuits simultaneously.

Even with this connection from 400 kV the electricity suppl authority imposes strict restrictions on the level of negativ phase sequence (NPS) voltage unbalance and harmonics which ar acceptable at the point of common connection. At Sellindge, th NPS restriction has been set at 0.25% and levels varying betwee 0.15 and 0.4 set for harmonics from the third to the 25th. Th fault level at Sellindge is normally in the region of 20 GVA however, under minimum fault level conditions, it may fall as lo as 6 GVA.

Hence, the maximum level of unbalance allowed at Sellindge i 0.25% on 6 GVA i.e. 15 MVA. To solve this problem a loa balancer is required on the UK side, and this is located in th main HV sub-station.

French Side

The same principle of connecting to a strong network applies o the French side and the connection will be made to the 400 k sub-station at Les Mandarins.

This part of the French network is particularly "strong", bei well supported by nuclear plant, thus giving a consistently hi fault level.

e maximum fault level is of the order of 20.5 GVA, and the nimum, which is more significant to our system, is 11.7 GVA.The ench supply authority EdF also allows NPS voltages of 1% and rmonic voltage levels of 0.6% for even harmonics and 1% for odd rmonics, subject to an overall distortion level of 1.6%.

is allows an unbalance of 117 MVA at the point of common nnection (1% of 11.7 GVA), and thus removes the need for any ad balancing equipment to meet this need. However, the pedance of the 400/225 kV transformers reduces the minimum ult level on the main intake sub-station busbars to 2030 MVA. the modern design of motors only allows for 1% of NPS voltage ntinuously, this would effectively limit the unbalance ceptable to 20.3 MVA.

the distance between Les Mandarins and Coquelles is short, proximately 2.5 Km, it was decided to provide a separate nnection for the auxiliary system such that the EdF point of mmon coupling is the same as the point of common coupling of e traction and auxiliary supplies.

nsequently, the French grid connection consists of three rcuits, one normally associated with the traction power and one th the auxiliary power and the third (emergency bar) switchable tween the two. This switching is effected by automatic itching devices.

e grid connection on the French side comprises two 400 kV rcuit breakers connected into the 400 kV mesh at Les Mandarins, ch one feeding a 400/225 kV 300 MVA autotransformer. ansformer 1 is normally connected to the emergency busbar. The ergency busbar is normally connected to the auxiliaries busbar a a bus coupler circuit breaker. The Echingen and Les Attaques rcuits are also connected to the auxiliaries busbar.
is makes good use of the equipment as it enables EdF to support e 225 kV system using the supergrid transformer when both ansformers are available while giving security to the auxiliary pplies from Echingen and Les Attaques when one of the supergrid ansformers is out of service.

There are three 225 kV 630 mm^2 XLPE cable circuits, each rated at 210 MVA summer rating connecting between the associated bars at Les Mandarins and Coquelles.

MAIN HV INTAKE SUB-STATIONS

The main sub-stations take in power from the grid connections and transform this down to the required voltages for utilisation, namely 25 kV single-phase to earth for traction and 21 kV three-phase for the auxiliary systems.

<u>French Side</u>

To ensure that the traction and auxiliary systems are kept segregated and to have the flexible switching required, the main sub-station also has three busbars; traction auxiliary and emergency, mirroring the system at Les Mandarins.

The traction system uses 25 kV single-phase to earth. The Terminal is fed from the Y-phase while Running Tunnel South uses R-phase and Running Tunnel North B-phase.

The feed for each 25 kV phase is obtained from 225/27.5 kV, 60/7 MVA ONAN/ONAF single-phase transformers. There are three transformers connected to dedicated phases R-Y, Y-B, B-R, plus further spare transformer which can be selected to any pair of phases on the HV side (see figs 1 and 2).

These traction transformers have an impedance of 19.8% on ONA rating to limit the maximum fault level on the 25 kV system to 12 kA, which is the maximum acceptable to the locomotives.

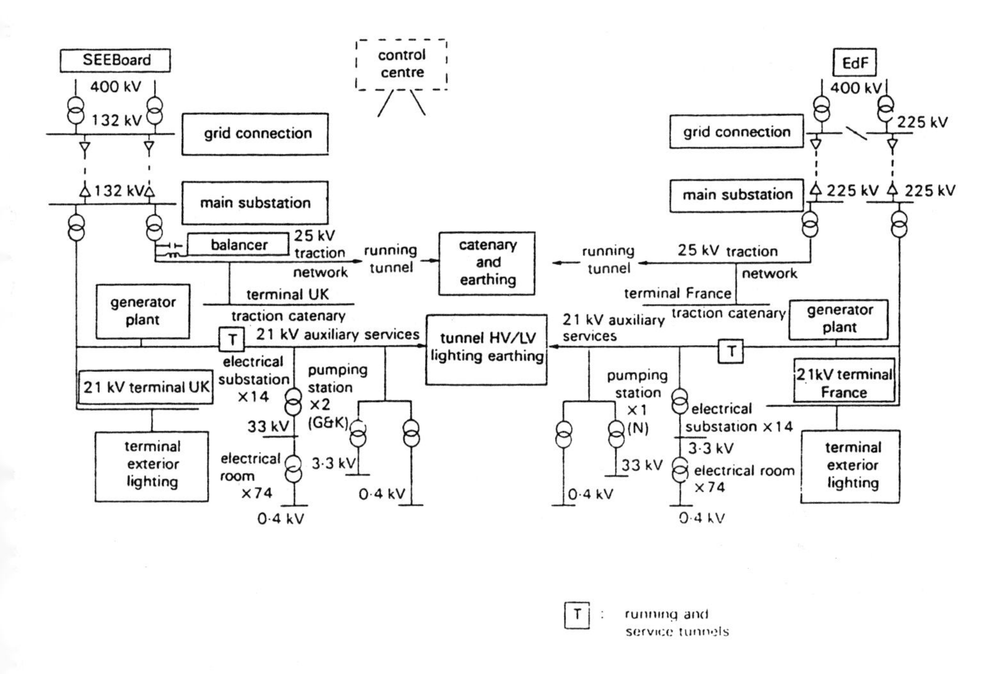

Fig. 1. Overall diagram of power supplies

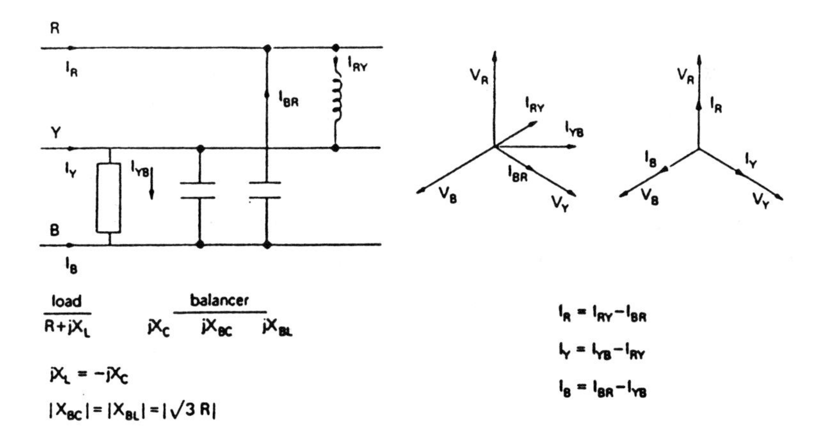

Fig. 2. Steinmetz balancing principle for delta-connected load

The voltage on the traction overhead catenary system is allowed to vary between 27.5 kV and 19 kV dependent upon the traction load. All the 225 kV and 25 kV equipment is conventional outdoor equipment.

The auxiliaries supply system is secured by two 225/22.5 kV auxiliary transformers rated at 30/40/45 NVA ONAN/ONAF/OFAF, having impedance of 17.5% on rating to limit the fault level to 12.5 kA with two transformers in parallel. The neutrals of the transformers are each earthed through 500 A neutral earthing resistors, thus limiting the 21 kV earth fault current to 1000 A with both transformers in parallel.

The transformers are connected to an indoor 21 kV single busbar switchboard using SF_6 switchgear. This switchboard is divided into five sections located in three separate rooms segregated by fire walls. The two transformers feed to the two end sections with the outgoing circuits being spread across all sections. Provision has been made for the addition of a third transformer in the future should this be considered necessary.

UK Side

The UK main sub-station performs the same function as the French sub-station, but the incoming voltage is 132 kV. The 132 kV system is a double busbar with a section/coupler arrangement in the middle between the traction half and auxiliary half of the sub-station.

The normal arrangement is with the system run solid and both grid connection circuits connected. The auxiliary system feeding arrangement is exactly the same as for the French side, except that the primary voltage is 132 kV instead of 225 kV.

The traction transformer arrangement was also originally designed to be the same; however, the interaction of the balancer has necessitated a development from single phase to three phase traction transformer design.

To understand the reasons for the differences in the main sub-station designs, it is necessary to look in some detail at the problem of unbalance caused by the traction load. Initially the Terminal is fed from the B-phase with Running Tunnel North fed from R-phase and Running Tunnel South from the Y-phase.

The load on each phase will vary according to how many trains are on that section of catenary and whether the trains are driving, oasting or braking. Consequently it is a continuously luctuating load on each phase with continuously changing atterns of unbalance. To present a balanced load to the 132 kV ystem without using real power, a load balancer using the teinmetz principle is employed.

f we consider a single-phase load connected between two phases f a three-phase system (FIG 2) then this unbalanced load can be alanced by first power factor correcting the load and then dding capacitive load equal in magnitude to $P/\sqrt{3}$ between two ther phases and an inductive load equal in magnitude to $P/\sqrt{3}$ etween the other two phases.

t can be seen from the vector diagram that the resulting line urrents drawn from the system are then balanced and in phase ith the voltage vectors, i.e. it appears to the system as a alanced unity power factor star-connected load. Any combination f loads on the three phases can be considered by superposing the olution obtained assuming each phase-to-phase load as a ingle-phase load.

is explains simply how any fixed set of unbalanced loads can be lanced but, as explained, the traction system is generating a ntinuously changing pattern of unbalance.

is is solved by connecting to each phase a fixed capacitive nk which can be continuously adjusted by a thyristor-controlled actor (TCR). A sophisticated control system monitors the stantaneous loads and calculates the amount of capacitance or actance required in each phase and sets the firing angle of the R to achieve the required effect.

The traction load, although connected phase-to-earth, would appear as a phase-to-phase load at the high-voltage side of the transformers. However, to avoid the use of costly and space-consuming transformers, the balancer is connected at 25 kV in parallel with the traction load.

This method of connection of the balancer effectively eliminates the negative phase sequence voltages and produces balanced currents at 132 kV, but the side-effect is that it doubles the zero sequence current flow in the secondary 25 kV windings of the transformer. The effect of this zero sequence current flowin through the transformer impedance is to cause highly unbalance voltages on the 25 kV side.

This phenomenon is more easily understood by reference back t the simple case of balancing a single-phase load. It can be see that the resultant three-phase loads to create balanced 132 k currents are one phase resistive load, one phase capacitive loa and one phase inductive load. Consequently, the resistive loa basically causes a phase shift through the transformer impedanc with little change in magnitude. However, the capacitive loa causes a significant voltage rise and the inductive load create a significant voltage drop.

This voltage unbalance causes problems for the operation of the 25 kV system.
The substation 25 kV busbars need to be maintained within voltage range of 25 kV minimum to ensure adequate voltage at th pantograph of the trains at the most distant point in the centr of the tunnel and to 27.5 kV maximum to prevent damage t traction equipment from over-voltage.

The problem arises from the voltage changes caused by ze sequence current flow. Consequently, if a transformer with l zero sequence impedance is used, this effect can be reduced. T use of an inter-connected star or zig zag winding was chos (similar to that used in earthing transformers).

The connection of single-phase transformers in zig zag together with a switchable spare is not a viable solution practically; consequently the decision was made to use three three-phase star/zig zag transformers each 50% rated.There are two special requirements for the specification of these transformers. First, although low zero sequence impedance is required, the positive and negative sequence impedances must remain high to limit the traction power fault level to 12 kA. Also, although the line currents are balanced on the 132 kV side, the currents flowing in the low-voltage windings are unbalanced and can exceed the normal maximum load current that would occur on a normal balanced three-phase system.

The result is that the balancer eliminates the negative sequence effect while the zig zag connection minimises the effect of the zero sequence current, as seen on the 25 kV system(see figs 3 and 4).

The traction equipment generates harmonics and additionally the thyristors required for the balancer aggravate the situation by adding additional harmonics. It is therefore necessary to provide filters to keep the harmonic distortion within the tight limits specified by the supply authority. These filters are incorporated into the capacitor banks required for the balancer by providing a mixture of damped and fully tuned filter arms to make the best use of the available capacitance. (FIG 3).

TUNNEL AUXILIARY SYSTEM

The tunnel auxiliary system has been developed to meet the special requirements of the system. These may be summarised as follows.

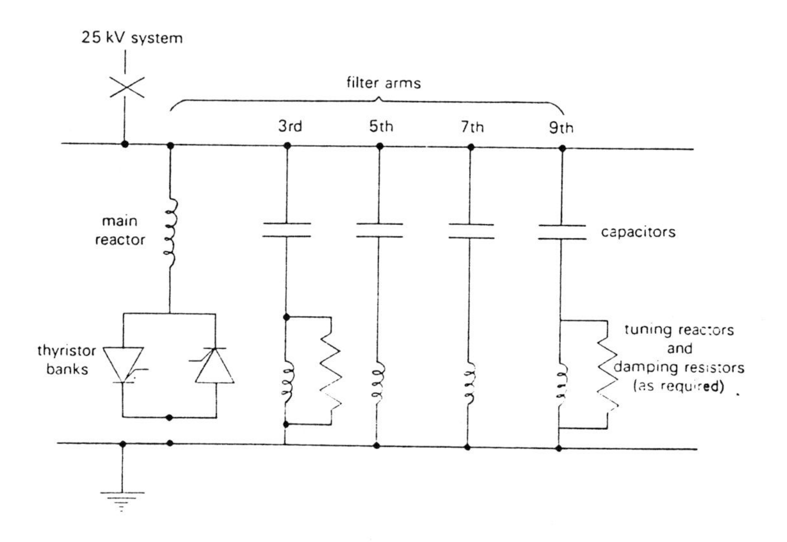

Fig. 3. Diagram of one phase of balancer

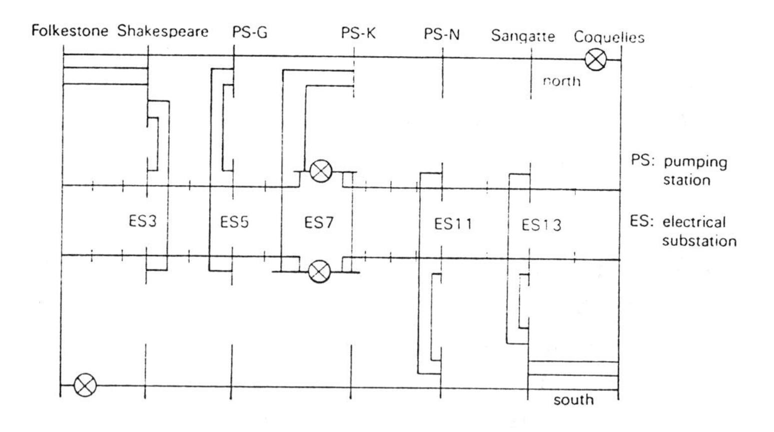

Fig. 4. Tunnel 21 kV distribution system

'irst, although it is an integrated system, it will normally be fed from both ends, but under no circumstances are these two infeeds to be allowed to be paralleled.

Secondly, the load to be supplied by this system splits into three basic parts.

- The largest part of the normal load which has a high motor content is concentrated at the two access shafts, Shakespeare Cliff and Sangatte.

  The pumping stations which result from the tunnel profile are located at the low points of the tunnel.

  The distributed small loads, lighting and socket supplies which require a number of sub-stations and electrical rooms spaced at regular intervals through the tunnel.

hirdly, the system needs to provide security of supply to allow lanned and unplanned outages. The system has also to have the bility to be rapidly reconfigured to allow for the total loss of upply from either the UK or France or both simultaneously.

rom economic considerations, 21 kV has been chosen as the ominal voltage with operations tolerances of ± 5%, giving ypically 22 kV on the busbars at each main sub-station with no ess than 19.95 kV at any point on the primary voltage system.

ne 21 kV system consists of two feeders used to feed the pumping tations, one of which is normally fed from the UK over its full ength and one of which is normally fed from France. (FIG 4). nis method of feeding has the advantage that one circuit is aintained alive to all essential loads e.g. ventilation, fire ghting and pump stations, even under loss of one Grid system.

nis is supplemented by two cables feeding the distributed loads a a system of 14 electrical sub-stations. Substations 1-7 are rmally fed from the UK and 8-14 from France, with the circuits ened on bus section breakers at ES7.

These four cables provide the capability of dealing with all th
priority loads. However, at Shakespeare Cliff and Sangatte, th
non-priority load of the cooling is connected into the pumpin
station feeder fed from the "home" side. To support this loa
and to improve security and voltage drop conditions, tw
additional 21 kV cable circuits are run between Folkestone an
Shakespeare Cliff No 1 board and between Coquelles and Sangatt
No 2 board.

To ensure the necessary security of supply and improv
operational flexibility, inter-connectors are provided betwee
the "pumping station" circuits and the "electrical sub-station
circuits at both shaft locations and at the pumping stations.

In the event of a loss of a Grid, the system has load-sheddin
applied to reduce the load to that for the downgraded conditio
and the system is reconfigured to be run solid with all fou
cables in parallel to reduce the voltage drop problems under thi
onerous condition.

At those electrical sub-stations not associated with a
inter-connector, ring main units consisting of two disconnector
and a fuse switch are used. At electrical sub-stations wher
inter-connection takes place circuit breakers are provided t
sectionalise the 21 kV electrical sub-station cable feeders a
these locations.

To ensure fast effective discriminated fault clearance, the prir
feeders and inter-connectors are fitted with pilot wi
protection. The system is also equipped with over-current a
earth fault relays, multiple in some locations to allow for t
changing requirements under normal, downgraded and stand
generator operation.

LOW VOLTAGE DISTRIBUTION AND LIGHTING

The low voltage distribution system is required to distribu
power from the electrical sub-stations to the many and vario
auxiliary loads distributed throughout the tunnel, such as

- lighting
- piston relief duct dampers and cooling valve actuators
- fire fighting valve actuators
- catenary isolators
- cross passage door electro/hydraulic units
- control and communication gear and switchgear battery chargers
- socket outlets

These items all take power at 400 V, and this level has been adopted in advance of the CEGELEC and EEC voltage harmonisation directives. Originally it was intended to feed these from the electrical sub-station locations at 400 V. However, with the long distances between 2.8 and 5.1 Km, this concept was reviewed together with the location of the 400V switchgear and distribution boards, and an intermediate voltage of 3.3 kV was introduced (see Fig. 5).

ach electrical sub-station is divided into two parts, North and outh fed, by separate 21 kV cables. (FIG 5). Each part has a 1/3.38 kV step-down transformer feeding a main 3.3 kV board. his board then feeds onto radial 3.3 kV feeders, one feeding lectrical rooms to the West and one feeding the electrical room djacent to the sub-station (see Fig. 6).

f a cable is faulted or taken out of service between two lectrical rooms, then the electrical rooms downstream of the aulted cable can be restored by linking onto the end of the adial feed from the adjacent electrical sub-station.

ach electrical room, except the adjacent ones, houses a 3.3 kV ing main unit feeding a 3.3/0.419 kV transformer which feeds a 00 V distribution board.

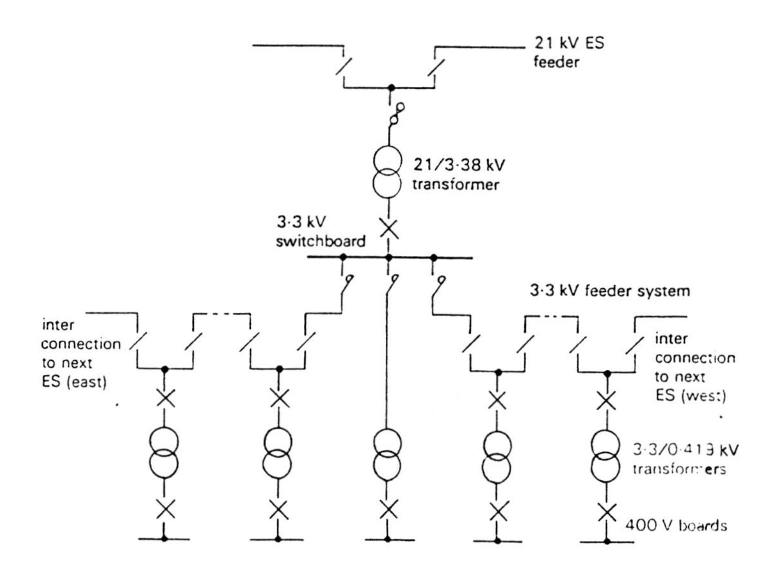

Fig. 5. Typical 3.3 kV radial distribution

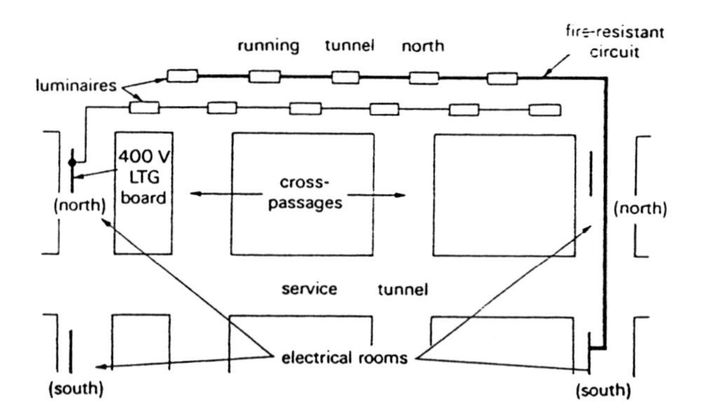

Fig. 6. Distribution for main lighting circuits

These electrical rooms are spaced at approximately 750m intervals. The 400 V boards at each electrical room are inter-connected by a 400 V inter-connector equipped with an automatic changeover with three out of four interlock system. The lighting system (FIG 6) uses an insulated earth principle with continuous monitoring of phases and neutral-to-earth by a DC monitoring system. To create this separate insulated earth (IT) system 0.4/0.4 kV isolating transformers are required at each electrical room. This insulated earth system enables the lighting circuits to remain in service, even with an earth fault on one cable line, but gives an alarm so that maintenance personnel can investigate the problem.

The lighting is a critical safety item under tunnel evacuation requirements and this was the subject of much discussion before the present solution was adopted. The lighting of each 750m section of tunnel is covered by two overlapping circuits. One circuit is fed from the electrical room to the east of the section, and the other from the electrical room on the other side of the Service Tunnel and to the west of the section. Each circuit feeds every alternate lamp so that loss of one circuit will leave every alternate luminaire lit.

One of these two circuits for each section of tunnel uses special fire-resistant cabling to BS6387 Class CWZ giving 3 hour performance under 950°C fire conditions in the presence of water and with mechanical shock. This is to secure half the lighting for the remainder of a section in the event of a localised fire. This solution was used in preference to battery-backed fittings, because the maintenance required for the batteries was considered impractical under tunnel operating conditions.

Battery-backed fittings have been retained for the information markers indicating the locations of the Cross Passages and in these cases the batteries are located in the Cross Passages for ease of maintenance. The method of overlapping with one fire-resistant circuit is also employed in the Service Tunnel.

The lights are switched such that initiation of the lighting for one section brings on the lights in the adjacent section both to the East and to the West, thus illuminating approximately 2250 m of tunnel.

Initiating one section of Running Tunnel lighting illuminates 2250 m of Running Tunnel together with 2250 m of Service Tunnel lighting and all associated Cross Passages, but leaves the opposite Running Tunnel in darkness. Initiating of the lighting can be either remotely from the control centre (the normal method) or from illuminated pushbuttons located approximately every 75 m along the walkway inside the Running Tunnels.

The luminaires have had to be specially developed to provide aerodynamic shaping to reduce the drag in the Running Tunnels and also to be able to achieve the required IP65 rating under dynamic pressure conditions. They provide a 20 lux lighting level with 0.5 uniformity after allowing a 0.75 downgrading factor for dirt and ageing. This is achieved by lighting mounted 4.1 m above the walkway with spacing of 8 m using 18 W fittings.

SPECIAL CONSIDERATION FOR TUNNEL EQUIPMENT

The physical locations of the switchboards and the cable feeder have been carefully selected to avoid a single incident affectin more than one of the duplicate supply arrangements. (TABLE 1).

Running Tunnel North		Service Tunnel		Running Tunnel (South)
Pumping 21 kV Feeder No 1	pumping sub-stations (North)	pumping 21 kV Feeder No 2	pumping sub-stations (South	
	electrical sub-stations (North)	sub-stations 21 kV Feeder No 1	electrical sub-stations (South)	sub-stations 21 kV Feeder No 2
Shafts 21 kV Feeder No 1				shafts 21 kV Feeder No 2
3.3 kV room feeders (North)	electrical rooms (North)		electrical rooms (South)	3.3 kV room feeders (South)

TABLE 1
Segregation of cabling and rooms

At each pumping station and electrical sub-station, the duplicate switchboards (north and south) are located in separate rooms either side of the Service Tunnel, i.e. one room located between the Service Tunnel and Running Tunnel North and the other between the Service Tunnel and Running Tunnel South.

With regard to the four prime 21 kV cable circuits, one of the pumping station feeds is located in Running Tunnel North and the other is located in the Service Tunnel. The electrical sub-station cable feeders are located one in the Service Tunnel and the other in Running Tunnel South. For the underland part between the shafts and the main sub-stations, the two additional cables are run in each of the Running Tunnels.

The equipment to be located in the pumping sub-stations, electrical sub-stations and electrical rooms has to be very compact because of the restricted space available and must not provide a significant fire risk. This has led to the use of SF_6 switchgear for 21 kV, vacuum for 3.3 kV and air gear for 400 V. The transformers are all dry-type cast resin.

The environment in the rooms is relatively dry and so the requirements for special ingress protection are not essential. However, equipment to be located in the tunnels themselves where tunnel cleaning will be used, requires IP65 rating.

All equipment which uses inherently flammable materials is rigorously tested for the following aspects:-

flame propagation	- the materials must not ignite easily nor propagate flame along the tunnel
smoke density	- when burning, the material must not produce dense smoke which would obscure visibility and hinder escape
toxicity	- when burning, the materials must not produce toxic or corrosive gases

These types of test apply to all flammable equipment, although the detail of the test is tailored to suit the specific item of equipment under test. All cables to be installed in the tunnels undergo these tests and are classified as low smoke and fume (LSF) and have flame retardancy characteristic in accordance with IEC 332-3, the detailed category depending on the voltage rating of the cable concerned.

The cable-supporting system and installation method had to be designed to meet the following criteria:-

- safety under normal and fire conditions
- resistance to corrosion
- minimise installation time in the tunnels
- minimise the earthing requirements
- co-ordinate with the temporary services

This has resulted in a system of non-metallic "Modar" guttering and trays which have been submitted to the fire testing referred to earlier. This system means that cables are laid directly onto a supporting surface, and do not depend on cleating or trying to keep them in place during cable laying.

Because of the large quantities of cables to be laid and the logistical problems of access from the shaft locations only, an innovative method of cable laying from a slow moving (0.5 km/h) train has been developed.

The cable is anchored to the tunnel wall at the start point. As the train moves slowly forward, the cable is fed out from the drum through a tensioning wagon. This wagon is there to give an alarm if the cable comes under excessive tension. It then passes to the cable feed wagon where it is raised over rollers to the working level where the operatives guide it onto the support system.

SHAFTS AND STANDBY GENERATION

The shaft locations at Shakespeare Cliff and Sangatte are the major load centres for the tunnels, both for essential and non-essential loads.

The distribution system at the shafts is basically on the surface. There are separate 3.3 kV and 400 V switchboards associated with each of the systems, normal ventilation, supplementary ventilation, fire fighting etc.

In the event that all the supplies from France and the UK are lost simultaneously, standby generators are located at both shaft locations to support the essential services for tunnel evacuation, and for the integrity of the tunnel. These loads are essentially lighting, ventilation, pumping and control and communication power supplies. All other loads have to be shed under these extreme operating conditions.

Use is being made of the construction generators already existing at Shakespeare Cliff and Sangatte. The generators are connected via step-up transformers, one per unit at the French side as lready existing, and one per pair of units on the UK side to a enerator 21 kV switchboard.

he 21 kV system is a substantial cable network and when energised on no load generates approximately 4.5 MVAr onto each et of generators. This self-excitation of the system would ause instability of the generators and it has been found ecessary to add a 3 MVAr 21 kV shunt-connected reactor to each enerator busbar to improve the stability of the machines.

n the event of loss of both Grid connections, the generators are ın up, synchronised to each other, loaded with the shunt reactor nd then connected to the 'home' board at their location.

The network is re-configured to split both pumping station feeders at Pumping Station K and loaded progressively to secure first the lighting, then ventilation, pumping and last the control and communication power supplies which have 3 h battery-backed autonomy to survive through the AC system interruption.

TERMINALS AND EXTERIOR LIGHTING

The Terminals are fairly conventional distribution systems with 21 kV as the primary voltage and 400 V as the utilisation voltage.

The UK side uses a ring main concept with duplicate RMU's (ring main units) at strategic sub-stations such as the Control Centre and single RMU's at other locations. At those locations where only one RMU is provided, the 400 V switchboard is divided into priority and non-priority sections. The priority section is secured by a 400 V cable inter-connection from the adjacent sub-station.

The French side, where the size of the Terminal is significantly larger, has used duplicate radial feed systems, which can be connected as rings at the remote end.

The exterior lighting consists basically of street lighting, car park lighting, railway sidings lighting and the vehicle loading platform lighting. The majority of the lighting is by high pressure sodium lamps on conventional lamp posts, whereas the platform lighting uses catenary-supported light fittings.

The lighting design, as well as meeting the functional requirements, has endeavoured to take account of the architectural and aesthetic aspects required by the Client and the environmental considerations such as minimising 'glow in the sky', direct light affecting residents and reducing the general 'forest' appearance of lamp posts in daytime as required by the planning authorities.

Certain lamp posts in restricted access areas, e.g. maintenance sidings, have been developed with H-frame luminaire support heads which can be lowered vertically down the support post for maintenance.

In conclusion, the development of the power system for the Channel Tunnel has basically been the application of well proven and reliable technology to meet the specific and unique requirements of this particular project. Special consideration has been given to Safety aspects, for load balancing on the UK side and for solving the logistical and environmental problems of the tunnels.

Ventilation and cooling

A. G. Fairbairn, Manager, Special Projects, TML, Folkestone, England

1. INTRODUCTION

The Channel Tunnel is unique in many respects. It is both very long, at 50km between portals, and difficult to service, having only two other surface connection points which are at the coastal sites, 37.5km apart. Forecast traffic density is high with up to 10 shuttles and 5 through trains per hour in each direction at Opening, rising to 30 train movements per hour per direction at ultimate. Considerable power is required to move the 2,400t shuttle trains at speeds up to 140km/h against the resultant high aerodynamic friction forces in the Tunnel. Almost all of this power is degraded into heating the air in the Tunnel. The Tunnel may also contain up to 15,000 people on 20 trains at any one time on their 25 minute journey between portals. Providing an acceptable tunnel environment, even for everyday air condition and temperature, is not, therefore, straightforward. Some new and unusual combinations of design features have had to be developed for both ventilation and cooling systems.

Considerations of passenger safety in abnormal conditions also impose stringent requirements upon the overall design. The provision of a "safe haven" within the Tunnel, intended to ensure a place of safety with a fresh air supply and acceptable temperature, even in the most extreme emergency scenarios, is one such feature responding to these requirements.

This paper will describe the requirements to be met by tunnel ventilation and cooling systems, referring also to the origin of certain requirements and the circumstances in which they must be met. Development of the system designs to achieve these requirements will be covered before providing a description of the as-built systems, their chief parameters and performances.

A description of the systems in action to meet operational requirements will also be given.

2. THE COOLING SYSTEM

Generally speaking, it is only the relatively short tunnel sections of surface railways which do not have to consider the need for cooling.

Longer surface railway tunnels usually have ventilation shafts to the surface which also serve to reject waste heat to the atmosphere, by means of the warmed, vitiated airflow. Subways also use surface ventilation shafts, with either natural or forced draft, to ventilate and cool their longer sections in tunnel.

Apart from the portals and the two coastal sites, the Channel Tunnel does not have surface connections. The capacity for heat exchange with the atmosphere at the portals by means of vitiated air has been estimated at 1.8MW, whereas the heat rejected in the Tunnel as a result of train movements will range from 60MW at opening to more than 100MW at ultimate.

2.1 <u>"Natural" Methods of Heat Removal</u>

In addition to the net flow of warmed, vitiated air from the tunnel portals, there are other "natural" methods of heat removal.

The mass of the train itself is warmed as it passes through the Tunnel. Heat is also lost to the tunnel linings, the surrounding ground and to the sea bed. Air is also expelled at the portals additional to net vitiated ventilation airflow due to the piston effect of trains exiting the Tunnel. Table 1 below shows the relative value of these effects.

HEAT SINK	OPENING	2003	ULTIMATE
Vitiated Airflow	1.8	1.8	1.8
Train Mass	8.6	10.2	15.5
Mass of Earth (long term)	4.5	5.0	7.6
Piston effect of trains	2.5	3.0	3.6
Net Amount of Heat to be removed	17.4	20	28.5

Table 1: Relative values of "Natural" Methods of Heat Removal (MW)

However, the calculated average value of heat input to the Tunnel is well in excess of these values. Figure 1 shows the forecast rise in Tunnel air temperature should the Tunnel have been opened without supplementing the "natural" means of heat removal.

2.2 <u>Heat Input to the Tunnel</u>

Heat input is largely due to the tractive effort of shuttle trains, overcoming aerodynamic and frictional resistance to movement (80% and 20% respectively at 140 km/h) and degrading as heat.

Catenary and other electrical loses in the shuttle power train and the waste heat from on-board auxiliary equipment further contribute to the overall heat load. Indeed, apart from the effect of minor speed differences on tunnel entry and exit and of the 60m height difference between UK and French portals, all traction energy supplied to the tunnel by the catenary is eventually rejected as waste heat to the tunnel air or the mass of trains.

The losses from Fixed Equipment also contribute to the tunnel heat load. Lighting, ventilation and drainage system losses generally appear as heat rejected to tunnel air.

The relative amounts of heat rejected are as follows:

SOURCE	OPENING	2003	ULTIMATE
Train Movements (average for peak week of the year)	60	69	101
Fixed Equipment:	3.0	3.0	3.0
TOTAL	63	72	104

Table 2: Heat Input to the Tunnel (MW)

The figures in Table 2 are based on round trip in-tunnel energy losses per tourist shuttle of 9.8MWh and average levels of train movements in the peak week of the year measured in shuttle "equivalents", where:

	Shuttle Equivalence
Tourist Shuttle	1.0
Lorry Shuttle	0.94
National Passenger Train	0.2
TGV (or TMST)	0.15
Goods Train	0.28

Thus a TGV or TMST (TransManche Super Train) takes only 15% of the energy of a tourist shuttle to travel through the Tunnel, reflecting the considerable differences in train length and cross sectional area in relation to the Tunnel cross section, which are the parameters largely determining the aerodynamic resistance or "drag" factor.

2.3 The Need for Cooling

The excess of Heat Input to the Tunnel over "natural" methods of cooling is set out in Table 3 below,

ITEM	OPENING	2003	ULTIMATE
Heat Input from Table 2	63	72	104
"Natural" Heat Removal from Table 1.	17	20	28
Net Amount of Heat to be removed	46	52	76

Table 3: Forecast Cooling Loads

2.3.1 Design Criteria

Acceptable environmental conditions must be provided in the Tunnel for:

- passengers travelling in shuttles and through trains,
- maintenance staff,
- staff and passengers in the Tunnel during an evacuation,
- mechanical, electrical and electronic equipment.

Furthermore, the normal service provided to customers by the Transport System as a whole is to be, inter alia, high speed and high quality, setting a tighter limit on the temperature conditions for the Tunnel.

However, the nature of the service must also be taken into account:

- all weather, 365 days a year,
- passengers on tourist shuttles travel with their cars,
- long periods of loading and unloading with doors open for 40 minutes out of the 110 minutes of cycle time.

In the circumstances of limited environmental control, a target temperature range of 15 to 28°C during transit has been determined for tourist shuttles. Whilst these temperature limits are dictated primarily by the range of external ambient conditions, they can only be maintained by means of practical sizes of on-board heating and air conditioning systems if the tunnel ambient temperature is also maintained between 20 and 30°C. This temperature range for the tunnel is also appropriate:

- to those situations where passengers and staff may be required to detrain in the Tunnel for evacuation purposes,
- for maintenance staff within the Tunnel complex who may also be subjected periodically to the chill factor of air speeds approaching 10-12 m/s; and
- for mechanical, electrical and electronic equipment located in underground technical rooms which reject heat to the service and running tunnel areas.

This temperature range is taken as the main performance criteria for the cooling system. The range must also be maintained throughout the Tunnel despite the following variable factors:

a) daily, weekly and monthly traffic variations, varying the heat input over a wide range (see figure 2),

b) variable heat input along the tunnel as a function of gradient and direction of travel (see figure 3)

c) variable rates of heat removal by both natural and forced cooling as a function of local air velocity in the tunnel, determined, itself, by the number and speed of shuttles, (see figure 4).

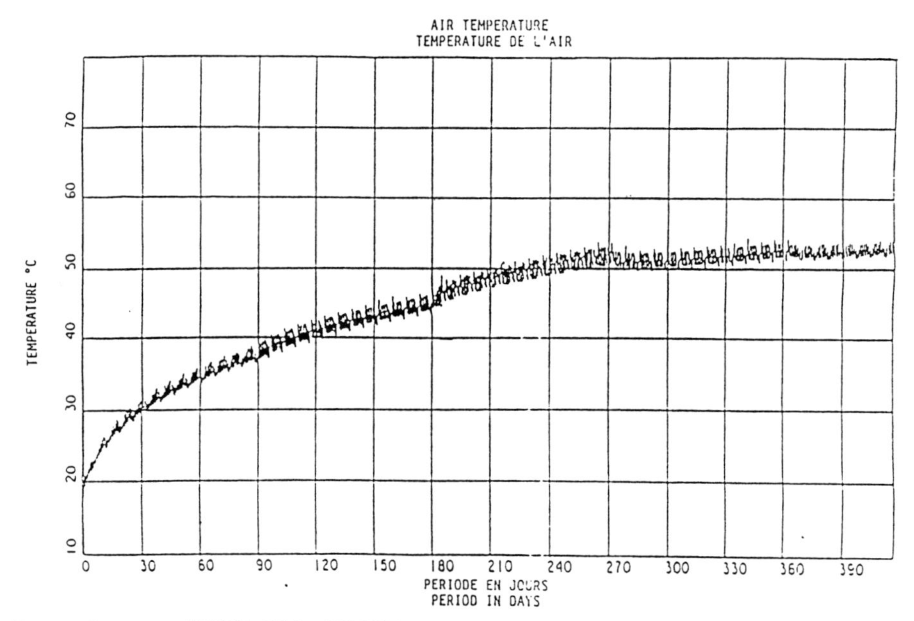

FIGURE 1 HAUSSE DE LA TEMPERATURE DE L'AIR DANS LE TUNNEL SANS REFROIDISSEMENT - TRAFIC 1993

RISE IN TUNNEL AIR TEMPERATURE WITH NO COOLING - 1993 TRAFFIC

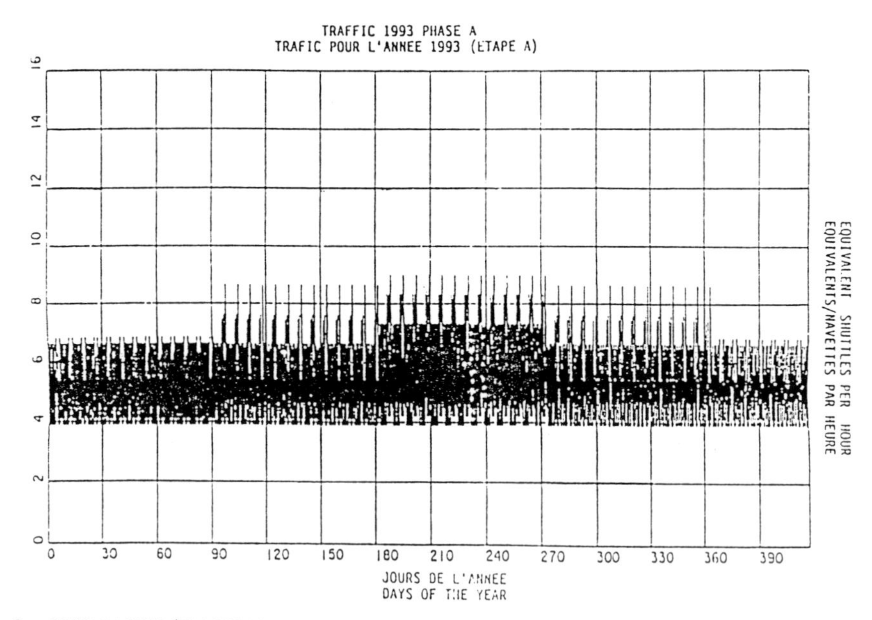

FIGURE 2 EQUIVALENTS/NAVETTES PAR HEURE CORRESPONDANT A LA MARCHE NORMALE EN 1993

EQUIVALENT SHUTTLES PER HOUR CORRESPONDING TO NORMAL 1993 OPERATION

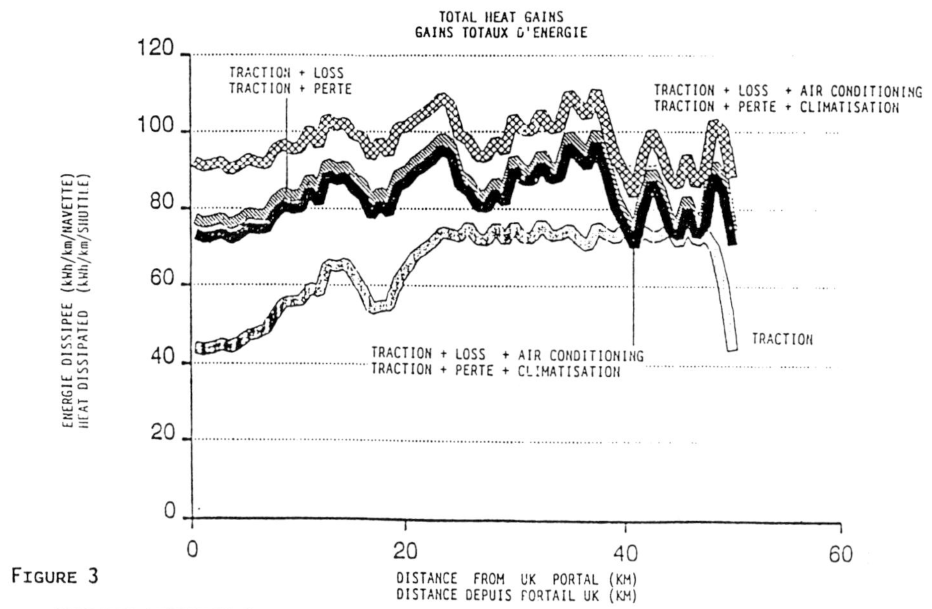

FIGURE 3

ENERGIE DISSIPEE CUMULEE DEPUIS UNE NAVETTE SIMPLE TUNNEL SUD - DIRECTION OUEST

DISTRIBUTION OF HEAT GAINS ALONG TUNNEL FROM TYPICAL SHUTTLE - RTN WESTBOUND

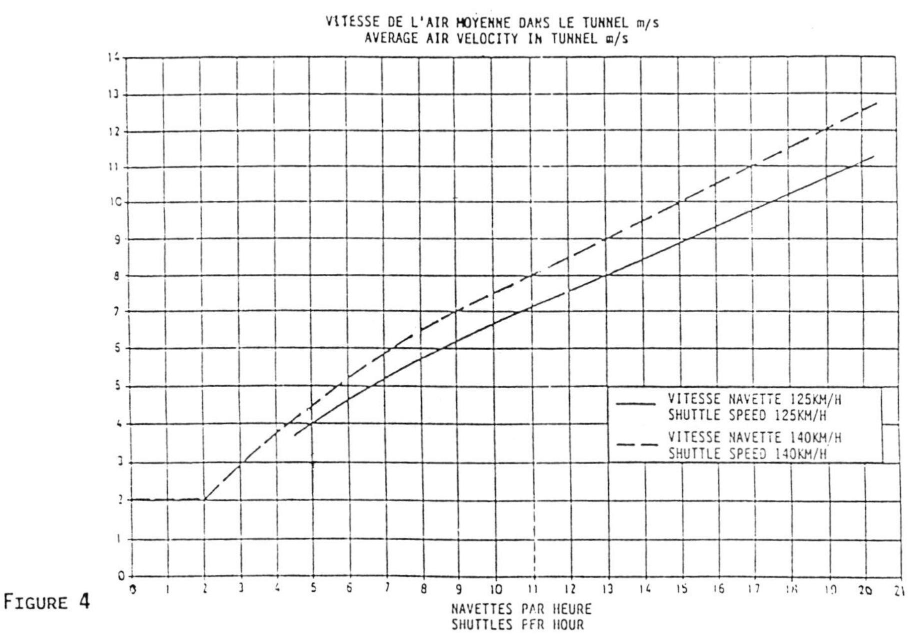

FIGURE 4

VARIATION DE LA VITESSE DE L'AIR DANS LE TUNNEL EN FONCTION DU NOMBRE DE NAVETTES A L'HEURE

TUNNEL AIR VELOCITY VARIATION DEPENDING ON NUMBER OF SHUTTLES PER HOUR

There are three main mechanisms which average out the effects on tunnel temperature of the variable heating and cooling factors mentioned above and which help to maintain temperatures within the specified range:

- variable rates of heat lost to the lining and surrounding ground which depends on air temperature and velocity.

- circulation of large volumes of air between tunnels, due to the piston relief ducts, and net longitudinal air movement (in opposite directions) in each running tunnel.

- design of the cooling system, which is described in the following section.

2.4 The Design of Cooling System

Various schemes of cooling have been considered for the Channel Tunnel. The 1974 scheme, which preceded the present Project, included a proposal to deposit ice in the Tunnel from the rear of a moving shuttle, heat being eventually rejected from the Tunnel via the tunnel drainage system. The present project first considered fin-fan cooling units to be located every 375m supplied by lagged cooling water pipework on a closed cycle with heat rejected to the sea via water/water coolers at the coastal sites.

2.4.1 Cooling System Pipework

Optimisation studies carried out in 1987 concluded that bare pipework circulating chilled water was a feasible solution.

Further studies and simulation of the heat transfer process in the Tunnel went on to conclude that:

- a hairpin pipework arrangement of bare supply and return pipes in each tunnel would provide both a sufficient level and satisfactory distribution of heat transfer,

- the pipework arrangement shown in figure 5 would be satisfactory with nominal diameters of 400 and 300mm for undersea (19km) and underland (10km - UK, 3km - FR) Sections respectively.

In the arrangement shown in figure 5, pipework in the underland sections is kept back from the portals (2.5km on the normal entry tunnel and 0.827km on the normal exit tunnel) to avoid overcooling. Furthermore, on the French side, where the underland section is only 3km long, a single circuit connects the two hairpin pipes in each tunnel.

The specific advantages of the bare pipe solution for the Channel Tunnel were considered to be:

- sufficient heat removal capacity taking into account space limitations for pipework and water temperature limits (+1°C inlet) for Opening and 2003 loads,

- extendible to ultimate cooling loads without needing further installation work in the tunnels (use of crushed ice in coolant is considered to be a potential solution, capable of successful development.),

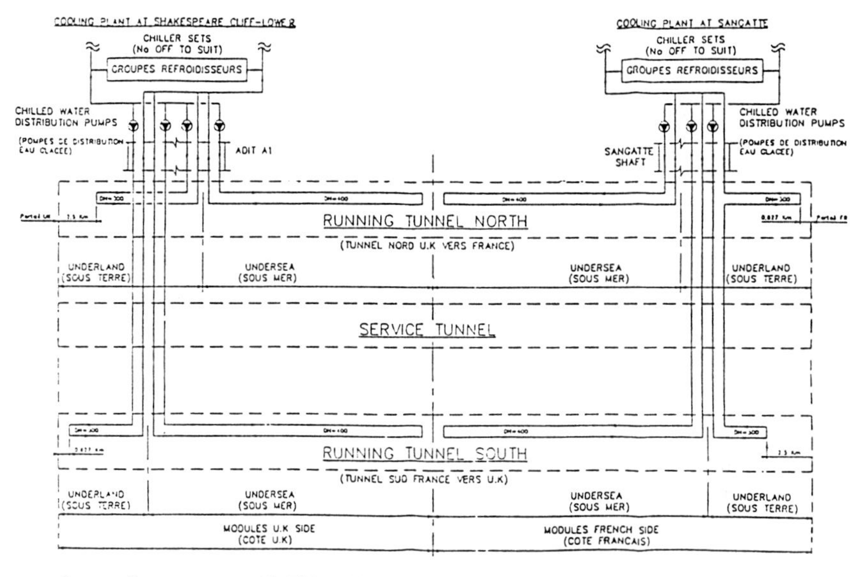

FIGURE 5 CIRCUITS D'EAU DE REFRIGERATION DANS LES TUNNELS
WATER COOLING SYSTEMS IN THE TUNNELS

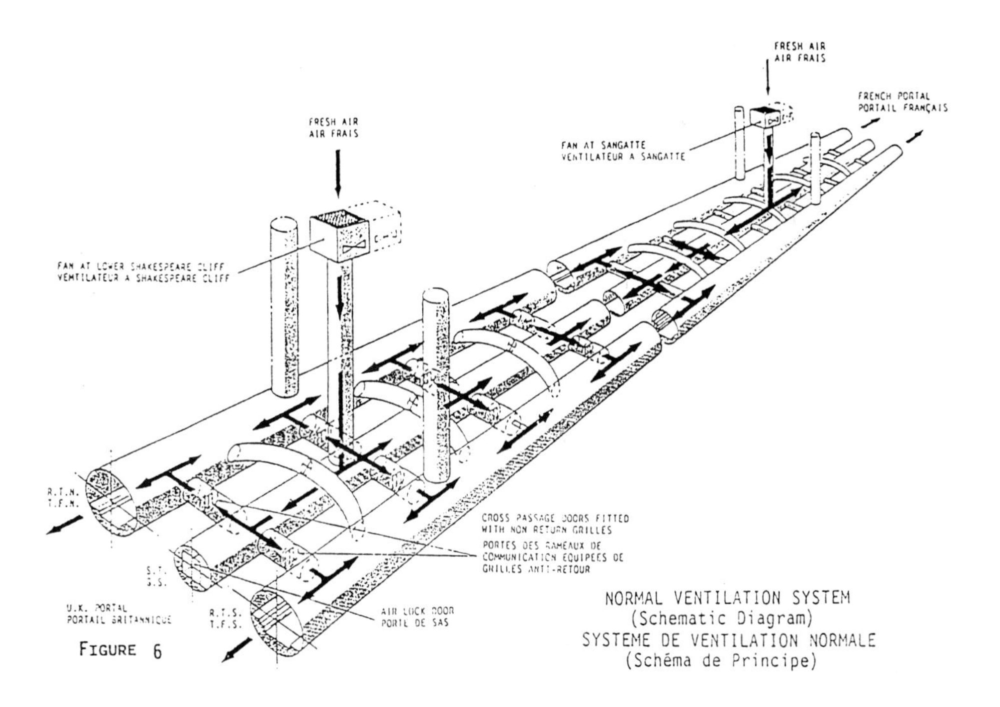

FIGURE 6 NORMAL VENTILATION SYSTEM
(Schematic Diagram)
SYSTEME DE VENTILATION NORMALE
(Schéma de Principe)

- bare pipework system offers the lowest possible aerodynamic resistance to train movement,

- static cooling system with no moving parts requiring access for periodic maintenance,

- simple hydraulic profile to ensure a flow rate of at least 1m/s at all points in the circuit.

Pipework material is seamless black steel with an external fusion bonded epoxy coating. The pipework was actually installed in 45m lengths from construction gauge work trains, although initial planning had envisaged 550m lengths erected from the permanent track.

Pipes are anchored at the tunnel inlet and outlet, at each undersea crossover and at nine other intermediate locations. Fixed supports prevent overall length variations due to temperature effects. Intermediate supports, at 12m intervals, permit local longitudinal movement whilst restraining lateral movement.

Automatic shut-off valves are provided for both supply and return pipework spaced at intervals in the tunnel ranging from 1160 to 2500m. The purpose of these valves is to limit, in the event of a fracture, the amount of coolant released in relation to the capacity of local drainage sumps in the tunnel before being pumped out via the drainage system. The valves may also be remotely operated from the Control Centre.

2.4.2 External Cooling Plant

Ultimate heat rejection to the sea as envisaged in the Proposal to Governments was opposed on environmental grounds. High first cost and ongoing corrosion problems were additional disadvantages.

The system finally adopted uses dry air coolers (in preference to cooling towers) which reject heat to the atmosphere either directly from the tunnel cooling system or indirectly via the heat rejection coils of an intermediate water chilling plant.

The specific advantages of this arrangement are:

- minimal environmental impact (elimination of plume effect, risk of legionnaire's disease, negligible water consumption);

- optimum use of "free" cooling from the outside air in winter;

- use of tried and tested cooler modules using an internationally accepted coolant (FREON 22);

- modular organisation of the cooling system whereby staged expansion is possible by adding modules and suitable levels of redundancy can be provided against maintenance and breakdown conditions.

2.4.3 Operation of the Cooling System

The system operates automatically with suitable remote control, alarm and other indications being provided as an integral part of the EMS -

Engineering Management System - operated from the main control centre at the Folkestone terminal.

Initially, the amount of cooling will be controlled from air and water temperature sensors located in the Tunnel. Separately, chilling plant will also be brought into or taken out of service and tunnel cooling water circulated directly, wholly or in part, to the dry air coolers depending on the season of the year and daily average ambient temperature.

As operating experience is gained with the cooling system further measures will be introduced to optimise overall operation and to minimise operating costs. The following factors will be considered:

- tunnel air and cooling water temperature profile
- forecast tunnel traffic
- weather forecasts
- electricity tariffs throughout the day
- substantial inertia effect of the mass of cooling water in the tunnel pipework (cycle time for one complete circuit is about 6 hours).

It is intended that this last feature will be exploited in a manner analogous to pumped-storage of electricity where cheap night time electricity (and lower overnight ambient temperatures) will be used to "store" cooling in the system, to be released later for the daytime increase in Tunnel traffic.

3. VENTILATION SYSTEMS

Various schemes were considered for the Channel Tunnel Fixed Link prior to the present design basis proposed in 1985.

In particular, whilst the design concept always included two separate running tunnels and a smaller, central service tunnel, initially, the three tunnels were not separated aerodynamically. Service and running tunnels were connected by open cross passages at regular intervals (250m) and air was free to circulate between all three tunnels, with the particular advantage of reducing the piston effect of train movement. Four key factors combined to require a change to this arrangement and a need for effective segregation of running and service tunnels.

- for maintenance access during normal operations, air velocities would be too high in cross passages and certain areas of the service tunnel due to the air piston effect of trains at high speed,
- it was not clear that ventilation air introduced at the coastal sites could be distributed effectively throughout the whole tunnel, particularly in the undersea sections,
- ventilation fans might have to withstand the full pressure of the piston effect of shuttles at high speed; and
- there was a growing perception of a need for a guaranteed "safe haven" for passengers, in the event of detraining in the Tunnel.

All four of these factors were resolved by providing bulk-head type doors in each cross-passage, thus isolating service and running tunnels. However, smaller Piston Relief Ducts (initially called draft relief cross passages) were provided between running tunnels at 250m intervals in order to mitigate the consequences of increasing the piston effect of moving trains by this segregation. (The consequences without this mitigation would have been significantly higher transient pressures generated by train movements and a considerable increase in the traction power necessary to overcome aerodynamic drag).

Isolation of service from running tunnels therefore brought important benefits but led to a need for a more complex design of ventilation which now comprises two main, separate systems - normal and supplementary ventilation.

The normal ventilation system (NVS) operates at all times, essentially to provide fresh air throughout the tunnel complex for physiological purposes.

The Supplementary Ventilation System (SVS) operates only under abnormal conditions to provide significant quantities of additional air directly to the Running Tunnels for a variety of purposes.

However, whilst comprising separate systems, during certain abnormal operations when emergency conditions apply in the Tunnels, it has become necessary to operate both NVS and SVS together, in order to support certain rescue scenarios. This requirement has required extensive study of the combined ventilation systems' characteristics and operating modes in relation to the development of emergency response strategies.

3.1 The Normal Ventilation Systems (NVS)

3.1.1 General Description

The NVS comprises fans located at the UK and French coastal sites of Shakespeare Cliff and Sangatte which blow directly into the service tunnel. From a ventilation point of view, the service tunnel then acts as a pressurised conduit distributing fresh air throughout the Tunnel. The service tunnel is closed to atmosphere at the portals via large air lock doors and by means of bulk head doors in each cross passage which give connection to the running tunnels. Airflow connections to the running tunnels are made at selected cross passages whilst airflow is ensured in the underland sections by atmospheric bleed-offs at the portal air locks. Figure 6 is an isometric view of the NVS, whilst figure 7 shows the design rates of airflow in each section.

Air is passed to the running tunnels through air distribution units (A.D.U's) incorporating non-return devices and a flow regulator. When the running tunnel pressure, due to train piston effect, exceeds the local service tunnel pressure, the non-return devices close, preventing air flow back into the service tunnel. By this means, the service tunnel always remains pressurised with fresh air.

3.1.2 NVS Design Requirements

The NVS has to fulfil the following requirements.

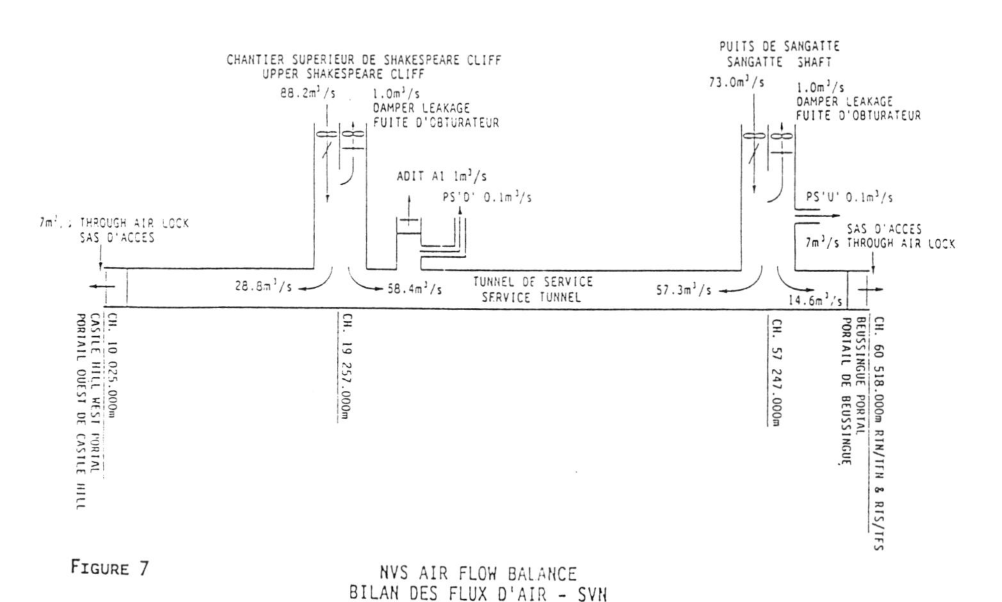

FIGURE 7 NVS AIR FLOW BALANCE
BILAN DES FLUX D'AIR - SVN

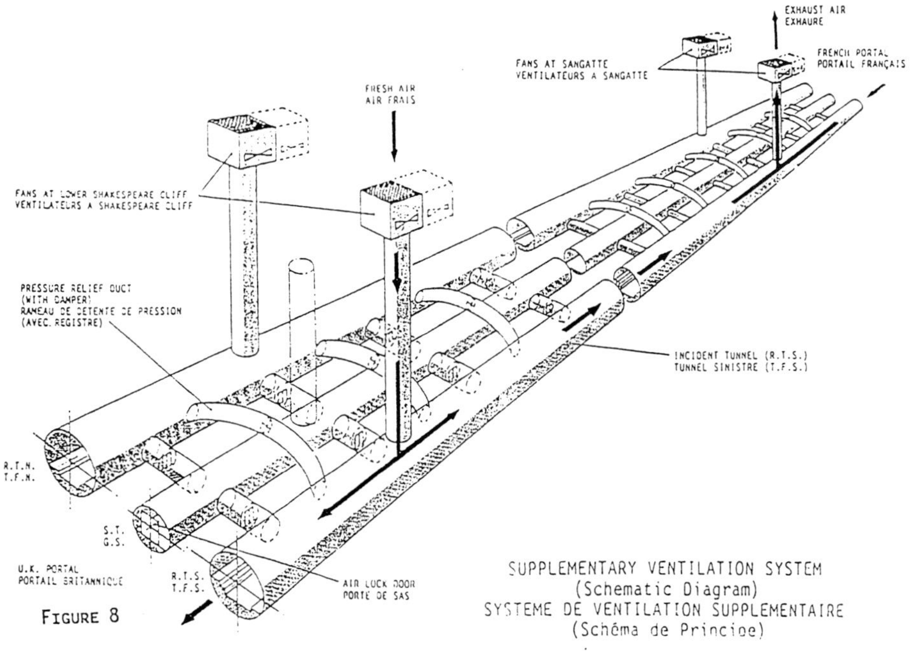

EXHAUST AIR
EXHAURE
FANS AT SANGATTE
VENTILATEURS A SANGATTE
FRENCH PORTAL
PORTAIL FRANÇAIS
FRESH AIR
AIR FRAIS
FANS AT LOWER SHAKESPEARE CLIFF
VENTILATEURS A SHAKESPEARE CLIFF
PRESSURE RELIEF DUCT
(WITH DAMPER)
RAMEAU DE DETENTE DE PRESSION
(AVEC REGISTRE)
INCIDENT TUNNEL (R.T.S.)
TUNNEL SINISTRE (T.F.S.)
R.T.N.
T.F.N.
S.T.
G.S.
U.K. PORTAL
PORTAIL BRITANNIQUE
R.T.S.
T.F.S.
AIR LOCK DOOR
PORTE DE SAS

FIGURE 8 SUPPLEMENTARY VENTILATION SYSTEM
(Schematic Diagram)
SYSTEME DE VENTILATION SUPPLEMENTAIRE
(Schéma de Principe)

a) During normal operation:

- to supply sufficient fresh air for the physiological needs of passengers on trains and shuttles and for maintenance personnel working in the tunnel and associated technical rooms,

- to provide adequate ventilation air for the diesel engines of the Service Tunnel Transport System (STTS) and any maintenance works trains in the running tunnel (eg during catenary maintenance).

- to supply ventilation and cooling air to technical rooms, some of which are equipped with chiller units.

b) During abnormal operation:

- to maintain a pressurised "safe haven" of fresh air in the service tunnel into which passengers can evacuate from a running tunnel incident. The safe haven must, therefore, be maintained even when a number of cross passage doors are opened.

- to provide a flow of air in either direction along the service tunnel to clear smoke and fumes in the event of a fire in the service tunnel.

- to dilute and remove Halon and the products of combustion in the event of a fire in a technical room.

3.1.3 NVS Fan Design

Two 100% duty axial flow fans are provided at each coastal site each capable of delivering 90m^3/second at 3kPa. The fan stations incorporate the following features:

- reversible flow and stepped blade pitch control.

- non-stalling design using anti-stall chambers.

- capable of continuous operation with ±7% cyclic change in system pressure caused by traffic movements in the Tunnel.

- windmilling capability.

- operation for 90 minutes exhausting air at 150°C.

- inlet air heater for frost conditions.

- full remote control.

- silencers fitted on the atmospheric and tunnel sides of each fan.

3.2 The Supplementary Ventilation System (SVS)

3.2.1 General Description

The SVS also comprises fans located at each coastal site except that connection is made directly to each running tunnel. Fans at each site also operate in tandem, in 'push-pull' fashion, in order to induce the requisite air flow in the undersea section. Fans would normally only be connected to one tunnel at any one time. Dampers in the piston relief ducts between running tunnels and doors at each crossover would normally be closed during an abnormal incident. This action isolates the incident running tunnel from the other tunnel which may be used to bring in a rescue train for final evacuation of passengers to the surface.

Figure 8 shows an isometric view of the SVS in operation.

3.2.2 SVS Design Requirements

The SVS only operates in abnormal conditions, when it is required:

- to provide a flow of cooling air to stationary shuttles and trains, primarily to enable the continued operation of on-board auxiliaries, such as a.c. units;
- in the event of a fire in a running tunnel, to control and effect the removal of smoke and fumes by means of a flow of air along the incident running tunnel;
- to provide adequate ventilation air to a diesel powered rescue unit in the event of a train being stranded by a catenary failure.

The performance requirement is to provide a minimum flow rate of $100m^3/s$ in one tunnel of the undersea section. In an open tunnel section, this flow rate corresponds to a velocity along the tunnel axis of 3m/s approximately. Shuttles in cross-section occupy 50% of the free space in the running tunnel, leading to an air flow velocity in the walkway alongside a shuttle of 5m/s approximately. This level of airflow is suitable for both evacuation purposes and for controlling the smoke from an uncontained fire. The air flow in underland tunnel sections is very much higher than in the undersea section, being limited only by the frictional resistance of the tunnel length to the portal. On the UK side [10km] the corresponding underland air flow rate is $160m^3/s$, on the French side [3km] the air flow rate is $200m^3/s$.

3.2.3 SVS Fan Design

Two 100% duty fans are located at each coastal site having the following characteristics:

- connectable to either or both tunnels by dampers
- axial flow type with symmetrically profiled variable pitch blades providing flow rates between ±100%
- 90 minute rating at 150°C
- full remote control
- 100% duty rating is - UK side: $260m^3/s$ at 1.7kPa
FR side: $300m^3/s$ at 1.8kPa
- fan motors are rated at 700kW UK side, 840kW on the FR side.

3.3 NVS and SVS Operation

The ventilation concept for the Channel Tunnel together with the unprecedented scale of the system and its possible modes of operation led directly to a need for extensive simulation work throughout all design phases.

Initial work was carried out using simple computer or analogue models. However, modelling work has become more sophisticated to reflect the developing requirements of simulation.

A very comprehensive set of simulation studies were carried out during the later design phases with the following objectives.

1. To calibrate the normal ventilation system for effective distribution of air by regulating the flow at A.D.U.'s.

2. To investigate the effects on air flows and pressure distribution throughout the tunnel for various combinations of PRD dampers open/closed, ADU's open/closed and Cross Passage Doors open/closed. These investigations included NVS and SVS operating alone and, finally, together in variable flow modes.

3. Based on the investigative studies of 2 above, to determine a simple set of operating rules for the ventilation system which provide the necessary support and environmental conditions for a wide range of normal, abnormal and emergency incident scenarios.

   The necessary design skill is to reduce the range of possible actions as far as possible without prejudicing the overall efficacy of the operational response. Examples include derivation of a simple set of revised NVS fan settings to be adopted prior to opening one, two or more cross passage doors, depending on:

   - status of PRD's and ADU's ie whether open or closed

   - location of an incident in the tunnel

   - presence or otherwise of a train or shuttle alongside

   - SVS operating or not and, if so, in which direction.

4. To produce an operational plan and a simple set of procedures for operation of the Ventilation Systems during all normal and abnormal conditions which is fully integrated with the operational requirements of the whole Transport System under these conditions.

5. To produce a commissioning programme for the ventilation systems integrated with other tests on completion, e.g. shuttle evacuation and aerodynamics, which allows ventilation simulation results to be tested and any necessary adjustments made as simply as possible.

Examples of simulation results are shown in Figures 9, 10, 11 and 12.

Figure 9 shows the distribution of air pressure and flow along the tunnel with the NVS operating normally. ADU regulators have been set to produce the desire flows without exceeding $2m^3/s$ at any one location. (Compare the

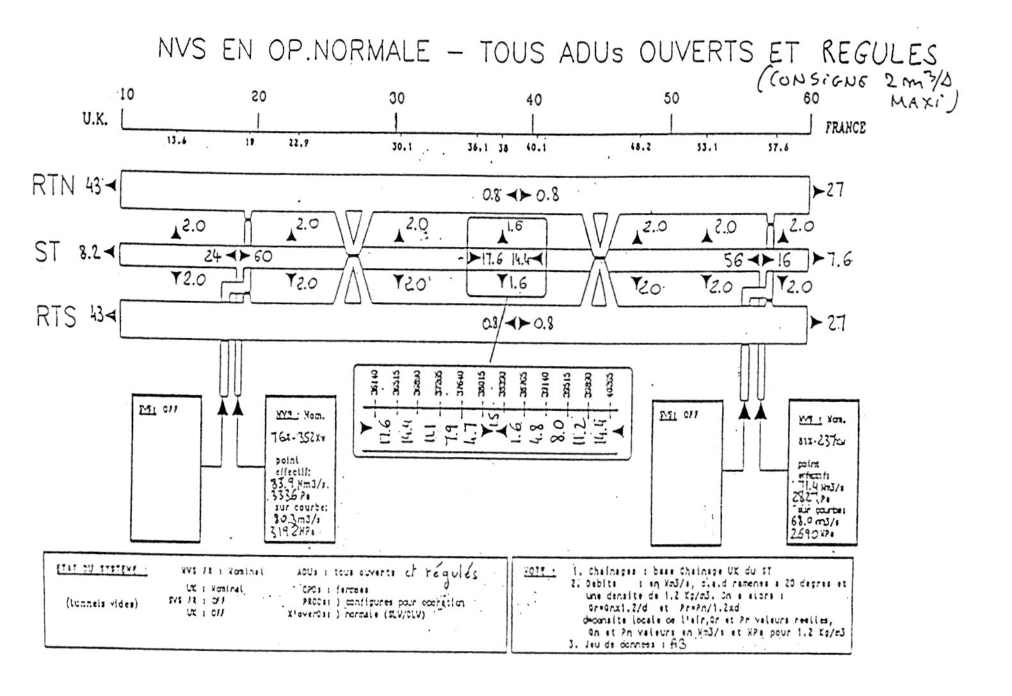
NVS EN OP.NORMALE – TOUS ADUs OUVERTS ET REGULES
(CONSIGNE 2 m3/s MAXI)
U.K.
FRANCE
10
20
30
40
50
60
RTN 43
ST 8.2
RTS 43
27
7.6
27
0.8
0.8
24
60
17.6
14.4
56
16
2.0
1.6
ETAT DU SYSTEME :
(tunnels vides)
NOTE :

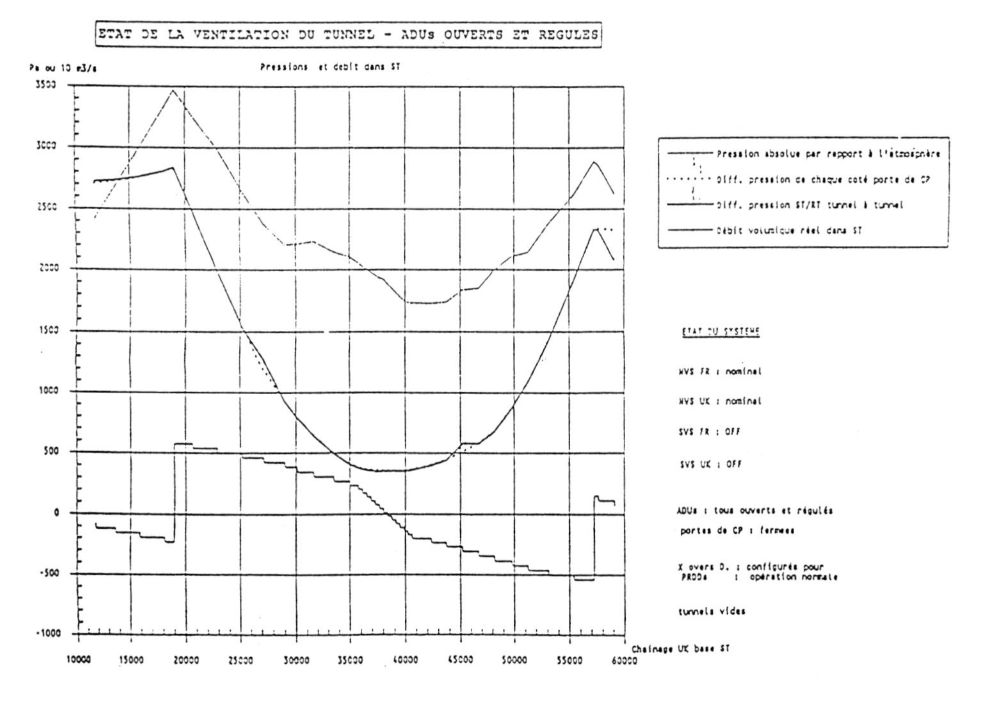
ETAT DE LA VENTILATION DU TUNNEL - ADUs OUVERTS ET REGULES
Pa ou 10 m3/s
Pressions et debit dans ST
Pression absolue par rapport à l'atmosphère
Diff. pression de chaque coté porte de CP
Diff. pression ST/RT tunnel à tunnel
Debit volumique réel dans ST
ETAT DU SYSTEME
NVS FR : nominal
NVS UK : nominal
SVS FR : OFF
SVS UK : OFF
ADUs : tous ouverts et régulés
portes de CP : fermees
X overs D. : configurés pour
PRDDs : opération normale
tunnels vides
Chainage UK base ST
3500
3000
2500
2000
1500
1000
500
0
-500
-1000
10000
15000
20000
25000
30000
35000
40000
45000
50000
55000
60000

FIGURE 9

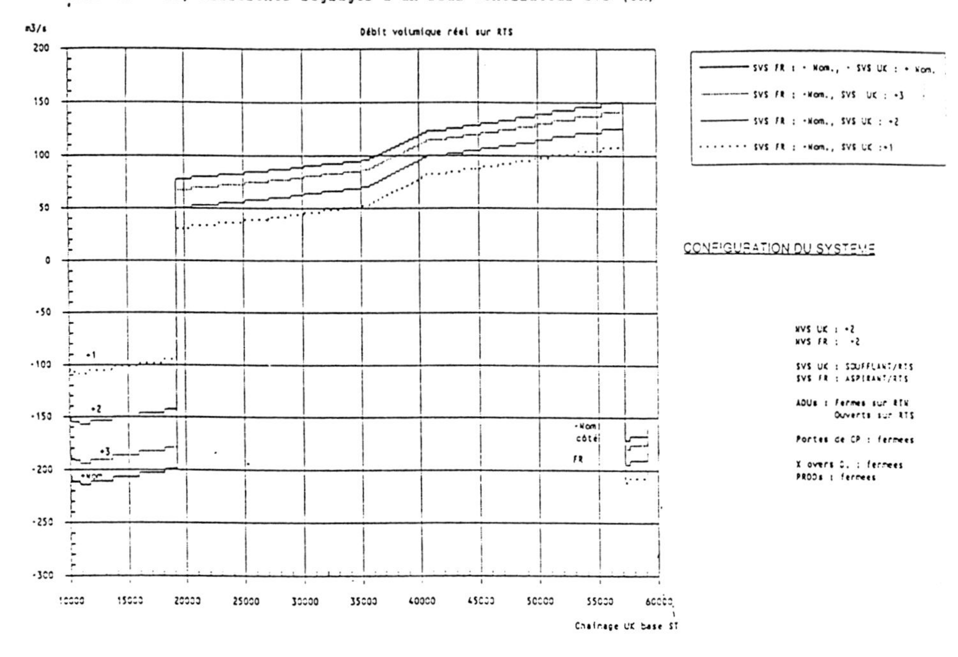
SVS FONCTIONNANT (AVEC NVS) SUR UN TUNNEL VIDE
OU TOUS LES ADUs SONT OUVERTS (RTS) ET TOUTES LES PORTES FERMEES
Sens UK -> FR, différents réglages d'un seul ventilateur SVS (UK)
m3/s
Débit volumique réel sur RTS
200
150
100
50
0
-50
-100
-150
-200
-250
-300
10000
15000
20000
25000
30000
35000
40000
45000
50000
55000
60000
Chainage UK base ST
CONFIGURATION DU SYSTEME

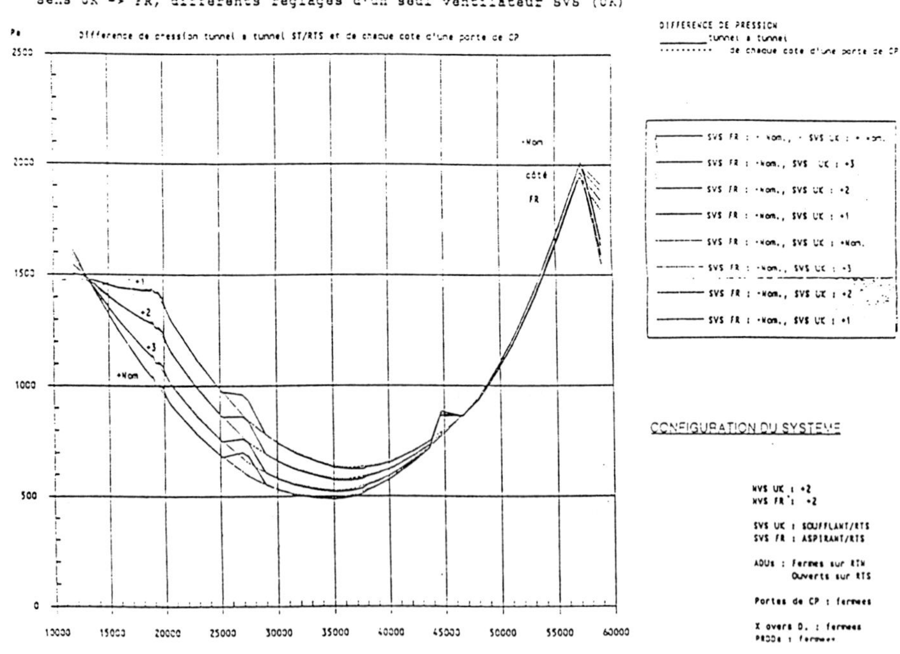
SVS FONCTIONNANT (AVEC NVS) SUR UN TUNNEL VIDE
OU TOUS LES ADUs SONT OUVERTS (RTS) ET TOUTES LES PORTES FERMEES
Sens UK -> FR, différents réglages d'un seul ventilateur SVS (UK)
Pa
2500
2000
1500
1000
500
0
10000
15000
20000
25000
30000
35000
40000
45000
50000
55000
60000
CONFIGURATION DU SYSTEME

FIGURE 10

1 **CONDITIONS MÉTÉO: Influence sur le débit en RT**

2 MODE INCIDENT EN RT AVEC NVS + SVS - 2 CPs OUVERTS SUR TUNNEL INCIDENTE

3 Valeur du débit en RT(m3/s) en aval SVS du 2nd CP ouvert et ecart par rapport aux valeurs en conditions méteo neutres(*) pour: T0(tunnel vide). T1(1 navette seule). Tm(plein sous mer). Tt1(plein sous terre des deux cotés + 1 navette).

4 FLUX SVS DIRIGÉ VERS FRANCE
[II.a (F)]

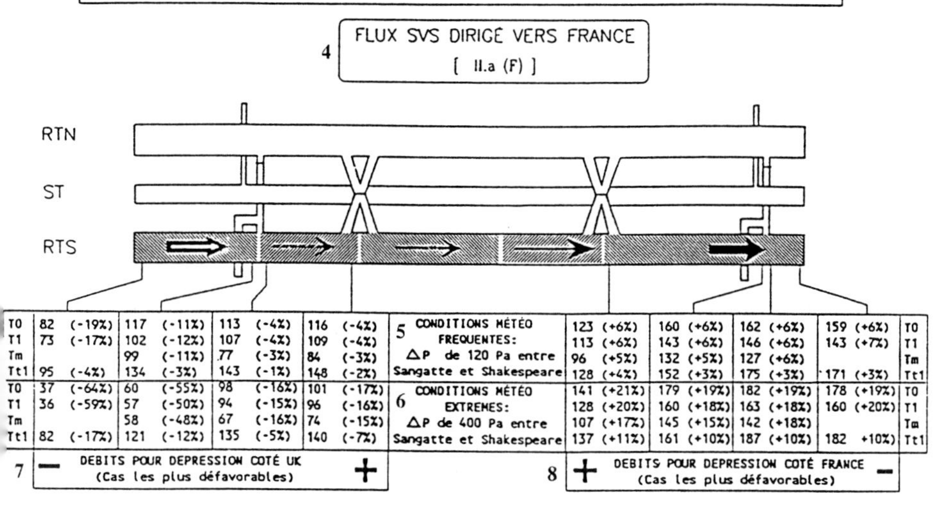

T0	82 (-19%)	117 (-11%)	113 (-4%)	116 (-4%)	5 CONDITIONS MÉTÉO FREQUENTES:	123 (+6%)	160 (+6%)	162 (+6%)	159 (+6%)	T0
T1	73 (-17%)	102 (-12%)	107 (-4%)	109 (-4%)		113 (+6%)	143 (+6%)	146 (+6%)	143 (+7%)	T1
Tm		99 (-11%)	77 (-3%)	84 (-3%)	ΔP de 120 Pa entre	96 (+5%)	132 (+5%)	127 (+6%)		Tm
Tt1	95 (-4%)	134 (-3%)	143 (-1%)	148 (-2%)	Sangatte et Shakespeare	128 (+4%)	152 (+3%)	175 (+3%)	171 (+3%)	Tt1
T0	37 (-64%)	60 (-55%)	98 (-16%)	101 (-17%)	6 CONDITIONS MÉTÉO EXTREMES:	141 (+21%)	179 (+19%)	182 (+19%)	178 (+19%)	T0
T1	36 (-59%)	57 (-50%)	94 (-15%)	96 (-16%)		128 (+20%)	160 (+18%)	163 (+18%)	160 (+20%)	T1
Tm		58 (-48%)	67 (-16%)	74 (-15%)	ΔP de 400 Pa entre	107 (+17%)	145 (+15%)	142 (+18%)		Tm
Tt1	82 (-17%)	121 (-12%)	135 (-5%)	140 (-7%)	Sangatte et Shakespeare	137 (+11%)	161 (+10%)	187 (+10%)	182 +10%)	Tt1

7 — DEBITS POUR DEPRESSION COTÉ UK (Cas les plus défavorables) +

8 + DEBITS POUR DEPRESSION COTÉ FRANCE (Cas les plus défavorables) —

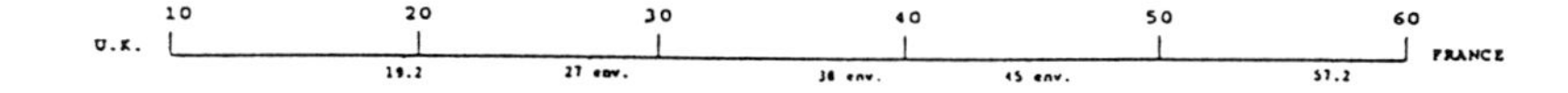

9 FLUX SVS DIRIGÉ VERS UK
[II.a (K)]

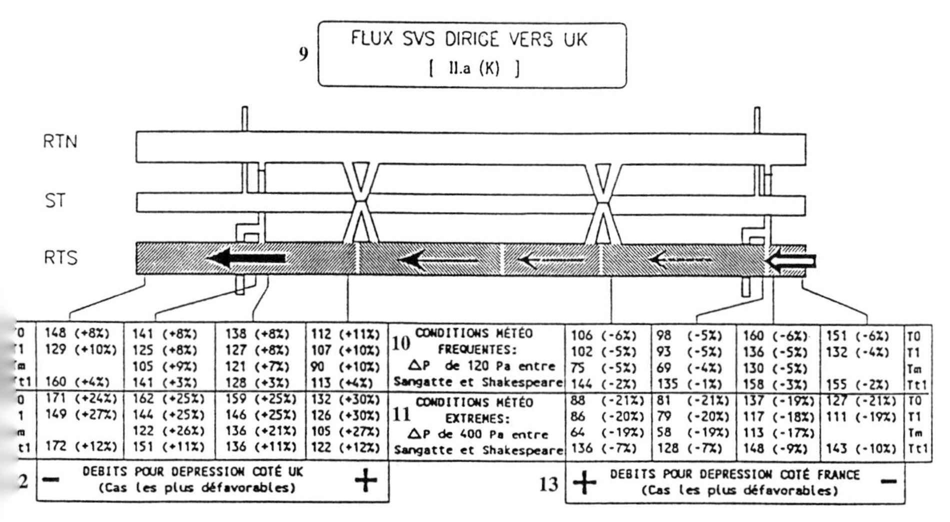

T0	148 (+8%)	141 (+8%)	138 (+8%)	112 (+11%)	10 CONDITIONS MÉTÉO FREQUENTES:	106 (-6%)	98 (-5%)	160 (-6%)	151 (-6%)	T0
T1	129 (+10%)	125 (+8%)	127 (+8%)	107 (+10%)		102 (-5%)	93 (-5%)	136 (-5%)	132 (-4%)	T1
Tm		105 (+9%)	121 (+7%)	90 (+10%)	ΔP de 120 Pa entre	75 (-5%)	69 (-4%)	130 (-5%)		Tm
Tt1	160 (+4%)	141 (+3%)	128 (+3%)	113 (+4%)	Sangatte et Shakespeare	144 (-2%)	135 (-1%)	158 (-3%)	155 (-2%)	Tt1
T0	171 (+24%)	162 (+25%)	159 (+25%)	132 (+30%)	11 CONDITIONS MÉTÉO EXTREMES:	88 (-21%)	81 (-21%)	137 (-19%)	127 (-21%)	T0
T1	149 (+27%)	144 (+25%)	146 (+25%)	126 (+30%)		86 (-20%)	79 (-20%)	117 (-18%)	111 (-19%)	T1
Tm		122 (+26%)	136 (+21%)	105 (+27%)	ΔP de 400 Pa entre	64 (-19%)	58 (-19%)	113 (-17%)		Tm
Tt1	172 (+12%)	151 (+11%)	136 (+11%)	122 (+12%)	Sangatte et Shakespeare	136 (-7%)	128 (-7%)	148 (-9%)	143 (-10%)	Tt1

12 — DEBITS POUR DEPRESSION COTÉ UK (Cas les plus défavorables) +

13 + DEBITS POUR DEPRESSION COTÉ FRANCE (Cas les plus défavorables) —

14 (*) Pourcentage par rapport au conditions météo neutres (même pression atmosphérique en UK et FR) :
(+) Augmentation de débit
(-) Diminution de débit

FIGURE 11

15 **CONDITIONS MÉTÉO: Influence sur le débit dans les CPs**

16 MODE INCIDENT EN RT AVEC NVS + SVS – 2 CPs OUVERTS SUR TUNNEL INCIDENTE

17 Valeur du débit dans les CPs ouverts (m3/s) pour: T0(tunnel vide). T1(1 navette seule). Tm(plein sous mer). Tt1(plein sous terre des deux cotés + 1 navette).

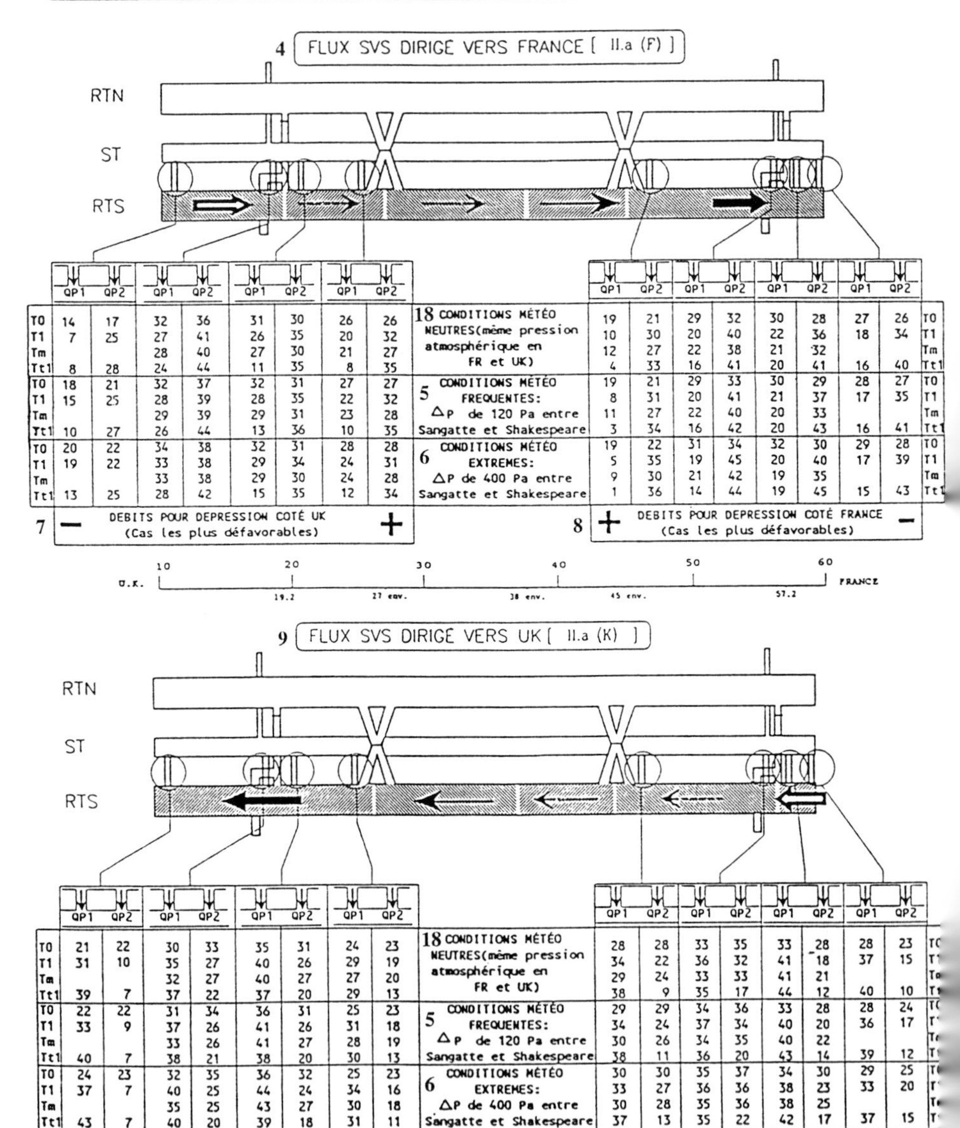

4 FLUX SVS DIRIGE VERS FRANCE [II.a (F)]

Conditions		QP1	QP2	QP1	QP2	QP1	QP2	QP1	QP2	QP1	QP2	QP1	QP2	QP1	QP2	QP1	QP2	
18 CONDITIONS MÉTÉO NEUTRES(même pression atmosphérique en FR et UK)	T0	14	17	32	36	31	30	26	26	19	21	29	32	30	28	27	26	T0
	T1	7	25	27	41	26	35	20	32	10	30	20	40	22	36	18	34	T1
	Tm			28	40	27	30	21	27	12	27	22	38	21	32			Tm
	Tt1	8	28	24	44	11	35	8	35	4	33	16	41	20	41	16	40	Tt1
5 CONDITIONS MÉTÉO FREQUENTES: ΔP de 120 Pa entre Sangatte et Shakespeare	T0	18	21	32	37	32	31	27	27	19	21	29	33	30	29	28	27	T0
	T1	15	25	28	39	28	35	22	32	8	31	20	41	21	37	17	35	T1
	Tm			29	39	29	31	23	28	11	27	22	40	20	33			Tm
	Tt1	10	27	26	44	13	36	10	35	3	34	16	42	20	43	16	41	Tt1
6 CONDITIONS MÉTÉO EXTREMES: ΔP de 400 Pa entre Sangatte et Shakespeare	T0	20	22	34	38	32	31	28	28	19	22	31	34	32	30	29	28	T0
	T1	19	22	33	38	29	34	24	31	5	35	19	45	20	40	17	39	T1
	Tm			33	38	29	30	24	28	9	30	21	42	19	35			Tm
	Tt1	13	25	28	42	15	35	12	34	1	36	14	44	19	45	15	43	Tt1

7 — DEBITS POUR DEPRESSION COTÉ UK (Cas les plus défavorables) +

8 + DEBITS POUR DEPRESSION COTÉ FRANCE (Cas les plus défavorables) —

9 FLUX SVS DIRIGE VERS UK [II.a (K)]

Conditions		QP1	QP2	QP1	QP2	QP1	QP2	QP1	QP2	QP1	QP2	QP1	QP2	QP1	QP2	QP1	QP2	
18 CONDITIONS MÉTÉO NEUTRES(même pression atmosphérique en FR et UK)	T0	21	22	30	33	35	31	24	23	28	28	33	35	33	28	28	23	T0
	T1	31	10	35	27	40	26	29	19	34	22	36	32	41	18	37	15	T1
	Tm			32	27	40	27	27	20	29	24	33	33	41	21			Tm
	Tt1	39	7	37	22	37	20	29	13	38	9	35	17	44	12	40	10	Tt1
5 CONDITIONS MÉTÉO FREQUENTES: ΔP de 120 Pa entre Sangatte et Shakespeare	T0	22	22	31	34	36	31	25	23	29	29	34	36	33	28	28	24	T0
	T1	33	9	37	26	41	26	31	18	34	24	37	34	40	20	36	17	T1
	Tm			33	26	41	27	28	19	30	26	34	35	40	22			Tm
	Tt1	40	7	38	21	38	20	30	13	38	11	36	20	43	14	39	12	Tt1
6 CONDITIONS MÉTÉO EXTREMES: ΔP de 400 Pa entre Sangatte et Shakespeare	T0	24	23	32	35	36	32	25	23	30	30	35	37	34	30	29	25	T0
	T1	37	7	40	25	44	24	34	16	33	27	36	36	38	23	33	20	T1
	Tm			35	25	43	27	30	18	30	28	35	36	38	25			Tm
	Tt1	43	7	40	20	39	18	31	11	37	13	35	22	42	17	37	15	Tt1

7 — DEBITS POUR DEPRESSION COTÉ UK (Cas les plus défavorables) +

8 + DEBITS POUR DEPRESSION COTÉ FRANCE (Cas les plus défavorables) —

FIGURE 12

Key to figures 11 and 12

1 METEOROLOGICAL CONDITIONS: Influence on the flow in RT

2 INCIDENT MODE IN RT WITH NVS + SVS - 2 CPs OPEN IN THE INCIDENT TUNNEL

3 Value of the airflow in RT (m3/s) downstream from the SVS of the 2nd open CP and difference compared with values for neutral meteorological conditions (*) for: TO (tunnel empty), T1 (1 single shuttle), Tm (full marine), Tt1 (full under-land on both sides +1 shuttle).

4 SVS Flow Directed Towards France
[11.a (F)]

5 FREQUENT METEOROLOGICAL CONDITIONS:
ΔP of 120 Pa between Sangatte and Shakespeare

6 SEVERE METEOROLOGICAL CONDITIONS
ΔP of 400 Pa between Sangatte and Shakespeare

7 FLOWS FOR DEPRESSION (LOW PRESSURE) ON THE UK SIDE
(Most unfavourable cases)

8 FLOWS FOR DEPRESSION (LOW PRESSURE) ON THE FRENCH SIDE
(Most unfavourable cases)

9 SVS FLOW DIRECTED TOWARDS UK
[11.a (K)]

10 FREQUENT METEOROLOGICAL CONDITIONS
ΔP of 120 Pa between Sangatte and Shakespeare

11 SEVERE METEOROLOGICAL CONDITIONS
ΔP of 400 Pa between Sangatte and Shakespeare

12 FLOWS FOR DEPRESSION (LOW PRESSURE) ON THE UK SIDE
(Most unfavourable cases)

13 FLOWS FOR DEPRESSION (LOW PRESSURE) ON THE FRENCH SIDE
(Most unfavourable cases)

14 (*) Percentage compared with neutral meteorological conditions (same atmospheric pressure in UK and France):
(+) Increased flow
(-) Reduced flow

15 METEOROLOGICAL CONDITIONS
Influence on the flow in the CPs

16 INCIDENT MODE IN RT WITH NVS + SVS - 2 CPs OPEN IN THE INCIDENT TUNNEL

17 Value of the airflow in the open CPs (m3/s) for: TO (tunnel empty), T1 (1 single shuttle), Tm (full marine). Tt1 (full under-land on both sides + 1 shuttle).

18 NEUTRAL METEOROLOGICAL CONDITIONS (same atmospheric pressure in France and UK).

results with figure 7 which shows the conceptual design flow rates). The flow rate is enhanced at the middle of the undersea section in order to avoid any stagnant areas of low or zero flow.

Figure 10 shows the operation of SVS and NVS together for various settings of SVS and NVS blade angles. Notice that the NVS flow through the open ADU's adds to the total flow in the running tunnel.

Figures 11 & 12 show an example of the synthesis of the basic simulations done to produce figures 9 and 10 into sensitivity studies of the effect of various factors on the operating parameters chosen for NVS and SVS fans.

In the example shown, the effect of meteorological conditions is being assessed for the important operational condition of two cross passage doors open for evacuation purposes. In the extreme, a difference of 400Pa in atmospheric pressure can be envisaged between the two fan stations located on either side of the Channel. Figure 11 shows the variation of total air flow at different points in the incident running tunnel under three different meteorological conditions and with four different train in tunnel combinations. Figure 12 shows the variation in air flow through open cross passage doors at different locations in the tunnel under the same variable meteorological and train in tunnel conditions. The test to be applied in this latter case is to ensure that the flow rate through any cross passage does not become either negative (ie from the running into the service tunnel, prejudicing the safe haven concept of the service tunnel) or too great (thereby exceeding a maximum acceptable velocity of 12m/s for passengers to walk against).

As indicated earlier, the objective of the studies is to produce a minimum set of possible actions, expressed as operational fan and damper settings. The settings must, individually, be sufficiently robust for the respective operational conditions envisaged and, generally, entirely consistent with the overall operational response in terms of speed and ease of operation, as well as flexibility of response to changing conditions.

Figure 13 is an abstract taken from a postulated scenario study setting out the actions which would need to be taken by the railway controller (RC) and the EMS controller (EC). The postulated scenario is a catenary pulled down by a tourist shuttle (no. 6387) and stopped at PK 3348 in running tunnel south (between the two undersea crossovers). As well as a number of trains running normally from the UK to France in running tunnel north at the time of the incident, there are two through trains ahead of the incident shuttle and four trains behind, three of which have not yet passed the French undersea crossover. The train immediately behind is an HGV shuttle (no. 7387). In view of the forecast time to repair and restore power to the affected sections, the decision is taken, 28 minutes into the incident, to evacuate passengers from the affected tourist shuttle to a rescue train to be brought alongside in the other running tunnel. The underlying objective is safely to evacuate all passengers in all trains, preferably to their intended destination, within 90 minutes.

In figure 13, those actions conditioned by air movement considerations and, therefore, based on circumstances studied by the ventilation simulation, are highlighted by underlining. The example is given to indicate something of the resultant simplicity in integrating the output from the simulations into a set of basic, essential actions suitable for final preparation of operating procedures and instructions. The overall simplicity achieved

	POSTULATED SCENARIO: CATENARY PULLED DOWN BY A TOURIST SHUTTLE	
TIME (Hrs)	RCC (RC: RTM Railway Controller; EC: EMS Controller)	Comments
14.34	EC: Notices a power alarm and loss of power to UK running tunnel South subsequent to opening to the main circuit breaker. Alerts RTM controller.	
14.35	RC: Orders all trains in RT South to stop (track-to-train radio). Sets tunnel approach signals to danger.	
.. ..	.. ..	
14.40	EC: Unable to restore power. Advises RTM controller.	
	RC: Switches on main lighting in area without catenary power and instructs drivers in this area to check catenary and that there is no smoke in tunnel before alighting.	
	RC: Instructs EMS controller to open the section switch in advance of tourist shuttle 6387 and attempt to restore catenary power after warning the drivers.	
14.44	RC: Orders driver of TMST 9006 in RT North to slow to 100km/h up to the French crossover. Closes PRDs in the area between the two crossovers.	
14.45	RC: Inputs a command for a 100km/h speed restriction in the middle part of RT North. Orders driver of the HGV shuttle to prepare to reverse.	
14.45	EC: Advises that power to the catenary in advance of the tourist shuttle can be restored.	
.. ..	.. ..	
15.02	RC: Concludes that it is impossible to use the diesel unit to bring the shuttle out, so decides to evacuate the tourist shuttle.	
15.03	RC: Decides to use an empty tourist shuttle waiting at a UK terminal platform as an "evacuation train" and sets a route for this train via RT North up to signal section marker 2612 protecting the UK crossover.	
15.03	RC: Prepares for backing out HGV shuttle 7387 located in RT South between incident train and French crossover (reverses signalling direction).	
15.05	RC: Authorises driver of HGV shuttle 7387 to reverse at max. speed 40km/h and stop at PK 4580.	
15.06	RC: Configures NVS and opens door to cross-passage 3349. Grants catenary maintenance team a Sel consignation and track possession and instructs them to earth the catenary in advance and rear of the train.	
15.21	RC: As the last train (TMST 9007) has passed the UK crossover, sets the route for the evacuation train and instructs the train to stop at cross-passage 3388.	
	RC: Gives order to prepare to evacuate the train located in the area without power via cross-passages 3349 and 3387 and advises EMS controller.	
	EC: Opens required cross-passage doors and notifies first line response team at scene that passengers are to be evacuated.	
	RC: Instructs EMS operator to open cross-passage doors 3388 and 3350 and evacuation train driver to prepare to receive passengers.	
.. ..	.. .. etc	

Figure 13

rather belies the breadth and complexity of the simulation work actually carried out. For example, much study and simulation of many parameters was necessary to determine the maximum authorised reversing speed of 40km/h for the single HGV shuttle (instructed at 15.05hrs). This speed is limited by the need to restrict induced air flow speeds at the scene of the incident and to maintain the safe haven of the service tunnel. The "following" HGV shuttle (no. 7387) must be moved simultaneously with the passenger evacuation from the incident shuttle (rather than simply remaining at rest until detraining to the service tunnel is completed) otherwise the 90 minute objective will not be achieved for the passengers on the HGV shuttle.

4. CONCLUSION

The ventilation and cooling systems for the Channel Tunnel are uniquely designed to meet the particular requirements of the Transport System.

For the cooling system, the large cooling load distributed over a distance of almost 50km is best met by the distributed cooling surface of a base pipe.

Heat rejection to atmosphere is either directly through dry air coolers or modular chilling plant. Flexibility for operation and future load growth is provided by the modular cooling approach. The bare pipe/chilling plant solution also lends itself to lower temperature operation including the development of crushed ice circulation in the future.

The ventilation system whilst using conventional fan stations to pressurise the system uses both novel non-return devices and carefully developed operational procedures to maintain the requirement for a fresh air "safe haven" under all conditions. The most intensive investigations have been carried out to predict ventilation conditions under many different operating scenarios and then produce safe, simple operational procedures for both normal and emergency conditions in the Tunnel.

FIXED SYSTEMS

Trevor JOHNS
Eurotunnel, Folkestone, England

INTRODUCTION

In this paper, I would like to describe the systems which comprise the balance of the other fixed systems within the Channel Tunnel itself and have not been the subject of a detailed paper themselves. These are principally the drainage, fire fighting, fire detection, and lighting infrastructure used by the Channel Tunnel rail system.

DRAINAGE SYSTEM

The drainage of the Channel Tunnel is handled by a series of seven pump stations within the tunnel itself.

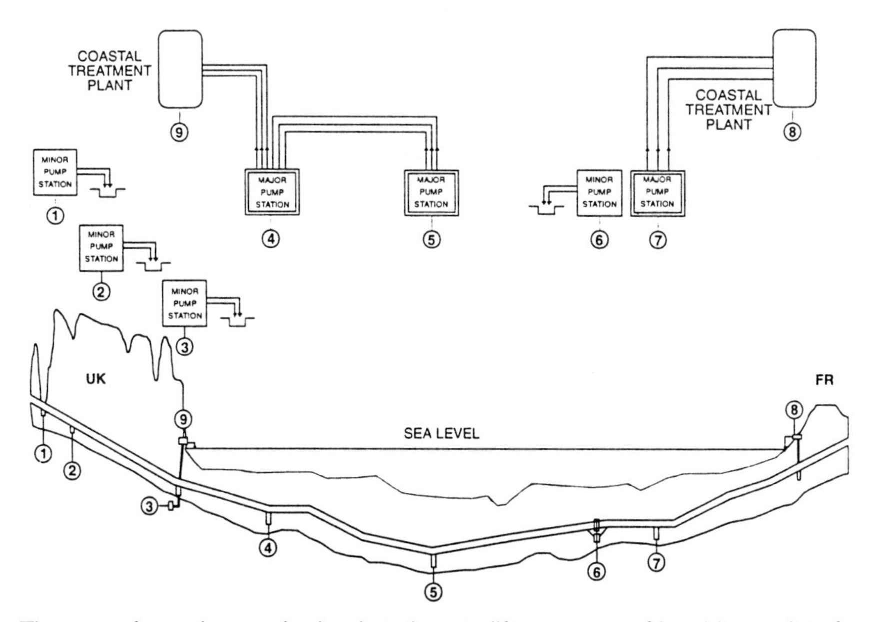

There are four minor under land stations to lift water out of local low points for transfer into the gravity drainage lines imbedded in the tunnel floor. All gravity drainage flows into low point catchment areas where three major undersea pump stations, pump water out of the tunnel network through three 406mm diameter lines situated in the roof of the service tunnel. These stations occur at approximately 15 kilometre intervals, and discharge into water treatment plants at the two coastal sites at Shakespeare Cliff and Sangatte.

Two of the three major stations discharge in UK and are configured as a cascade system, this represents the most economic manner of meeting the necessary pumping capacity.

The system has been designed so that each pump station is divided into two interconnected half stations situated at each of the tunnel low points. Each half station is capable of meeting the functional requirements of the pump station, and the duplication provides redundancy for both safety and maintenance requirements.

TYPICAL MAJOR PUMPING STATION

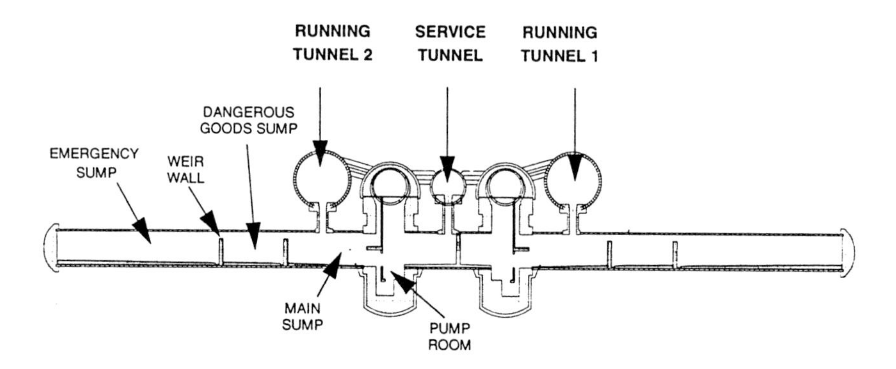

The pump station sumps are lined in cast iron and have been driven at right angles to the main tunnels. Each half station is split in to three areas: a main collection sump is used for the normal duty followed sequentially by a dangerous goods sump and an emergency sump positioned so as to complement the total storage capacity and to be able to isolate spillage's prior to transfer into special vehicles, which can be brought into either of the running tunnels. The two sump areas are separated by a water tight bulkhead and have separate access shafts and an independent ventilation system.

Each of the half stations is serviced by two multi-stage central-fugal pumps with cardan shaft transmissions to the motors which are located at the upper level of each shaft. The pump capacity varies from station to station with the largest being capable of pumping 668 cubic metres per hour, or in parallel operation, 985 cubic metres per hour with the second pump activated. These stations are run in an automatic manner by two PLC Controllers which also report on operating status to remote monitoring facilities at the Rail Control Centres. The functions monitored include ultra-sonic level detection, pump and motor vibration and motor temperature, together with discharge flows and pressures.

In addition to a conventional surge tank protection, a communications link between the stations provides sequenced ramp-valve opening and closing at the receiving end to minimise water hammer.

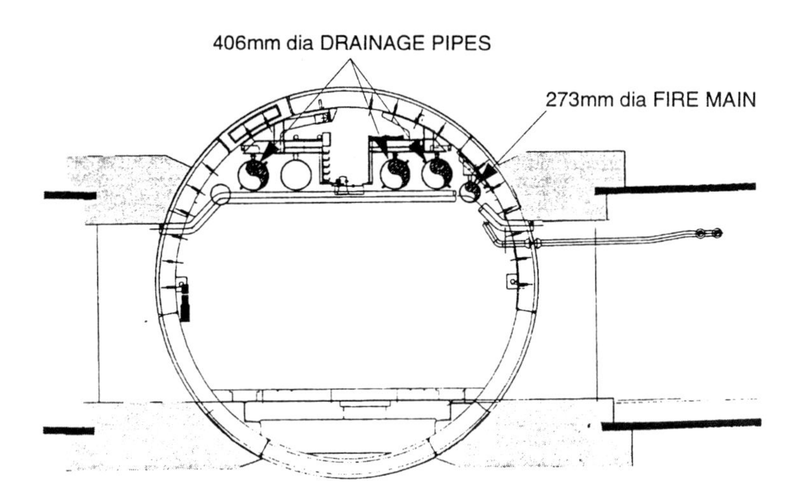

The drainage pipes mounted in the top of the service tunnel are 406mm outside diameter in 12 metre random length, 5.16mm wall thickness with an overall weight per pipe of around 600 kg, pipes are connected by Viking Johnson couplings and, tested to 35-bar. In each of the drainage lines, non-return valves have been fitted every 5km in order to ensure that any leakage is minimised and potential pump cavitation is reduced.

FIRE FIGHTING

The prime function of the Tunnel Fire Fighting System is to deliver water or foam from hydrants in the cross passages or running tunnels adjacent to the location of the fire. This is to be delivered at a pressure of up to 7-bar and a flow rate of 120 cubic metres/hour, with the potential use of up to four hydrants simultaneously. This requirement has been met by the provision of a 273mm main along the entire length of the service tunnel from Castle Hill Portal on the UK side to the Tranche de Beussingue on the French side, with operating pressures of up to 48-bar.

The fire main is sub-divided into four main sections. Each served by one of the four land based pump stations: located at, the UK Terminal, the Coastal site at Shakespeare Cliff, and similarly in France, one at the Sangatte Coastal site and at the French Terminal in the Tranche de Beussingue.

The fire main pipework loops in to each cross passage where a branch is taken off to the cross passage on the opposite side of the tunnel (see Appendix A). In each cross passage there are local control valve manifolds, hydrant connections and provision for portable foam generators. Branch pipes pass through the cross passage door bulkheads into the running tunnels and connect to hydrants situated either side of the cross passage.

In the event of an incident, the foam making equipment and hose reels will be taken to the nearest cross passage by the special service tunnel transport vehicles, used by the firemen based in the each of the two terminals.

The fire fighting stations are equipped with 600m^3 storage tanks, complete with biacide and anti-corrosion dosing systems. The operation of each station is controlled by a PLC, which has been configured to sequentially bring in the banks of both low and high pressure pumps as demand dictates. Jockey pumps ensure that the pressure head is maintained.

During operation, the fire fighting system can be configured so that with any one of the fire fighting pump stations out of service, sectioning valves can be opened to ensure that the adjacent fire fighting pump station can cover the requisite service. This provides for both an operational stand-by, in the case of breakdown, and also allows individual pump stations to be taken out of service for periodic maintenance whilst still retaining the necessary cover for the tunnel.

The fire fighting main feed line is a 273mm diameter carbon manganese line with a pipe wall thickness of 6.35mm. Each pipe being about 12 metres long and weighing approximately 500 kg. Each of the spools are mechanically jointed using the Viking Johnson couplings and hung from supports mounted in the service tunnel roof, adjacent to the drainage lines. Following the erection of the fire main, it was then tested to 61-bar and monitored to ensure that all deflections and loads on the brackets were within the design tolerances.

TUNNEL FIRE DETECTION AND PROTECTION

The main principals of the Fire Detection and Protection system are:

1. The provision of fire detection and protection for the equipment in the technical rooms.
2. Fire detection in the running tunnels.
3. Detection of the presence of a fire on a moving train in the running tunnels.
4. To relay this information to the fire control centre for display on a VDU together with suggested actions to be taken. Alarms indicate the exact location of occurrence and record the succession of events for subsequent analysis.
5. To continuously monitor the status of the system, displaying alarms and system operational availability. Additionally, the system is permanently self-checking in order to detect component failure.

The tunnel system itself forms part of the overall project fire detection system and is both supervised and monitored at each of the Fire Control Centres at the English and French terminals situated adjacent to their respective portals.

Technical Room Protection

This is provided by 74 local fire detection units installed in the northern cross passages. These monitor ionisation and optical smoke detectors installed in the 268 technical rooms within the tunnel complex.

Break glass units are mounted at the entrance of all protected zones allowing a manual alarm to be raised. Additional detectors are installed in the ventilation ducting of the electrical rooms with all sensors being wired to operate in a dual detection configuration. This is used in order to minimise the potential spurious alarms by requiring two adjacent detectors to be triggered simultaneously before releasing the extinguishant. The local fire detection unit is also interfaced with the ventilation control panel, stopping the ventilation fans and closing the vents to a room when a fire is detected.

The extinguisher chosen for the electrical rooms is halon 1301 stored in pressurised cylinders dependent on the volume of the room. In the event of a fire being detected, halon is automatically discharged by a diffuser connected to the gas cylinder, but only after a audible and bilingual illuminated alarm has sounded and after a short pre-set pause to allow personnel to evacuate the room. Manual release is also possible with a valve adjacent to the break glass unit.

The local fire detection units are interfaced by fibre optic links to ensure the transmission of all information to both fire control centres simultaneously. The local fire detection units also monitor detectors installed in the running tunnels which detect fire on a moving train as well as in the running tunnels. These comprise flame, smoke and carbon monoxide detectors, again relaying all data back to the monitoring centres at each portal.

The data transmission and communications systems which have been discussed earlier in this conference provide the link between these local fire detection units and the monitoring positions in both terminals.

TUNNEL LIGHTING SYSTEMS

The tunnel lighting system comprises of two types of lighting which are used throughout the Tunnel:-

a) Main lighting which is normally unlit but can be illuminated for maintenance and tunnel evacuation purposes.

b) Permanent Safety Markers (PSM) lighting which is permanently lit and incorporates an integral battery back-up with a 2 hour autonomy.

There are in total three independent power supplies for main and PSM lighting:-

- UK Grid
- French Grid
- Standby Generation.

Distribution

In general, the lighting is fed from its own 400V lighting switchboards in the north and south Electrical Rooms (ER), which are situated throughout the tunnel approximately every 750 metres. The lighting switchboards are fed via integral isolating transformers from the main 400V switchboards, this allows the electrical supplies to remain operational under first earth fault conditions. The north and south 400V switchboards are supplied from their respective independent 3.3kV ring mains from the various Electrical Underground Sub-Stations.

Reliability

To ensure lighting is always available the lighting switchboard power supplies are arranged to provide the following service reliability:-

- On loss of either National Grid, re-configuration of supply from the available National Grid.

- On loss on both National Grids, availability to supply from the Standby Generators.

- On loss of a 400V switchboard, an automatic changeover facility which will re-configure and supply from its opposite Electrical Room 400V switchboard (i.e. north to south or visa versa).

TYPICAL SECTION OF TUNNEL LIGHTING

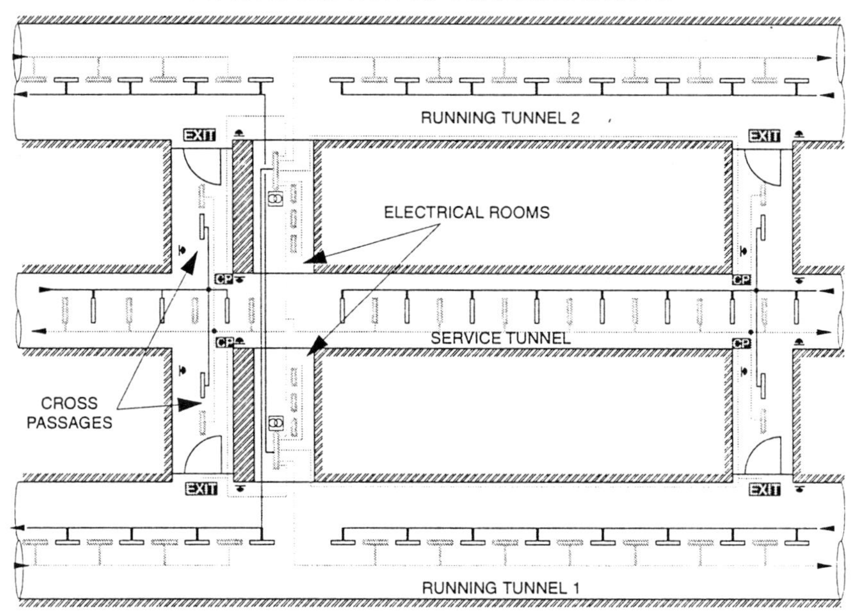

Standard Running Tunnels

A standard lighting section covers approximately 750 metres which consists a single row of main light fittings, with alternate fittings supplied by one of two overlapping circuits fed from different north and south ER's. The individual fittings are spaced approximately 7.75 metres apart above the evacuation walkways providing 20 Lux under normal conditions and 10 Lux with the loss of one supply. An additional safety feature is that one of the circuits is installed with fire resistant cables and the other with Low Smoke Fume (LSF) cables.

The main lighting is controlled by switching the associated circuit contactor from either local or remote. The normal method of operation is remote ON/OFF, initiated by the EMS controller, which will illuminate 3 x 750m sections of running tunnel as well as the associated service tunnel and cross passages. REMOTE ON control of similar sections of lighting is provided from the tunnel pushbuttons. Local ON/OFF of individual lighting circuits is available for maintenance purposes only.

Standard Service Tunnel

The standard lighting section configuration (normally unlit), is similar to that in the running tunnels with the exception that the light fittings are spaced at a nominal 8.7 metres, 2.5 metres over the roadway. With both power supplies available the illumination across the 3.8 metres wide roadway will be 20 Lux average with 5 Lux minimum and on loss of one complete supply this is reduced to 10 Lux average and 1 Lux minimum.

The main lighting is controlled by switching the associated circuit contactor from either local or remote. The normal method of operation is remote ON/OFF, initiated by the EMS controller, which will illuminate 3 x 750m sections of the service tunnel as well as the associated service cross passages. There are two REMOTE ON control push buttons, situated in the cross passages, one will illuminate 3 x 750m of running tunnels, service tunnel and associated cross passages and the other one will only illuminate 3 x 750m of service tunnel and associated cross passages. Local ON/OFF of individual lighting circuits is available for maintenance purposes only.

Transitional Lighting Zones

All tunnels are provided with transitional lighting zones which in the case of the running tunnels covers the first 1500 metres, and service tunnels the first 180 metres from the UK and French Portals. Although the tunnel standard lighting is not illuminated during ordinary traffic conditions, the areas by each portal are on to provide a limited graded transitional lighting facility. The intensity of lighting in the transitional zones can be adjusted for both day and night time operation.

Permanent Safety Marker Lighting

This sub-system provides permanent illumination of:

- Running Tunnel Cross Passage (CP) exit points;
- Running Tunnel CP telephone positions;
- Service Tunnel CP entrance points;
- Service Tunnel CP telephone positions.

It also provides Exit points and telephone locations for technical rooms, pumping stations, adits etc. The luminaire will provide clear point visibility to persons from front or sideways viewing up to a maximum distance of 200 metres.

The luminaires are supplied direct from the lighting switchboards, with no local switching facility. They are connected to a 230Vac LSF circuit supplied from the nearest ER. In the event of loss of the lighting switchboard supply an integral battery can maintain the illumination for up to two hours. The battery is automatically recharged on the restoration of supplies with a battery recovery time of 10 hours.

APPENDIX A

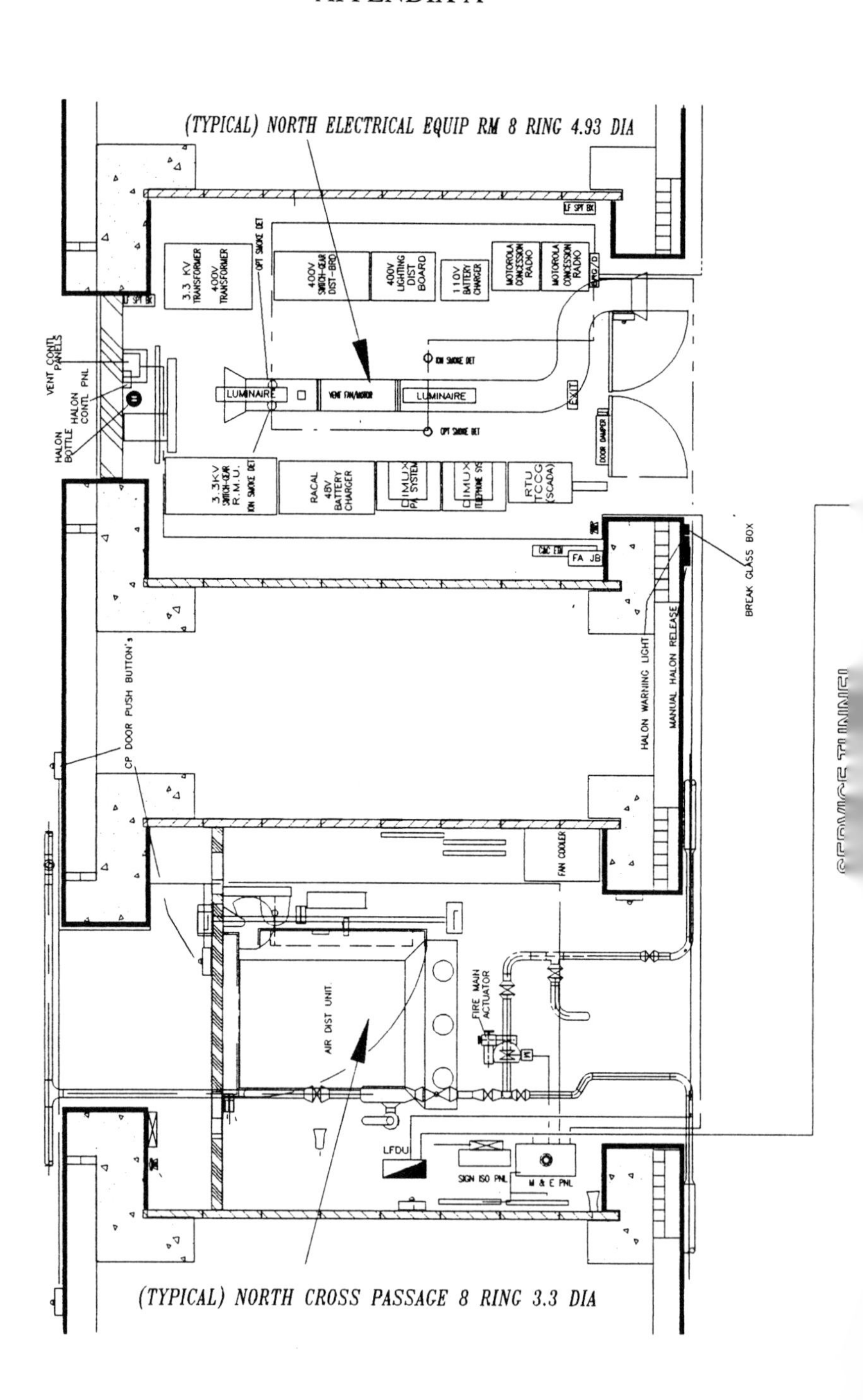
(TYPICAL) NORTH ELECTRICAL EQUIP RM 8 RING 4.93 DIA
RUNNING TUNNEL 2
3.3 KV TRANSFORMER
400V TRANSFORMER
OPT SMOKE DET
400V SWITCH-GEAR DIST-BRD
400V LIGHTING DIST BOARD
110V BATTERY CHARGER
MOTOROLA CONCESSION RADIO
MOTOROLA CONCESSION RADIO
VENT CONT PANELS
HALON CONTL PNL
HALON BOTTLE
LUMINAIRE
VENT FAN/MOTOR
LUMINAIRE
ION SMOKE DET
OPT SMOKE DET
EXIT
DOOR DAMPER
3.3KV SWITCH-GEAR R.M.U.
ION SMOKE DET
RACAL 48V BATTERY CHARGER
CIMUX PA SYSTEM
CIMUX TELEPHONE SYS
RTU TCCG (SCADA)
FA JB
BREAK GLASS BOX
HALON WARNING LIGHT
MANUAL HALON RELEASE
CP DOOR PUSH BUTTON's
FAN COOLER
AIR DIST UNIT.
FIRE MAIN ACTUATOR
LFDU
SIGN ISO PNL
M & E PNL
(TYPICAL) NORTH CROSS PASSAGE 8 RING 3.3 DIA

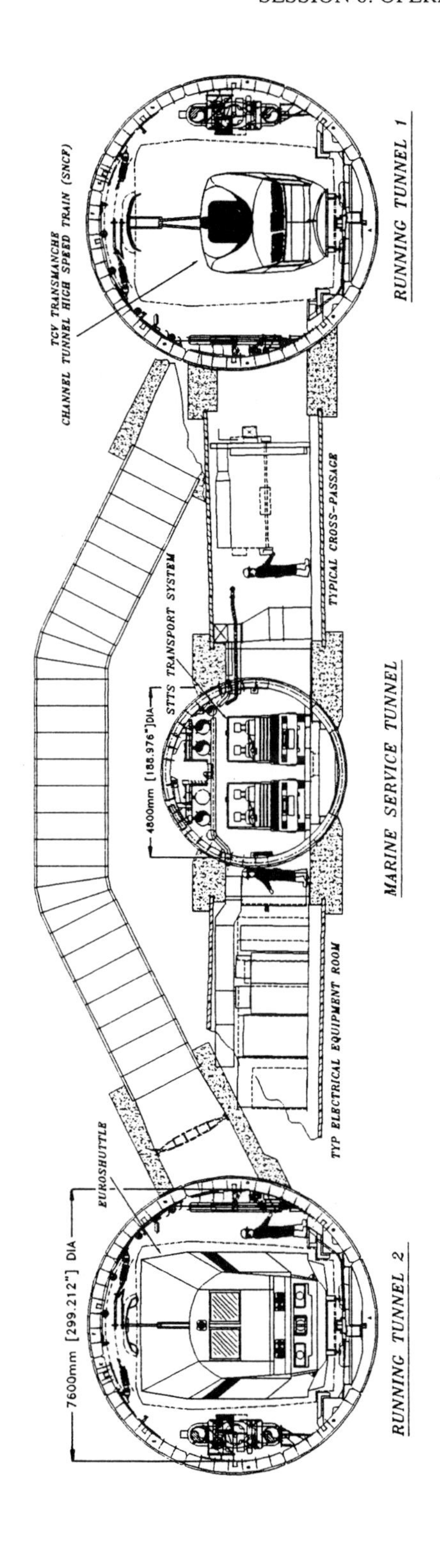
TCV TRANSMANCHE
CHANNEL TUNNEL HIGH SPEED TRAIN (SNCF)
RUNNING TUNNEL 1
TYPICAL CROSS-PASSAGE
STTS TRANSPORT SYSTEM
4800mm [188.976"] DIA
MARINE SERVICE TUNNEL
TYP ELECTRICAL EQUIPMENT ROOM
EUROSHUTTLE
7600mm [299.212"] DIA
RUNNING TUNNEL 2

Discussion on session 6

G. Tipper, *Heathrow Express (BAA)*

Please explain the measures regarding the control of dust in control rooms. Did Eurotunnel focus on safety culture during the psychometric testing?

R. Barnes, *Retired*

Why did the British go to the trouble of installing 132 kv oil filled cables on the UK side of the Channel Tunnel when the French used XLPE cables?

I recall that XLPE 132 kv cables were initially considered for the UK side. Why were they rejected?

B. J. Hardy, *EPD Consultants Ltd*

In hindsight would the author design any items of the electrical system differently?

N. Roth, *London Transport Planning*

Eurotunnel have been talking publicly about the possibility of building a second Channel Tunnel which would enable motor vehicles to drive through. How would such a tunnel be ventilated, given all the internal combustion engines that would be in the tunnel at any one time?

J. Anastassiades, *Attiko Metro*

Since HALON 1301 is being replaced all over Europe are there any provisions for changing the system and if so which system is the author planning to use?

Please explain emergency tunnel lighting?

R. Barnes, *Retired*

I think the 25 volt limit for 'touch' voltage inside the tunnel is excessively cautious and far too low. Most of Europe uses a 50 volt limit which I believe is a much more sensible figure and may have led to some savings on the earthing and screening systems.

P. T. May, *London Underground Limited*

What experience do the authors of session 6 have of rodent/insect infestation?

What are the effects of low gravity drainage flows on the performance of gravity drains?

Dr C. R. Bayliss
Reply to G. Tipper

Firstly it is very important to differentiate between the dust levels during the construction and initial commissioning, and the operations period and after rigorous cleaning. All tunnel technical rooms are pressurized with removable filters over the air access points. Keeping these filters clean after installation and towards the end of the construction period required a formal sizeable housekeeping/maintenance regime to be in place. Often such filters would need cleaning every other day until the tunnel cleanout had been completed and dust levels began to reduce. A similar regime was put in place in both UK and French control centres

Reply to R. Barnes

The 132 kV cables feeding the Channel Tunnel Main Intake Substation at the Folkestone Terminal from the Grid Substation at Sellindge were specified in terms of their performance so as to allow either paper insulated oil filled or XLPE solid dielectric cables to be purchased on a competitive tender basis. Oil filled cables were more competitive at the time of tender. This happens depending on the work in progress at different manufacturers at the time of tender. XLPE cables were selected on the French side for the similar 225 kV Grid infeed cables. It should be noted that paper cables have considerably higher capacitance per unit length than the equivalent XLPE insulated cables. This gave rise, in practice, to a voltage magnification effect under lightly loaded and transient conditions. In addition, the relative high charge on the cables led to a need to improve the rating of the 132 kV voltage transformers on the incoming circuits at the Folkestone substation. It should be noted that because of such capacitive effects it would have been much more difficult to engineer the 21 kV tunnel reticulation system if XLPE (or EPR) insulated cables had not been employed.

Reply to B. J. Hardy

The fundamental design has proven to be very sound indeed. As described, the tunnel 21/3.3/0.4 kV reticulation system is sufficiently flexible to be able to operate under a wide variety of normal, fault and outage conditions. The long cable systems have resulted in slight voltage rises under switching conditions at Sellindge substation and this effect would have been reduced if XLPE cables had been used for the Grid infeed connections on the UK side. However, it is not recommended to carry out complicated transient analysis studies on such a network at the early design stage because lack of system data would not produce meaningful results from the expended efforts. Very stringent harmonic and unbalanced design limitations were imposed upon the contractors at the design stage and this has probably led to a more costly balancer/filter design than otherwise required.

Reply to N. Roth

One of the main reasons for using a tunnel with electric locomotives is to remove the dangers imposed by car fumes.

Reply to J. Anastassiades

The halon system was designed before the introduction of the latest regulations. It would, of course, be perfectly possible to introduce more modern agents but these, and indeed the older CO_2 based systems, also have disadvantages.

The tunnel employs both 'main' and 'emergency' lighting systems. As explained in the text the lighting is classed as an 'essential' load such that is can still be operated from standby generation sets located at Shakespeare Cliff and Sangatte Shaft even in the very unlikely event of simultaneous loss of both UK and French National Grids. However, to improve further the security of the lighting system some battery backed 'emergency' lighting fittings are used to illuminate cross passage exits, technical rooms, telephone points, main lighting push buttons and illuminated arrow signs pointing to the nearest cross passage escape route along the length of the running tunnels. These emergency lights are operated from a float charged battery and inverter system with an autonomy in excess of 90 minutes.

Reply to R. Barnes

The UK has always taken a very cautious view with regard to earthing design. I do not, however, know of any figures to suggest that in Germany or France there are more fatalities from electric shocks because of the 60 V or 50 V design limits used in those countries. 25 V is the design criteria used for British Railways and is typical in the Channel Tunnel project, where there were differences between UK and French design limits the more onerous was normally employed for safety reasons. The extrapolations from IEC479-1 current/maximum disconnect time curves suggest that 25 V is a suitable continuous contact voltage design limit under wetted contact area conditions. It was felt by the safety regulators, Eurotunnel and TML that under an emergency scenario such conditions could exist. It is quite correct to note that considerable expense was incurred in producing a design which would meet such a stringent design criteria. Such problems were typical of those which increased the costs of the project.

Reply to P. T. May

The tunnel represents a very sterile environment for pests. With good house keeping there is no source of food for the considerable distance between UK and France. In addition the running tunnels experience high velocity winds under which animals would find it difficult to survive. Animal defence barriers have been fitted at both ends of all three tunnels. These essentially work on the principal of a typical farm electric fence which deters (as opposed to kill) any pests, such as foxes carrying rabies, from entering the tunnels. In addition, a high level of security (which I am not allowed to discuss) further reduces the chances of animals entering the tunnels.

The measured water seepage inflows are some tenth of those originally anticipated and allowed for in the designs. The gravity drainage pipes located under the trackbase have been designed with access manholes located every 90 m along the track. It is intended that these manholes will allow for regular maintenance and high pressure water jetting and cleaning of the gravity drainage pipework.

A. G. Fairbairn
Reply to N. Roth

Speaking from TML's point of view, the possibility of building a second Channel Tunnel is very much a matter for Eurotunnel, as concessionaires. In fact, the Concession Agreement requires Eurotunnel to submit a proposal for a drive through link by the year 2000. The Concession Agreement refers to the need for the technical feasibility to be assured and, I have to say, this is certainly relevant to the question of how 50 km of road tunnel could be ventilated.

I am not a ventilation system designer but, to my mind, the main problem may not be the need to cater for a large number of internal combustion engines running simultaneously in the tunnel, although this, as the question implies, will not be easy. Just as important will be the need to consider the ventilation response to emergency incidents, controlling and extracting smoke and other fumes in such a way that passenger and fire. fighter safety is adequately supported.

Reply to P. T. May

Measures were taken during construction to avoid encouraging infestation by not leaving foodstuffs and similar material in the tunnel. Other than this, the most stringent precautions have been taken to prevent the transfer of rabies through the tunnel. This has included electrified grids installed at two locations in all three tunnels in addition to the many other measures taken in the terminal area e.g. fencing, patrolling and trapping.

Also, it has to be said that the tunnels are not a good environment to support animal life. Very high airflows are generated each time a train passes through the running tunnels. Additionally, the service tunnel is sealed by air locks at each portal and is always pressurized, making any access through small holes very difficult. To my knowledge there has been no significant incidence of infestation either during construction or operation.

Concerning low gravity drainage flows, I am not aware of any adverse effects on the gravity drains themselves. It had always been expected that the tunnel would tend to dry up and that there would be relatively wet and relatively dry areas, either of which would lead to low local drainage flows. The main effect of low flows throughout the tunnel has been that the high capacity discharge pumps have to operate in a different manner to that forecast. Infrequent starting of the pumps followed by short periods of running now characterizes the duty cycle which can bring its own problems for machines designed for more frequent running.

Safety in the design

X. Laniray, Director, Operation and Railway System Division, Sofrerail

1. INTRODUCTION

From past experience, all projects creating a fixed link between an island and a mainland have generated strong feelings amongst the populations concerned. The Channel Tunnel is no exception. Moreover, by its nature, it was bound to be extremely 'safety sensitive'. The fixed link incorporates some of the longest tunnels in the world, at over 50 km in length, with 35 km undersea, which are intended to carry road vehicles with their tanks full of fuel. Considering the number of people who feel uneasy in an enclosed space, and considering the fashion for disaster movies, it is not surprising that all these facts were able to generate the most extraordinary phantasms.

It is against such a background of subjective or emotional opinions that the real Safety issues of the Channel Tunnel have had to be assessed.

2. THE CONTRACTOR'S APPROACH

When the Promoters of the Project, from which both the Contractor (TML), and the owner/operator (Eurotunnel) were derived, submitted their Proposal to the Governments, they were aware of the paramount importance of Safety. They had already outlined a strategy and a design allowing the incorporation of the best and most modern Safety features for a railway project known at the time (1985). Later on, after the Concession was granted from the two States to the owner/operator (Eurotunnel), a Construction Contract was established between the owner/operator and the Contractor on a type of performance Contract basis. The Contractor then developed a systematic approach to the Safety issues of the project through a complete methodology. Before looking at the details of this methodology, it is worthwhile addressing briefly the current safety approaches in transport systems

2.1. The "traditional" transport approach

The more traditional transport safety approach is based on regulations and procedures generated by experience from the past. Basically initiated from the railway industry in the 19th century, safety procedures and safety measures were reviewed and improved on a continuous basis, in particular after some incidents or quasi-incidents had revealed weaknesses and loopholes in the existing regulations and practices. During the early days of railway travel, safety was based on manual procedures with a clock, a pen, a pad and a flag, where the role of the person in charge was both paramount and central to the process. It was only later on that some sophisticated devices such as the telephone, then interlocking systems were introduced. The first interlocking was purely mechanical, then electro mechanical, by means of relays, and now is starting the era of electronic interlocking. In the railway industry, every phrase in the rule book has a history of its own and it is not uncommon that this very phrase was added after some mishaps occurred. The current level of safety of the railway industry is now very high and it is one of the safest means of transportation in existence. One major feature of the railway approach is that a stationary train is a safe train; therefore, many devices and procedures are geared to stopping trains when something goes wrong.

2.2. The "modern" safety approach

More recent systems, either developed from scratch with a high technological content, or based on a different philosophy, have adopted a different approach. For example; bringing the system to a halt as a safety measure is not viable with some other technologies. Imagine an aeroplane or a nuclear plant just stopping under any circumstances. This safety approach is based upon a thorough and exhaustive examination, prior to the event, of the consequences of all potential failures of the systems, including these from the men operating them. Measures are then incorporated into the design and/or the operating procedures in order to eliminate or

Channel tunnel transport system. Thomas Telford, London, 1996

drastically reduce the consequences of such failures to an acceptable level in terms of safety. If a failure cannot be avoided by, for example, duplication in equipment, it must then be demonstrated that the likelihood of this failure occurring is sufficiently low for the risk created by this failure to be of an 'acceptable' level. The word 'acceptable' being defined as below.

Acceptable levels of risk for public utilities are probably one or two orders of magnitude lower than the risk anybody is prepared to assume in the day to day life, in ordinary events such as walking the dog.

2.3. The main steps

The methodology implemented for the Project took advantage of both approaches, looking on the one hand at the most recent railway practice in the world and ,on the other hand, conducting a "modern" safety approach, from the very beginning to the completion of the project.

The "fast track" nature of the project, essential to the building of a financially viable transport system, imposed its own problems. The parallel running of design and construction presented a continual challenge to the Safety Studies. Any new system that had to be added to already built sections would have dramatically increased costs. The life of the Safety Engineers was always a struggle against time.

The first step was to carry out a set of 'Development Studies', where all the Safety features already embedded into the Project in mid 86 were reassessed in order to define the overall level of safety of the System

Design studies incorporated a Preliminary Hazard Analysis and a System hazard Analysis, which identified all hazards that any human being might face from the Channel Tunnel system.

Then, for each individual sub-system which was critical to Safety, a Failure Mode analysis and Reliability, Maintainability and Human Safety studies were conducted.

2.4. Safety has been considered throughout the life of the Project

Owing to the high safety sensitivity of the Channel Tunnel, a safety engineering approach was pursued during the whole life of the Project, during Construction, Installation and Commissioning phases. For example, all chemical and other products needed in the Tunnel at any stage were submitted to the Safety team for vetting before being installed. A considerable amount of paints, glues, etc.had to be either already certified by the appropriate bodies or else tested before approval.

It is necessary here to say a few words about this approach of authorised products in the Tunnel complex.

There was no definite regulation about the type of material which could be accepted in the Tunnel complex. The only words included in the Concession Agreement were:

> *'Materials and equipment to be used in the tunnels should be of fire resistant materials and of a nature that when exposed to fire or electrical discharge do not give off toxic fumes or dense smoke.'*

One of the best places where a methodology was available were the standards regarding railway and underground rolling stock in France and in Britain, where a quantitative approach is made of the acceptance of a product, depending upon its fire and smoke properties, as well as its level of toxicity when burning.

From that point, all products where classified, through laboratory tests, into different categories, and were either accepted without restraint, accepted in a limited quantity, or rejected according to their fire and smoke behaviour.

A full database of all the products located in the tunnels was produced and monitored, in order to know whether a new product could be added in some location or not.

A good spirit of co-operation between the construction sites and the safety Engineers was created and resulted in an early advice in almost all cases.

Within the central engineering organisation, a team of safety engineers was established at the start of the project and continued its function throughout the life of the Project. Recognition by Senior Management of the importance of Safety in the project gave this team a recognised role. This proved invaluable at times when strong decisions were needed.

Before going further into the details of the methodology, it is necessary to introduce some outside background to the project.

3. THE AUTHORITIES APPROACH OF SAFETY

After having selected the fixed link Project from the joint venture between France Manche S.A. and the Channel Tunnel Group, the two countries either side of the Channel firstly signed a treaty in Canterbury on the 12th February 1986, then granted a Concession in order to get the private sector to finance, build and operate this massive railway project.

3.1. The IGC

Under the same Treaty of Canterbury, the two states created an ad-hoc watchdog body in order to monitor the new entity and eventually deliver the Operating Certificate. It took the form of the Intergovernmental Commission, which was of course of a bi-national nature and comprised representatives of the various British Departments and French 'ministères' involved.

3.2. The Safety Authority

An organisation was also set up under the Treaty to monitor the design from the aspect of safety, environment and national security, and to give independent advice to the IGC.

The Safety Authority had 10 members, 5 from each side, comprising experts on engineering and safety issues in the design or operation of transport related projects.

3.3. Some post contract incidents

In order to fully understand the history of the Project, one must bear in mind that, unfortunately, a significant number of incidents occurred in the Transport and Large Systems field after the signature of the Concession. These incidents generated an even stronger feeling in the public at large and in the press regarding Safety issues in general. The problem of the responsibility and potential liability of the Public Bodies in charge of monitoring such systems was also raised.

In addition to the nuclear Chernobyl disaster (May 86), there was:

* the capsizing of the Herald of Free Enterprise in Zeebrugge,
* a major railway crash in Paris Gare de Lyon
* the King's Cross fire in the London Underground
* the Clapham Junction rail crash
* an explosion and fire on the Piper Alpha oil platform in the North Sea

It can be said that these disasters have had a profound effect on the project, by increasing the safety sensitivity of all parties involved.

4. TML SAFETY PLAN

We may now come back to the basics of the methodology.

The safety principles developed by TML were incorporated in a Safety Plan, which was discussed and approved by Eurotunnel, and presented to the Safety Authority. This Safety plan was elaborated in two stages. A phase one Safety plan concentrated on the studies to be carried out under the responsibility of TML; the phase two Safety plan described how the various suppliers of equipment would be involved in the safety approach of the Project. It described also the Contractor's actions to be undertaken during Construction and Commissioning phases.

4.1. The situation approach

The number of different risks of casualty encountered in the Channel Tunnel System is finite. The first step was to identify these hazards and to analyse the global response of the Transport System. This was the "situation" approach.

All possible incidents were grouped into typical situations, known as Emergency situations.

Each of these emergency situations was given an estimated level of severity and a probability of occurrence, resulting in a criticality grid.: For example, in the case of a fire taking place in a wagon within the tunnel, one would describe what is the status of the system after the incident which will minimise the risk of casualty: evacuation of passengers along the train, fire curtains closed, trains stopped or not, ...

4.2. A defined number of systems

The complementary approach was to split the global Transport System into a number of elementary subsystems and to analyse how these subsystems would make the hazards acceptable and how they would respond.

Examples of subsystems: railway signalling, tunnel cooling, tunnel doors, ...

4.3. The definition of safety classes

In parallel with the split in subsystems, three safety classes were determined, depending upon the severity of the consequences of a failure of a given subsystem.

Classification 1 comprised the structures, systems and equipment the failure of which might be the direct cause of a serious incident, such as a derailment or a collision at high speed; an example of such subsystems is the railway signalling subsystem.

Classification 2 comprised the equipment of which the failure would lead to a potentially dangerous situation, and any detection or protection equipment used to bring an emergency situation under control; an example of such subsystems is the lighting of the tunnel.

Classification 3 comprised the equipment the failure of which would have no consequences on safety; an example is the cooling plants.

4.4. A safety classification per system

A safety classification was allocated to each subsystem of the Project.

Where the systems were classified as level 1, several types were defined:

> Where accommodation of failure could be envisaged, such as Railway Signalling, a fail safe approach was made, designing the system in such a way that any consequence of a failure would be geared towards safety. For example, a signalling fault would slow down or halt a train.
>
> Where the system could not accommodate a failure, such as a wagon axle, a quantified safety objective would be set for each severe event.

4.5. The evacuation studies

Evacuation studies were derived from analysis of situations and all the most critical cases requiring passengers to be moved out of a wagon, or eventually out of a train in the tunnel were studied. The systems necessary to perform these evacuations were in turn scrutinised in order to ensure that no single failure would impede the evacuation process.

4.6. The computer programmes

The overall safety of the system is dependant upon some key software and hardware equipment in the Control and Communication field. Specific studies were undertaken in order to assess the required integrity of the computer based elements of the Control an Communication systems.

The integrity of a system is defined as 'freedom from impairment' or 'the quality of being unimpaired'. It is depending upon the risks and benefits associated with the system and its application.

The integrity studies consisted in 3 logical stages which were performed during the typical production cycle of each component:

1. determine the integrity level
2. design and built in order to reach this level
3. ensure that this level has actually been achieved.

Of course, two additional stages 0. and 4. should be kept in mind:

0. preliminary hazard analysis
4. operational phase.

During the development process, the required integrity level must continually be borne in mind in order to avoid design or development decision which might detract from the desired integrity level.

Methods and techniques used for the development of software depended also upon the status of the software, whether it was coming : out of a catalogue, or being modified from existing material, or being entirely new.

5. THE PROJECT AS DEVELOPED

Since the Proposal to Governments which formed the basis of the Project Safety Policy, the project has evolved in several important aspects whilst still retaining the fundamental principles.

5.1. The basic principles

Three main principles were set, which have had a strong influence on the design of the whole concept.

5.1.1. The safe haven principle

Any human being within the System must have available a safe haven to shelter him from an aggressive environment such as fire, smoke and fumes. This would apply in two stages: if an incident would occur in a wagon, other wagons would provide a safe haven. If the whole train would be affected by the incident, then the Service tunnel would provide the safe haven.

5.1.2. The run as long as you can principle

The normal assumption that railways reach maximum safety when at a complete stop is not directly applicable to the Channel Tunnel. When considering safety strategies for postulated incidents occurring in the tunnel the possibility of difficulty of controlling large numbers of passengers, some of whom may be concerned at being "stranded" in a confined space below the Channel, may present a greater hazard to safety than the initiating incident. The general policy is therefore to continue running as long as possible with a view to exiting the tunnels before evacuating a train. The principle applies even in the event of a fire in a wagon, the effects of which are contained by the design of the rolling stock and far more predictable than of frightened people.

5.1.3. The 90 minute evacuation principle

Embedded in the concession agreement, because it was thought of paramount importance, is the obligation to get all passengers out of the tunnel within 90 minutes in the case of a train becoming immobilised in the Tunnel for any reason. The 90 minute figure was derived from the findings of psychological studies of an increase of stress after some period of time between one hour and a half and two hours.

5.2. The consequences

These three principles had important consequences on the design of the system as a whole.

5.2.1. Duplication of equipment

The required level of safety led to a great amount of duplication of equipment.

It was clearly unacceptable that a failure in the electrical supply of one country might leave a section of the tunnel without lighting. The safety studies showed quite clearly however that the lighting of the tunnels was not the only issue. Drainage pumps, , ventilation, communication and control equipment, all are essential to achieve the 90 minutes evacuating principle.

Therefore, not only the tunnels but all the Concession can be fed by either country. As the electrical networks of both countries are not synchronised, great care must be taken in order to avoid coupling the two networks, when SEEBOARD supplier feed Coquelles terminal or conversely when EDF feed the Folkestone Terminal.

On top of this duplication, the remote case where both supply would suffer a common mode failure was also contemplated and emergency generators were provided in order to provide energy for the most critical subsystems such as the tunnel lighting, and ventilation.

The communication system has been also very carefully duplicated in order to minimise the risk of a command not reaching its destination. Two physically different cable routes have been defined, using different tunnels and different computers, located in different rooms.

The Control Centre it self has been fully duplicated: in case of an serious incident affecting the main control centre in Folkestone, the control centre of Coquelles is ready to take over the command and control of the entire system. Only a few ergonomically desirable devices, such as the large mimic panel, have not been duplicated for obvious reasons of costs.

5.2.2. The ventilation systems

The ventilation systems were also is designed for the maximum safety of the Project. It was from the start divided into two systems: the normal ventilation system and the supplementary ventilation system.

The normal ventilation system designed to provide air to the 20,000 passengers that could be within the tunnels. Its working principle is to blow fresh air into the service Tunnel which percolates into the running tunnels by controlled air distribution units. It reinforces the safe haven principle through an over pressure of the Service tunnel with respect to the Running Tunnels. By this means, anyone opening a door from the running tunnel to the service tunnel, in order to escape from an incident, would be moving into an area of fresh air supply in a maintained safe haven.

The supplementary ventilation was designed in order to provide proactive control of the smoke coming from a fire in the running tunnel using reversible fans in shafts located at both ends of the undersea sections of the tunnels which allow the smoke to be driven in either direction.

5.2.3. The wind fences

A slightly unexpected side effect of the huge size of the shuttles, some 1.6m higher than a British or a French train was a significant sensitivity of the wagons to side winds. This effect was increased by the unusually square shape of the wagons. A risk analysis was conducted and as a result structures were designed to protect the wagons against the winds. After modelling in French and British wind tunnels; full size mock-ups were erected. The solution implemented of a half solid half porous screen tends to break the strength of the wind without creating the flow reversal which can prove as damaging as a direct gust. The final design was calculated to ensure that the risk to shuttle passengers of being killed in an overturned wagon would be no greater than that defined as the "acceptable" level of risk.

6. THE CHANGES TO THE PROJECT

As the project design developed and as a result of the transport industry accidents which were mentioned earlier, some further requirements were introduced which led to further changes in the Project.

6.1. The "Non segregation" issues

The first major issue was the one of "non segregation". This somewhat awkward wording was a way to say that the vehicle users are authorised to stay within their vehicles during the travel, unlike the ferry regulations. From the start of the Project, this hypothesis had been taken on board, as being fundamental to a viable transport system.

The difficulties of loading tourist cars and coaches on one train and then transferring passengers to another train, within a time scale compatible with the crossing time stipulated in the concession, would have been insurmountable and the cost of running two trains economically prohibitive. It is, however, a relatively simple matter to transfer a few lorry drivers to another part of the HGV shuttle. However, the project was started on the basis of a full non-segregation principle for both types of road users.

The Safety Authority required a full demonstration of the safety of the project as it was being designed and constructed. After a long debate and many tests and studies, the non objection from the Intergovernmental Commission to the non segregation of tourist passengers was given in December 89. The non-objection excluded HGV drivers and any LPG propelled vehicle or any caravan or camping cars.

Five main requirements were made, which are summarised below:

The platforms at one side of each train should be continuous in order to facilitate evacuation of passengers during the loading/unloading phase.

The design of the tourist wagon was to be improved regarding fire resistance of the internal deck in the double deck wagon, whilst a highly sophisticated video surveillance system was to be implemented, linked with the alarm system. A smoke extraction system was to be implemented;

Fire barriers between wagons were to be improved, to the width of the pass-doors increased to 0.7m permitting longitudinal evacuation to an adjacent wagon.

Additional fire detection and extinction systems were required to be fitted in the tourist wagons; no other vehicle would be allowed in a wagon together with a coach. This significantly changed the overall capacity of the system;

Special measures were to be taken for disabled.

6.2. The wagons pass-doors

The project was started with the concept of a smoke curtain within each wagon, preventing the spread of smoke. This concept was progressively hardened into a fully fire resistant bulkhead at each end of the wagons, These bulkheads were to be fitted with pass doors allowing evacuation from one wagon to the other. The Authorities required an increase of the width of free opening for the doors from 0.6m to 0.7m and this required almost a total redesign of the bulkhead.

6.3. The disabled policy

During recent years, there has been in all developed countries an increasing objective to provide access for disabled people. This policy required that some special measures were taken in the Channel Tunnel in order to allow disabled people in the shuttles.

The evacuation cross passages had to be designed in order to accommodate wheel chairs, and are generally limited to a 10% slope. Where stairs were unavoidable, space was to be provided in order to park the wheel chairs during the evacuation of able bodied people. The continuous tunnel walkways were redesigned in order to facilitate disembarkation both from a shuttle and from a Eurostar train, which is narrower and has a different door configuration. This led to a design of a double level walkway.

As this walkway cannot accommodate standard wheelchairs, special ones are provided in each end wagon of a rake. The loading procedures were therefore redesigned to ensure the disabled are located in special areas of the end wagon.

6.4. A fail-safe automatic train protection (ATP)

Another identified risk in the Channel Tunnel system, as in any railway, is the risk, for any reason, of overspeeding by the train driver. This might cause the train to overshoot its stopping point and eventually hit any obstacle on its route such as another train, a point in the wrong direction or, in our case, a cross-over door. A remedy to this problem is to fit the system with what is called an Automatic Train Protection system. This system needs devices fitted both on the track and on the locomotives. The principle used for the Channel Tunnel is that the track based device tells the loco based one what is the maximum speed allowed at this location, considering the track status, the routes set and the trains in front. The on board device compares this authorised speed with the actual one, and, if the latter exceeds the former, triggers an emergency braking of the train.

The few systems of this type which have been in existence for some years are not fully automatic, i.e. where there is still an active driver, it is generally accepted that a failure of the ATP system is not critical as the driver is still able to drive the train manually, therefore acting as a safety net. However, for our project, it was required by the Safety Authority that this system was rendered fail safe: any breakdown of any component of the system must not create a potentially dangerous situation. This requirement generated extra developments to the signalling system.

6.5. The seismic issue

At the start of the project with the exception of underground civil tunnel structures where a seismic loading of 0.05 g was applied, no particular attention to seismic events was given, as the regulation of both countries were either silent or considered the geographic area as being of negligible seismicity. However a significant earthquake had occurred in AD1580 in the Channel area, which had brought down a few church steeples.

The matter was taken up by the Safety Authority which required studies and improvements in the design in limited areas to facilitate evacuation in certain more onerous scenarios. The philosophy expressed was to study what damage would occur under the conditions of the 1580 earthquake, which was scaled at VI on the Richter scale. The forecast damage should not put the lives of passengers in peril. Therefore, demonstration was to be made that evacuation of passengers immobilised in the tunnel could be carried out prior to any flooding of the tunnel, with backup energy provided by emergency generators, should both national grids be out of service.

6.6. The consequences of the Open sided HGV wagons

As the project developed, some thought was given to reduce costs. One possibility was the HGV carrier wagons. The decision to segregate the drivers from their lorries had already been taken, for various technical and commercial reasons. They were to travel in dedicated areas of the HGV shuttle.

In 1990, the HGV shuttle wagons were totally redesigned resulting in an open body shuttle rather than the fully enclosed and complex tourist shuttles.

But the Concession had specified smoke containment, implying therefore enclosed wagons. Consequently, a derogation was necessary from the IGC.

The IGC was concerned that, in the event of a fire on a lorry, it would not be contained and there could even be a sort of torch effect carrying the fire from one lorry to the other. Therefore, significant studies were requested from Eurotunnel, which were performed either by themselves or through TML in order to investigate all consequences of this change. A lorry was set on fire in a laboratory in Norway; tests of fire detection systems were carried out in railway tunnels. Various studies were carried out regarding the speed of spread of smoke, should a fire occur.

The IGC eventually gave their non objection to this change provided some extra modifications were carried out to the project. One requirement was to install a fire detection system in the tunnel, together with a fire detection system on board the HGV trains. The emergency evacuation procedures had to be revised and a restriction imposed upon the signalling system to prevent any train being "too close" behind a HGV shuttle from a smoke and fume point of view. The minimum distance was 4km from the tail of an HGV shuttle.

6.7. The fire detection/protection policy

It has always been considered that one of the major risks in the Channel tunnel was fire. Events such as the King's Cross disaster have obviously reinforced this feeling. A strong fire detection and protection policy has therefore been applied within the Channel Tunnel complex.

The bulk of the electrical and control equipment has been located in Technical rooms which are equipped with a fire detection and automatic fire extinction system by automatic discharge of Halon in case of a fire detection.

In addition to a general material requirement of non flammable and low smoke and fume generation, the tunnel itself, due to changes in the design of the HGV shuttles, has been fitted with a sophisticated fire detection system, which is in itself triplicated, detecting smoke, infra-red and ultra-violet radiation coming from a fire on a moving shuttle. This system is duplicated in its function by an on board fire detection system fitted onto the loading wagons of the HGV shuttles.

6.8. Other changes

Some further changes were demanded by the IGC in other fields, such as the fire suppression systems: the fire main length in the running tunnels was extended to reduce the hydrant spacing to a minimum, and the fire hydrant outlets were duplicated throughout the tunnel in order to accommodate both the French and the British standard fire hoses.

7. CONCLUSION

At the Proposal stage in 1985, help had been obtained from some of the best railway organisations in the world and the proposed level of safety was at the best of the state of the art at the time.

However, during the implementation phase of the Project, an even higher level of safety was obtained through various changes in the project.

It is unfortunately not possible, in our imperfect world, to state that no incident will ever occur in the system, because of the frustrating behaviour of the probability laws, any event which has been forecast as having a return period of one million year has a remote probability of occurring tomorrow.

But it can be said that new grounds were broken, not only within the Channel chalk marl but also in the field of engineering and implementation of safety in large projects.

Recruitment and training for a new system

B. Watson, Eurotunnel Services Ltd, Folkestone, England

1. INTRODUCTION

1.1 This paper principally describes the arrangements for recruiting and training new people to operate the transportation system in France and UK.

1.2 To set these arrangements in context, it outlines the philosophies of the operating company which have helped define its human resource policiès.

It looks at organisation structure and the factors which have influenced the Company in the way it has defined its people needs and planned for them.

1.3 In describing training, particular reference is made, amongst other aspects, to language training and to the training given to cope with abnormal and emergency situations - two aspects which reflect the unique nature of Eurotunnel's operation.

2. HUMAN RESOURCES POLICIES

2.1 Eurotunnel faced a choice early in the planning process, either to operate its system with two workforces, working together but under separate French and British employment regimes or integrated into a bi-national structure with the greatest practicable harmonisation of work practices and employment conditions.

2.2 There are advantages and disadvantages to both strategies and neither choice is without risk.

The integrated nature of the railway operation, requiring unified control and management, was the prime determinant in the choice Eurotunnel made to set up an integrated bi-national company.

The logic of a single transport system and single crew planning and maintenance requirements led to operations management in particular to demand a single set of staff management assumptions. For this reason, the Eurotunnel workforce in France and UK were employed under a common philosophy. Those terms of employment which impact on day to day management are common - overtime arrangements, shift pay, call-out and annual holidays, for example. National law and custom intervene to create or preserve differences in a number of areas - bank holidays is one example.

2.3 This bi-national focus is suffused with a single set of core values held in common throughout the operation in UK and France.

1. A total quality approach.

2. Commitment to Customer Service.

3. Dedication to the Safety and Security of the system.

4. Respect for national differences.

5. The importance of the individual.

6. Long-term relationships, with employees and with the communities of Kent and the Nord Pas de Calais.

7. The need for profitable operation.

The core values and the essential bi-national nature of the enterprise have important consequences for recruitment and training.

2.4 Whilst the Concession Agreement requires that a broad balance between French and UK nationals should be preserved in the top 60 jobs in Eurotunnel, a policy decision has been made to maintain this broad parity throughout the organisation. 27 nationalities are employed in Eurotunnel, the majority, of course, being British and French. Despite cost differences, the operation has broadly the same numbers of French and British throughout the Company. Care has been taken also to ensure that where managers are French, their deputies are British and vice versa to maintain national parity.

2.5 i) Concern for the long-term nature of Eurotunnel's involvement in the local communities of Kent and Nord Pas de Calais has also influenced recruitment. Our policy gave preference to local people wherever possible; it gave opportunity to all ages, including to the over 40's, and acknowledged the claims of the disabled. Concern for these groups is a declared aspect of recruitment policy.

ii) Similarly, because the requirements of start-up created a short-term peak these were met in non-core activity by temporary contracts rather than open-ended employment contracts which disappear when start-up activity subsides after opening.

iii) A number of activities have been specifically contracted out including terminal access control and cleaning, to enable management to focus on core service activities. Whilst contracting of on-board customer services was considered, this activity was retained in-house because of the importance of the direct customer contact roles.

The policy has been to recruit a core workforce to which the Company can offer high quality, secure employment, with peaks catered for by sub-contract or temporary labour.

2.6. In return, Eurotunnel demands a high level of commitment and flexibility and a very open attitude to change. Whilst the early training has focused on specific job training, ultimately the Company is committed to multi-skilling and wide job flexibility.

Given the sophistication of the technical systems employed in fixed equipment installations and rolling stock in particular, multi-skilling in these technical areas represents a training rather than a recruitment challenge.

2.7 All these policy issues have contributed to defining the Company's people needs. These are quantified and described in the next section.

3. ORGANISATION

3.1 Definition of the numbers needed in the organisation has been driven by line management, each directorate presenting its proposals which have been subject to a process of budgetary approval.

3.2 The headcount plan for core activities has changed over time, as policy has firmed up on issues such as sub-contracting , and as the commercial organisation in particular has been specified to provide the level of market penetration necessary in a start-up situation.

3.3 Staffing of the core activities, despite these changes, has remained at around 2,500 in full operation. These numbers are employed approximately equally between UK and France.

3.4 The headcount in full operation will be, for the major employee groups, as set out below:-

Operations Directorate

Control Centre	50
Train Crew	550
UK Terminal	500
French Terminal	420
Rolling Stock Maintenance	200
Fixed Equipment Maintenance	200
	1920

Commercial Directorate	250
Support Services (Finance, Human Resources, Information Services, Media Relations, New Works	250
	2,420

There follows a brief description of how these major groups are organised.

3.5 Control Centre

Railway Systems Controllers (bi-lingual) operate from both the main UK Centre and the French auxiliary Control Centre. This is a bi-national team living in both France and UK with individuals working in both Control Centres.

3.6 Train Crew

About 260 are Drivers/Chefs de Train, equally employed in UK and France. On each Shuttle there is a driver in the front locomotive and a Chef de Train in the rear and these alternate their duties. They also act as on-board customer service staff when needed, illustrating the Company's commitment to flexibility. With the exception of the experienced drivers recruited to help Eurotunnel commission rolling stock, the majority have been recruited without a rail industry background.

About 260 are on-board customer service staff (both French and British), six on each passenger shuttle, whose role is to load and off-load passengers, provide customer support in transit and assist in emergency procedures in the event of an incident.

3.7 The UK and French Terminal organisations consist of Traffic staff, directing traffic flows to the shuttles, Tolls staff carrying out the transactions at toll booths with paying customers, and a number of security staff operating the Euroscan X-Ray facility in the UK. The numbers in UK exceed those in France because of the additional manning requirement of Euroscan. Access Control is contracted out in UK, to a private Security Company, and in France to P.A.F

3.8 Rolling Stock Maintenance is based principally in France where the workshops are. With the exception of a dozen or so British Troubleshooter Technicians based in the UK and charged with first response intervention to problems in the UK, returning rolling stock to the French workshops, the rest of the rolling stock team is French. The bi-national ideal is kept alive by a British Workshop Manager based in Calais.

3.9 Fixed Equipment Maintenance is a fully bi-national operation with equal numbers of French and British. The management are organised in the classic Eurotunnel fashion with both French and British Department Managers with their Deputies being of the other nationality. This team provides the technical maintenance of fixed installations:-

Power Supply/Mechanical-Electrical Systems

Signalling/Control & Communication Systems

Civils & Structures

Support Group

Working teams are bi-national. There is no territorial demarcation of responsibility.

3.10 The Operations Directorate accounts for 80% of the Company's human resource.

3.11 The Commercial Directorate is worth some description as the second largest investment made in people. Commercial Management is principally based in Operational HQ in Calais. Its people are in France, UK, Belgium, Netherlands, Germany and Spain.

The Commercial Directorate has around 150 people in UK. The principal activity (in terms of employee numbers) is a Customer Service Information and Telesales activity in Cheriton responding, since January 1994, to customer enquiries and offering a pre-booking facility in the period until the British public is educated to our turn-up-and-go-system. A direct Sales force is employed throughout the UK promoting the service to travel agents and selling direct to the Freight and M.I.T. markets. These operations are mounted also in France, with small presences in the other European countries mentioned. The Commercial organisation demonstrates the commitment made to growing our business from a standing start.

3.12 Other support activities - Finance, Human Resources, Information Systems, New Works, Administration, Media Relations, Legal, Quality and Safety - are based in France and UK also. Operational Headquarters are in Calais which is the centre of gravity for the transportation service. All functions are bi-national and both languages are spoken. The language spoken in meetings often depends on which nationality is in a majority or in which country the meeting is held but individuals are free to use their own language, particularly for the expression of complex ideas.

3.13 The organisation structure and headcount, defined by the philosophies and policies described, represent the starting point for recruitment, which is described in the next section.

4. RECRUITMENT

4.1 In the build up to opening Eurotunnel will have recruited 1500 people.

4.2 Recruitment in 1991 and 1992 was concentrated on middle management in all functions, recruited to plan for operation, and technical staff in fixed equipment and rolling stock maintenance required to enable Eurotunnel to fulfil its commissioning responsibilities.

4.3 Recruitment decisions have been viewed as amongst the most critical managers can make and the process has been designed to reflect the value of the investment made when a decision to employ is reached. A £15,000 p.a. employee, with employment costs, working in the Company for 25 years, represents an investment of almost £500,000.

4.4 A competitive tender process was instituted to select a recruitment consultancy which could handle the logistics of recruiting 1500 people in France and UK., using a common process and, most importantly, deploying common psychometric test procedures. Mercuri Urval were chosen because of their strengths in psychometrics and their well-developed organisations on both sides of the Channel.

4.5 Recruitment planning was made quite difficult by changes in the opening date and uncertainty about the delivery of rolling stock which affected the phasing of operational service build-up to full capacity.

4.6 For this reason, recruitment plans were revisited monthly, sometimes weekly, to react to changes, with lead-times calculated for each position by reference to the length of time required to process a candidate, make an offer, allow for notice periods and complete training, in order to establish the latest date by which recruitment must commence to enable us to deliver the people needed.

4.7 The recruitment process has been thorough and time consuming. For an individual candidate the whole process, spread over a number of weeks or months, has extended to 10-14 hours, depending on the position.

4.8 The process has consisted of a number of stages:-

i) Application

ii) Assessment event

iii) Aptitude Testing

iv) Interview

v) Medical Examination

iv) Security Clearance

Each is described below:

4.9 <u>Application</u>

All applications were logged into two candidate databases, one in France and one in the UK. The UK database handled over 10,000 applications and the French 16,000. These candidates resulted from advertising, unsolicited enquiries or the Department of Employment in UK , and its equivalent in France, with whom Eurotunnel worked closely.

Advertising was necessary in any volume only for technical or specialist recruitment. High technology maintenance technicians were hard to find in both France and UK, especially in railway-specific disciplines like signalling. Railway Systems Controllers have also been hard to find mainly because of the need to be bi-lingual and these positions have been resourced nationwide, extending even to Ireland, Belgium and Netherlands as well as UK and France.

Unsolicited enquires ranged from the very relevant local Kent or Calais people registering an interest with a new major employer in the area, to the bizarre sprinkling of disillusioned Stock-Brokers or Bankers seeking a mid-life change of career and willing to train as Drivers/Chefs de Train.

Staying in touch with 26,000 applicants represented a major logistical challenge.

4.10 Assessment events were the key feature at the heart of the recruitment process enabling Mercuri Urval to reduce (26,000) candidates from the database down to (6,000) for interview and further stages of selection.

At Assessment Events, up to 60 candidates would be briefed on Eurotunnel and the job(s) for which they were under consideration. They would undergo psychometric testing, which will be expanded on later, go through at least two short interviews, and complete one or two group exercises designed to show social skills, so important in customer contact roles. The detail of the Assessment Events differed by job but the framework of the methodology was common.

4.11 Psychometric Testing

Testing of personality and aptitudes has played a key role in the recruitment process. Personality testing has enabled a profile to be established for each candidate, to be compared with an ideal profile established for each job. Some attributes of personality have been sought as a common feature in all recruitment - open mindedness, flexibility and positive customer-orientation. Other features have varied in each job profile. Aptitude testing has been used extensively also. Even in recruitment of experienced technicians, a battery of mechanical aptitude tests was used. Aptitude testing was an essential component in driver recruitment enabling us to select outside the supply of experienced railway people and recruit from a range of backgrounds. A test battery supplied by S.N.C.F and operated by S.N.C.F personnel was used for driver selection.

4.12 All candidates referred by Mercuri Urval were intensively interviewed by a member of the Human Resources team and by line management.

4.13 Medical Examination

Common medical standards have been established in the French and British teams, not an easy task when B.R and S.N.C.F's medical standards are different in almost every respect.

In positions designated safety-related in particular, it was felt important to apply common standards and preferably ones accepted in the railway industry of each country. Eurotunnel medical standards were established with the assistance of input from B.R's Occupational Health Service, the S.N.C.F Medical service and the local Medicin du Travail in Calais. The most critical medical criterion proved to be hearing which eliminated a number of candidates at the eleventh hour. All Eurotunnel pre-employment medicals include a drug screen both in France and UK.

4.14 Security Screen

The process differs slightly in France and UK but all appointments are security vetted. The UK and French process are assisted by government by reason of Eurotunnel's unique cross-border situation.

4.15 The recruitment process has been an important unifying factor in building a bi-national company. It has been based on a common philosophy, with a common methodology, seeking, within the limitations of national differences, a common product.

Some of these national differences are minor - it is, for example, unlawful to seek and supply written employment references in France. Some are more important. The French workforce is, by and large, better educated and qualified than the UK equivalent. In some positions, French management have sought a Baccalaureat qualification (equivalent to our "A" levels) where the UK position has specified no formal qualification. These cultural differences sit alongside the basic common attitudinal profiles in our recruited population to add richness to our Company.

5. TRAINING

5.1 Training to operate the system prior to start-up has represented a Herculean task, both because of its complexity and as a result of sheer volume.

5.2 The subject is best analysed under the following subject headings:

i) Technical System Training

ii) Basic job training

iii) Language Training

iv) Emergency Training.

5.3 Technical Training

With most equipment supplied to the system being state-of-the-art technology, there was a strong need for Eurotunnel personnel to be trained in the operation and maintenance of equipment. This need covered track and catenary systems, power supply systems, signalling systems, cooling and ventilation systems and the myriad systems and equipment with which the Institute of Civil Engineers will be fully familiar.

T.M.L was responsible for organising and delivering both theoretical and practical training to Eurotunnel's technical staff, amounting, between August 1992 and March 1994, to nearly 57,000 delegate days.

This supplier training has updated the skills of a group of employees already skilled when recruited.

5.4 Basic Job Training

a) The majority of employees in volume positions, such as Drivers/Chefs de Train and On-Board Customer Service Crew, have required a basic job training programme to bring them to a necessary state of readiness. These programmes have varied, of course, according to the position.

b) Some elements are common to all programmes and a common methodology has underpinned all job training programmes

i) All employees went through an induction process, introducing Eurotunnel, in mixed French and British groups. Despite language difficulties, this mixing gives emphasis at the outset to the bi-national nature of the Company.

ii) Training has been prepared and delivered in a cascade process by Managers and Supervisors reinforcing the responsibility of the Line for training.

iii) Customer Service and Safety have been elements which appear in all programmes.

iv) Specific attainments were detailed for each programme which were examined, either by written test or practical demonstration, and certified by the Trainer. In order, for example, to test the Customer Service Information training, two week-end exercises were mounted in which employees phoned in with scripted queries and afterwards completed reports on the responses obtained.

c) The differences arise from specific programmes:-

i) Railway System Controllers were under training for 18 months preparing for operation. They visited the signalling system supplier in France to understand how it functions, they have been through theoretical instruction in operating procedures, they have carried out simulations using a model rail system, and practised emergency procedures.

ii) The programme for Drivers/Chefs de Train extended to 6 months covering theoretical instruction in operating procedures, introduction to the locomotive controls and systems in a simulator and, of course, practical application in the locomotives to gain certification.

5.5 Language Training

a) The bi-national nature of Eurotunnel poses a particular challenge in language competency.

b) A desired level of language ability profile has been established for every job. This profile is established by reference to a matrix (referred to as a referential) which identifies 8 levels of ability against different types of language skills.

These differentiate:

. listening skills

. writing skills

. speaking skills

. reading skills

In some jobs, the ability to understand written French is needed, but little need to speak the language.

c) Training needs were established by assessing the existing level of language competence by reference to the same referential and identifying where the candidate profile differed from the job profile.

d) Given the low level of language ability amongst English people, the language requirement was and is enormous. The French generally are better at speaking English but amongst direct customer contact staff there has been a large training need in France, especially since 2/3rds of customers were expected to be British.

e) Training has been prioritised to those jobs for which French or English is an operation requirement:

. Railway Systems Controller

. Train Drivers/Chefs de Train

. On-board Customer Service Crew

. Customer Service Agents

. Fire-fighters

. Maintenance Technicians.

An enormous investment has been made in language training in these areas - 8,500 delegate days between August 1992 and March 1994.

f) To assist training and safety, an agreed vocabulary has been standardised in Eurotunnel which minimised the possibilities of misunderstanding.

g) Language training for Eurotunnel will be like painting the Forth Bridge. There is a strong demand in the Company for opportunity to progress beyond the assessed job level. The company supports employees at evening classes and makes available open-learning materials.

5.6 Emergency Training

a) Eurotunnel has been very concerned to ensure that its people are trained to cope with emergency situations. Every job training programme in the Operations Directorate has included this training, which involves not just learning the procedures to be applied in the event of an emergency, but also practising them. The programme of training covered Railway Systems Controllers, Drivers/Chefs de Train, On-Board Customer Service Crew, Maintenance Technicians and Terminals staff in UK and France.

b) The effectiveness of this training has been tested and enhanced in a series of Command Procedure Exercises (CPX's) which have been designed to require the Eurotunnel departments to work together and to co-ordinate with the external services.

c) Before the beginning of the service, 7 CPX's were held, each based on an emergency scenario requiring co-ordinated response within the Company and outside. The following emergencies have been enacted:

CPX1: Derailment in the Tunnel

CPX2: Fire in the Tunnel

CPX3: HGV fire in transit

CPX4: Derailment in the Crossover

CPX5: Derailment in the Crossover

CPX6: High Speed derailment

CPX7: Tunnel Evacuation of 800 passengers in a Eurostar

d) Eurotunnel's staff have been involved in every CPX. The UK emergency services have been involved, as observers or participants in CPX's 3,4,5 and 7. The French emergency services were involved in CPX's 5,6 and 7. CPX 7 was a full exercise involving the emergency services of both countries.

e) These CPX's have enabled Eurotunnel and the French and British authorities to test and improve co-ordination procedures, response times, equipment readiness, decision-making and, most importantly, confidence to handle emergency situations safely.

We have been able to discover how the emergency services of both countries work together, the issues involved in calling in additional fire tenders after first-response measures have been taken, the technical solutions to communication problems using back-up systems when the main systems "fail".

f) The experience gained in these exercises has been invaluable and leaves us confident we can cope with any emergency situations. Most importantly, these exercises have enabled the Safety Authority to satisfy itself that Operating Certificates can be awarded with confidence to Eurotunnel.

6. CONCLUSION

6.1 This paper has addressed the recruitment and training of personnel to operate the transportation system and has ignored the recruitment and training of many non-operational staff which has gone alongside it.

6.2 The Finance staff, Information Systems personnel and others in support functions who have been working hard to set up Eurotunnel have also played an important role. Their situations have not been germane to the topic this paper was asked to focus on but should be mentioned, even if only in conclusion.

6.3 In establishing a bi-national organisation with new locations in Folkestone and Calais, a lot of Eurotunnel employees have been transferred from UK to work in Calais Operational Headquarters, or from Calais to Folkestone, and new people recruited to staff new functions in the Headquarters. In addition to the normal challenges, this recruitment has had to grapple with the complexities of social security and tax regulations applicable to cross-border and multi-state workers.

6.4 In addition to the training described in this paper, a good deal of other training was been carried out. For example, 200 Managers and Supervisors have been through a 5 day programme which provides a common frame of reference for managing in Eurotunnel to replace the 200 different perceptions these Managers brought with them from their previous organisations.

6.5 Whilst the recruitment and training effort has been focused clearly on opening the system for operation, it is clear that this is only the beginning. The next challenge is to ensure that this newly recruited and trained human resource remains enthusiastic and committed to the Eurotunnel vision.

BWW

Service Tunnel Transport System

J. Kennedy, Eurotunnel, Folkestone, England

INTRODUCTION

The Channel Tunnel comprises three parallel tunnels. Two of these are the running tunnels for the trains and the third tunnel which lies between the two running tunnels is the service tunnel. This tunnel accommodates the drainage pipes and other services. It also acts as the fresh air supply duct and the safe haven in the event of emergency. As the tunnel is 50 km long some form of powered transport is required in the service tunnel. This is the Service Tunnel Transport System or STTS.

THE CONCESSION REQUIREMENT

The concession granted by the Governments of France and the UK stipulates that "The service tunnel shall be provided with an independent transport system with an independent means of traction to allow emergency services teams to gain access to any part of the underground structure."

THE TASKS OF THE STTS

The STTS has to be designed for several tasks.

1. The transport of maintenance staff, their tools and replacement equipment.
2. The transport of the emergency services in the event of an incident.
3. The transport of various inspectors and visitors such as immigration, customs and security.

STRUCTURE GAUGE

The size of the service tunnel dictates the structure and kinematic envelopes of the transport system. The 250 m length of service tunnel built during the abandoned 1974 attempt to build a Channel Tunnel was used as the start of the 1986 successful design. That small length of tunnel is 4.5 m diameter. The rest of the service tunnel is 4.8 m diameter except for the UK land tunnel which is 4.9 m diameter. Evaluations of the merits of single line working in the 4.5 m section concluded that it was preferable to retain two way working at reduced speed and reduced clearance and allow more margin in the remainder of the tunnel. In practice the 4.5 m section was built very straight with no significant misalignments to reduce its nominal 4.5 m clearance.

After allowances for all tolerances and misalignments it was concluded that the vehicle should be no more that 1510 mm wide at axle height. The body gauge is tapered to 1.350 mm at roof level to allow for roll or flat tyres. The roof height was set at 2220 mm. These dimensions are sufficient to allow a very practical vehicle.

THE BASIC CHOICES

The first choice is to decide whether the STTS should be rail vehicles or rubber tyred. At the start of the project a rail system was contemplated. There would be a railway in the tunnels which would be used for construction. This could be refurbished and form the permanent system. However, there are a number of disadvantages of using a railway for the tasks in the permanent system.

The adhesion of steel wheels on steel rails is low and therefore braking distances are long. Either a signalling system is required or the speed must be kept low if the driver is to drive on sight. A railway is very inflexible. If you take an emergency train to an incident it is not possible to separate the wagons and change the order easily, eg. if an ambulance wagon is at one end of the train it cannot be detached and passed ahead of the train without great difficulty. Raised rails cause a tripping hazard so the rails must be sunk in the tunnel surface where they are difficult to maintain. The maintenance of a railway is a further task which increases the traffic, the disruption, and the costs. A system based on rubber tyred vehicles is much more flexible but it normally depends on the driver steering the vehicle and controlling its speed. The service tunnel is only 4.8 metres diameter so that the road width is only about 3.6 m or the width of one motorway lane. To use this for two way traffic means that the vehicles must be narrow and passing will be very close. There was also a lack of knowledge of whether it was difficult to drive a long distance in a narrow tunnel. Despite this it was clear that the flexibility of a rubber tyred system was preferable.

In order to be sure that it was practical to drive at a good speed in the tunnel various guided rubber tyred systems were investigated.

GUIDANCE SYSTEMS

There are several guided rubber tyred systems in use or developed ready for use. The German 'O' bahn which uses kerbs to guide horizontal wheels on the steering is in use in Essen and Australia. The system needs kerbs through out the tunnel. It can pass breaks of 2 or 3 metres such as would be needed at a cross passage but it is not possible to change lane without a larger break in the central kerb. The BN system which guides by a single rail in the centre of each track meets the flexibility requirement as it is easy to detach from the guidance and reattachment points can be provided at frequent intervals. However there were disadvantages in cost, noise and braking performances. Unsteered side guided vehicles were another possibility. The tunnel lining could not be easily adapted to take the side guides and these systems were not developed.

Guidance by following a buried wire has been used extensively at low speed for factory material handling. In Germany two experimental wire guided bus systems had been developed to the stage of running trials in public service. These had been successful from a technical point of view but had not resulted in mass application.

Bids were sought for all these systems. It was found that the best solution was to use wire guidance and a contract was placed with AEG. AEG provided the guidance system and Mercedes designed and produced the vehicles.

MOTIVE POWER

The service tunnel is the fresh air supply duct and thus electrical motive power is preferable. That means either batteries or current collection. Batteries give great flexibility of movement and avoid the costs and maintenance of a current collection system. Batteries are heavy and they limit the payload of the vehicle. It is possible to make a vehicle which will go 25 km to the middle of the tunnel and back again but then the battery needs 8 or 10 hours for recharging. It would be necessary to have a large fleet of vehicles or a large number of exchange batteries.

A current collection system combined with a small battery for local manoeuvring is a practical possibility but the installation and maintenance costs are high and the collection system makes access to the multitude of services in the tunnel crown more difficult. It was concluded that diesel power should be investigated to see whether the pollution could be low enough to be acceptable.

The diesel engine emits several pollutants of which the ruling ones are NO_x and smoke. CO is also emitted but the tolerance level is higher than that for NO_x. There are two basic forms of fuel injection for diesel engines: direct injection and indirect injection. In direct injection the fuel is sprayed into a hollow in the top of the piston. This is an efficient way of burning the fuel but it results in high levels of NO_x. Indirect injection uses a pre combustion chamber linked to the cylinder space. The combustion is not as efficient but the NO_x is only about one third of that for a direct injection engine. In the tunnel, as in mining, the loss of 5-10% in fuel efficiency is less important than keeping the NO_x low. The principal components of NO_x are NO and NO_2. The Threshold Limit Value (TLV) for working 8 hours per day is 15 ppm for NO and 3ppm for NO_2. At the exhaust outlet the NO_2 content is usually about 10% of the total. Thus the NO_2 will be within its limit if the NO is within its limit. Unfortunately NO changes slowly to NO_2. In the tunnel the air will be several hours before it reaches the portal and thus the rate of conversion is important. There is usually an initial conversion which brings the NO_2 proportion to around 20%. This means that it is as near its limit as the NO. Fortunately NO_2 is more soluble in water than NO and thus any wet patches in the tunnel will gather the NO_2 and dissolve it. While that is a great benefit for the tunnel atmosphere it is not so good for the tunnel itself as the NO_2 then converts to nitric acid. During the construction phase the tunnel was not fully sealed and there were plenty of wet areas to absorb NO_2. Now that the tunnel is fully grouted and the wet areas are few and far between the NO_2 level may become more important than the NO level.

Calculations indicate that the rate of conversion is slow, ie: several hours for a doubling of the NO_2 content, so it should be sufficient to control the initial NO_x emission and that will take care of both NO and NO_2.

The engine selected is a 5 cylinder, 3 litre indirect engine with a maximum power output of 62 kW. This is a small engine for a heavy vehicle but the gradients in the tunnel are small and moderate acceleration is acceptable. The advantages of the small size and weight of the engine are more valuable in a vehicle designed to fit the narrow confines of the tunnel.

In order to ensure that there is no risk from exhaust fumes, each vehicle is equipped with a detector which monitors the level of CO and NO_x.

CHANGE OF DIRECTION
The service tunnel is only 4.8 m diameter. A vehicle which can turn round in the tunnel has to be no more than about 3 metres long. The principal vehicles need to be much longer than 3 metres in order to carry the payload or provide working space inside. The vehicles must therefore be capable of being driven and steered from either end. The AEG proposal was to provide two identical cab ends complete with diesel engine and drive train. This enabled them to use a standard axle and gearbox. To provide an axle which could be driven at speed in either direction would have required a development and test programme. On the prototype vehicle the battery and fuel tank were also duplicated but in order to reduce weight this duplication was eliminated and now the vehicles only have one battery and one fuel tank.

Steering from either end is accomplished by locking or unlocking the appropriate axles. When a vehicle stops, and the driver thinks he may have to go in the opposite direction he engages the axle lock at that end before he switches off the engine. If he tries to start the engine at the other end without locking what is now the rear axle an interlock prevents the engine from starting . Thus the vehicle can only be driven if the rear axle is locked and the front axle unlocked.

THE BASIC VEHICLE
The result of the basic choices was a rubber tyred vehicle with the following characteristics:

Length :	10.1m
Width :	1.5m
Height:	2.2m
Unladen weight	6000 kg
Laden weight	8500 kg
Maximum service speed	80 km/h
Engine indirect injection diesel	62 kW
Payload	2500 kg
Range	200 km

A vehicle with a maintenance container is shown in figure 1. The antenna for the guidance system is mounted behind the bumper. A small hydraulic power pack controlled by the two on-board guidance computers drives two cylinders acting on the steering arms. The manual steering wheel is permanently engaged and operates through a standard steering box. There is no power steering when the guidance is not being used. The antenna senses the magnetic field from the two guide wires which are spaced 300 mm apart in the centre of the desired track. When the concrete surface is good the vehicle keeps to within 2 or 3 cm of the nominal centreline but where the concrete surface is rough the deviation can be a little larger. However, it keeps well within the tolerance of the kinematic envelope so that while the vehicle runs close to the wall it always has a clearance and when passing other vehicles there is a good space between them.

Connecting to the guidance is very simple. One drives at 20 km/h at a slight angle to the guidance and switches to guided mode. As the vehicle approaches the wires it takes over the steering and continues on guidance. To leave the track, for example to pass a stationary vehicle, one switches off the guidance and steers manually.

Fig. 1. STTS vehicle with maintenance container

Fig. 2. Ladog vehicle with personnel pod

In each slot in the road surface there is a wire with two cores. Each core carries a current of about 200 mA at a frequency of 8 kHz or 10 kHz, on the north track and 9 kHz or 11 kHz on the south track. The vehicle automatically selects the two strongest frequencies so that the driver does not have to select anything. He just drives towards the desired track and the guidance takes over when the signal is strong enough.

As noted previously, the engine is small for a vehicle of 8500 kg fully laden. The normal speed in the tunnel is 50-60 km/h. The vehicle will attain this in less than 40 seconds. The maximum speed allowable in emergency is 80 km/h and this can be achieved in less than one minute on the down gradient in the tunnel. On the level it takes nearly 90 seconds to reach 80 km/h but that is not important as the principal need for high speed is for the emergency services entering the tunnel down the gentle gradient of the land tunnels.

The braking system gives a deceleration of at least 0.5 g and usually 0.65 g on dry concrete. A braking distance of around 50 metres is needed to stop from 80 km/h. In the tunnel the sight distance is at least 200 m and generally more as the curves are a minimum of 4200 m radius except close to the portals. There is thus no difficulty in driving at 80 km/h on line of sight.

MODULAR CONCEPT

The variety of tasks required of the vehicles necessitates a modular concept for the load carrying element, so that the remainder of the vehicle can be standardised and variations kept to a minimum. The solution proposed by AEG was to have interchangeable containers on a common chassis.

This is very good for easy transfer of containers if a chassis unit becomes defective. For example the first line fire vehicles must have a very high availability. In the event of major maintenance on the chassis the container can be transferred to another chassis and be back in service quickly. On the other hand there is a penalty in weight and space within the container. In hindsight it would probably have been better to use a common chassis with various openings in the side and use smaller exchange units within the body to provide the different tasks. The weight saving would have eliminated the need for special uprating of the axles which had to be undertaken to provide sufficient payload.

THE SIZE OF THE FLEET

The size of the fleet is determined by the tasks to be performed. For the vehicles to be used in emergency it was necessary to consider various sizes of possible incident requiring intervention of the emergency services in the UK and France. It was essential to provide enough transport for men and equipment for a major incident but to use it economically so that the vehicle cost could be reasonable and the number of drivers to be kept trained and available is minimised. As standard fire appliances and ambulances will not fit in the tunnel it is only possible to use the human resources from a wide area and not their vehicles. The studies led to a response of seven vehicles on each side of the channel. This is made up of three sections.

- The first line

At each portal there is a duty crew of 9 firemen. These man two vehicles which enter the tunnel immediately or one with its crew of 4 may already be on patrol in the tunnel. The third vehicle of the first line is the control and communications vehicle which is manned by police who are on duty at the police stations at the far ends of the terminals. This vehicle should be able to enter the tunnel less than 5 minutes after the first line fire vehicles.

- The second line fire

This is two vehicles each capable of carrying up to 12 firemen. These vehicles are not expected to enter the tunnel together. The first two crews to arrive from the outside fire stations, probably Folkestone and Dover on the UK side and Calais on the French side will enter in one vehicle. Crews from stations further way will arrive later and take the second vehicle.

- Ambulance

Two ambulance vehicles on each side are manned by the medical services. The ambulance can carry a crew of 8 including the driver. There is also room for another 3 sitting on a cabinet but it is unlikely that the crew will exceed 8.

In order to maintain full availability of these vehicles there is a spare ambulance and a spare fire container mounted on chassis and a further spare container of each type.

MAINTENANCE

There is a multiplicity of equipment in the service tunnel and the technical rooms branching off it. The hours of work needed to maintain the equipment and the tunnel fabric were assessed. This resulted in an estimate of the number of staff who would be working in the tunnel and their transport needs. From this it was possible to assess the number of vehicles. However, there are numerous possibilities of ways of grouping movements and this combined with different shift patterns made it difficult to determine the optimum number of vehicles.

In addition it was originally considered that some of the transportation requirements for both maintenance and the emergency facilities could be partially met by access via the running tunnels.

In the event 8 maintenance vehicles were provided by TML and Eurotunnel supplemented this by purchasing 15 small vehicles.

For the movement of heavy equipment such as replacement transformers TML provided 3 flatbed trailers and Eurotunnel has purchased a number of small trailers.

PAYLOAD

The design payload was determined by analysing the equipment carried on fire appliances, ambulances and maintenance requirements. In practice the fire vehicles have the largest requirement and the other vehicles are well within that limit. The chosen payload was 2500 kg.

THE FIRE VEHICLES
A normal fire appliance has a large tank carrying water and an engine driven pump to increase the low pressure which is available at the hydrants. In the tunnel there is a firemain with hydrants at appropriate places and therefore there is no need for the fire vehicles to carry water. The hydrants are pressurised to about 7 bar so there is no need for a mobile pump.

For fire fighting with water the STTS only needs to carry hoses and branchpipes. However, as there is liquid fuel on the vehicles carried on the shuttles a foam making capability is needed.

This means that the vehicles have to carry the emulsifier for foam creation. Emulsifier is mixed into the water at a concentration of 3 to 6%. As modern vehicle fuels may include alcohol it is necessary to use an alcohol resistant emulsifier. The older types of emulsifier needed 6% concentration in order to prevent alcohol breaking down the foam. Fortunately it is now possible to obtain an FFFP with alcohol resistance and a utilisation ratio of only 3%. This means that the quantity of emulsifier on each first line vehicles can be kept to 500 litres. Even so, the foam emulsifier with its tank, pump and proportioning valve takes up about 750 kg of the payload.

The second task of the firemen is rescue. For this they need a variety of tools including hydraulic cutters, spreaders, jacks and air bags. To provide motive power for the hydraulic power pack, power tools and for portable lighting there is a 3 kVA diesel driven generator. Further items to be carried include breathing apparatus, stretchers and first aid. In all, there are over 150 separate pieces to be carried.

In analysing how all this should be carried it became apparent that the normal practice of each vehicle carrying all the equipment that its own crew needs would be less efficient than a division whereby the first line would take the bulk of the equipment with a crew of only four in each of the two vehicles and the second line would have supplementary equipment and space for as many crew as possible. This division also helps in the later stages of a long incident as the second line vehicles can be taken away to bring in relief crews without taking away all the vital equipment. From the point of view of design of the vehicles this led to all fire vehicles having a payload of just under 2500 kg. It was also possible to construct the containers to the same design with the first line vehicles having some extra partitions and shelves and the second line having some bench seats instead.

The stowage of the equipment was a major exercise in itself. One factor which makes intervention in the tunnel different from intervention outside is the distance that equipment may have to be moved away from the fire appliance. The STTS is confined to the service tunnel but it may be that the hydrant to be used has to be accessed by a cross passage and then along the running tunnel walkway. The hydrant to be used may be the one by the door or it may be one at 125 m or 250 m along the walkway. One good aspect of the tunnel is that the floor is generally fairly level concrete and not rough ground. It is thus practical to fit wheels to all the heavy items so that they can be pushed easily instead of being carried.

This principle was extended to the hose storage. Each vehicle has 8 hose boxes on wheels. Each box takes 3 hoses and is easily lifted out of the vehicle. It is then fitted with a handle and connected to a second box. One man can then move 6 hoses plus a few items piled on top such as an adapter or branchpipe. The diesel generator, the hydraulic power pack and the hydraulic tools are on their separate trolleys so that they can be pushed along the walkway easily and are manageable weights to remove from the vehicle and carry up the stairs in the non standard cross passages. The reserve cylinders for the breathing apparatus are also in removable boxes but without wheels. The boxes are used to provide safe storage on any vehicle such a maintenance vehicle which might be used to take empty cylinders back to the compressor for recharging.

AMBULANCE EQUIPMENT

The problem is much the same as for the fire vehicles: How to provide for a major incident with the minimum of vehicles. The ambulance container is designed with 4 stretcher positions, ie: 2 stretchers one above the other at each end of the container. However, it is unlikely to be used in this mode because it is not possible to give serious treatment to two patients who are stacked one above the other with little room in between. Furthermore, in the event of a major incident the small number of patients who could be moved by the ambulances would be insufficient and the main evacuation would be via a rescue train. The ambulance has been divided into two functional ends. One end has one stretcher position ready for use and a full set of medical equipment readily available. In the event of a staff injury, this end of the ambulance is always available for immediate use. The other end is almost filled with equipment for use in a major incident. There are stretchers of various kinds, dressings, splints, first aid boxes and oxygen bottles.

This equipment would be unloaded at the incident site and used to set up a local dressing station and transport patients out of the tunnel on a rescue train.

One of the difficulties in selecting equipment for the ambulances is the differences of medical practice on the two sides of the channel. On the UK side the interventions are principally by the ambulance service who are trained to a certain level and bring their own paramedic kits, on the French side the treatment is only performed by qualified doctors and the paramedic equipment for them has to be kept on the ambulance. There are other differences because similar equipment does not have regulatory approval in both countries.

THE MAINTENANCE VEHICLES

The requirements for maintenance vehicles differ considerably from those of the emergency vehicles: there is less need for high speed, the payload is usually quite small and the crew may be only two people. On the other hand there can be times when major works are in progress, such as replacing pipes or cables, when a team of 6 or more is required and they will spend a whole shift at a site. The six large maintenance vehicles have containers equipped with washing and toilet area and a workbench/travel area with four seats. This provides well for the larger tasks.

Most of the interventions in the tunnel will only need 1 or 2 technicians with a small amount of tools and replacement parts such as electronic cards. The vehicle only needs two seats and a small amount of equipment space. It is possible to use a small car but it is not easy to turn round in the tunnel and it is likely to get damaged easily as the clearance for passing other vehicles is quite small.

A review of various potential vehicles discovered that there are small municipal vehicles which have the right characteristics. These were basically a speed of 50 km/h, a width of 1.3 m or less, length of about 3 m and a good turning circle. The Ladog series of vehicles, see Figure 2, has these characteristics and in particular has four wheel steering which makes it very easy to turn in the tunnel. It has a hydrostatic transmission which provides a built in speed limit of about 50 km/h and thus prevents the possibility of drivers ignoring the speed limit.

The standard form of the vehicle is a pick up truck but it has a range of modules which can be mounted on the platform. Particularly useful modules are the sweeping and cleaning pack and the washing pack. The vehicle can drive at about 50 km/h to the part of the tunnel to be cleaned and work for a good period before coming out for emptying, again at 50 km/h. Another good feature of the Ladog is that it is always built with an indirect injection diesel so that pollution is low.

An initial fleet of 15 of these vehicles has been purchased. The attachments include two high pressure wash units, two sweeping and vacuum units, manhole lifter, winch, crane arm and snow clearance. The latter being for use in the terminal and not the tunnel. A further batch of a simpler model is to be purchased. The vehicles will retain 4 wheel steering so that turning in the tunnel is easy but the drive will only be 2 wheel and the engine will be smaller. The top speed will remain at 50 km/h.

TRAILERS

In the longer term there will be a programme of replacement of some of the equipment in the service tunnel. It is also possible that there may be premature failures. The electrical equipment in the sub-stations is either heavy, such as transformers, or bulky such as switchgear units. To transport these there are 3 heavy load trailers which have a platform that can be lowered to the floor to provide the maximum headroom for large switchgear units. The same trailer is also used to carry a pipe handling unit. The drainage pipes and possibly the firemain may need replacement in the long term and the way to do this is to take a pipe handling unit on a trailer and bring pipes alongside it on simple trailers. The fleet of vehicles can be used to tow the trailers. In order to avoid having to travel the whole length of the tunnel to reverse the trailers they are constructed with steering axles and towing points at either end. The Ladog can be detached, turned round and coupled to other end of the trailer when it is necessary to come out of the tunnel. The STTS has a towing point at either end.

CONCLUSION

The two types of vehicle with the addition of some trailers provide a very flexible transport system which meets all the diverse tasks. When the vehicles need replacing it will be interesting to see whether the vehicles designed to meet what is imagined to be the need are replaced with something quite different because of the results of real experience in the world's longest road tunnel.

Management of safety

R. Morris, Director of Safety, Eurotunnel, Folkestone

'Salus populi suprema est lex'
(The safe-keeping of the people is the chief law)

So wrote Cicero in the 1st Century before the birth of Christ, although these sentiments would be immediately recognised within Eurotunnel, encapsulating as they do one of our main objectives.

The company is entirely cognisant that quite apart from any other consideration, the commercial success of the Channel Tunnel depends on the travelling public being satisfied that the system is safe.

To this end, the project has been driven by five major factors.

1. A relentless search to design, engineer and manufacture safe equipment, and provide a safe system of work through the systematic identification and reduction of hazards.
2. The recruitment of staff of an extremely high calibre and relevant profile, trained within a positive and proactive safety culture.
3. The compilation of the Rules by which Eurotunnel will operate, produced by the operators, in conjunction with safety experts.
4. The establishment of a dynamic Safety Management System, based on the theory of Loss Control, which will provide constant measurement of safety performance and be available to everyone in the company.
5. To ensure intentions are translated into reality, Eurotunnel has compiled a full Safety Case - the first of its kind in the transport industry.

Our aim, based on these initiatives and our drive to succeed, is simply to become a world leader in safety management.

1 INTRODUCTION

The Channel Tunnel system is one of the largest and most exciting engineering projects in Europe this century, although there is little new about the concept. The principles of twin-bore, one-way railway tunnels date back to the 19th century. The carriage of road traffic by rail shuttle under the Alps has flourished without serious accident or incident for over 30 years.

The Channel Tunnel is a railway system connecting terminals near Folkestone and Calais through single bored tunnels laying generally between 25 and 40 metres below the seabed. The tunnels are 50 kilometres long with a motorway-to-motorway crossing time of one hour. The system will carry four main types of traffic.

Two are operated by Eurotunnel:
- cars, coaches and motorcycles in passenger shuttles;
- Heavy Goods Vehicles (HGVs) in freight shuttles;

and two operated by the national railways:
- through passengers trains;
- through freight trains.

The passenger and freight shuttle system for road vehicles is designed to provide a "turn up and go" service, 24 hours-a-day, throughout the year, in virtually all weathers. Passengers travelling with their cars or in coaches will remain with their vehicles throughout the journey. Drivers of HGVs will be segregated from their vehicles for the journey through the tunnel and will be carried in an amenity coach marshalled into the train.

The signalling system can permit 20 paths per hour through the tunnel in each direction. The number of paths can be increased without major modification to 24 paths per hour. An increase to 30 paths per hour could be made but would require some minor alteration to the software of the signalling system.

2 DESIGN FEATURES

2.1 The Tunnels

The choice of rail as the mode of transport was in no small way influenced by safety considerations, as rail is known to be a far safer option than road. The two running tunnels are single track and separate, joined at only two points by undersea crossovers. In this way the risk of head-on collisions is minimised. Both tunnels are fully reversibly signalled, affording an efficient and easy means of effecting maintenance work or continuation of service in the event of an obstruction through the provision of properly protected single line working arrangements.

A third tunnel, the service tunnel, runs between the running tunnels. This provides four main functions. Firstly, it acts as a duct providing fresh air to the running tunnels. Secondly, it provides a safe refuge in the event of an incident and is maintained at a higher air pressure than the running tunnels to prevent ingress of smoke. Thirdly, it acts as an access for the Emergency Response Organisations and maintenance personnel, and fourthly it carries some of the tunnel services, i.e. fire mains, power and communication cables etc.

Every 375 metres, cross passages passing through the service tunnel join the two running tunnels, creating an evacuation route either from one running tunnel to another, or from a running tunnel to the service tunnel. In order to provide access to cross passages, a continuous walkway runs along the offside of each running tunnel whilst along the nearside tunnel wall a continuous maintenance walkway has been constructed.

Rubber-tyred vehicles constantly patrol the service tunnel conveying personnel trained both for maintenance and emergency procedures. These vehicles are designed to transport special equipment for the Emergency Response Organisations. In normal operation the Service Tunnel vehicles use an electronic buried wire guidance system laid so that two vehicles travelling in opposite directions can travel at speeds of up to 80 kph. At all times a central control is aware of the exact location of each Service Tunnel vehicle.

2.2 Ventilation

Perhaps the most vital life-sustaining service to any tunnel is ventilation. Two systems have been installed to cater for normal operations and for emergencies, particularly those requiring the control of smoke.

The normal ventilation system supplies air to the running tunnels through air distribution units located above the evacuation cross passage doors, from the service tunnel from a ventilation plant located on each coast. Each plant contains two variable pitch axial fans, each capable of supplying the required air flow. One fan at each plant will be operational at any one time with the other on permanent stand-by, available for immediate use should a fault develop with the duty fan.

In the event of the need to control smoke by redirection of flow, a supplementary ventilation system is available, controlled and co-ordinated by the Railway Control Centre. Two pairs of axial fans in parallel are located at coastal sites near to either end of the tunnel. The air flow can be modified or reversed by varying the blade pitch, thus avoiding loss of control of air movement which would be caused by reversing the motor direction.

Trains passing through the running tunnels act as a quasi-piston and produce both positive and negative air pressures. In order to provide relief, piston relief ducts have been constructed between the two running tunnels every 250 metres. Each duct is provided with a butterfly valve which can be operated remotely as necessary, whilst pressure restrictors are also provided at each PRD to reduce the effect of air on passing trains.

2.3 Cooling

The air friction created by the passage of trains and the heat given off by equipment require a cooling system which has been installed through both running tunnels in the forms of cooling loops. The pipework, which extends for some 120 kilometres, consists of 300mm and 400mm welded pipes divided into seven individually controlled cooling loops. These are served by sea water drawn from offshore intakes, and the water is cooled in chiller plants located at Lower Shakespeare Cliff and Sangatte before being circulated through the various loops to maintain the ambient tunnel temperature between 18° and 30° Centigrade.

2.4 Pumping

Three major pumping stations in the undersea length of the Tunnel system have been constructed to remove spillage or water collected through gravity. Although the likelihood of sea-water entering the Tunnel is virtually nil other possibilities must be catered for i.e. ground water leakage, damage to water mains, spillage from rail traffic, fire fighting, etc.

Four pumps are installed in each major pumping station, but under normal operation only two pumps are in use. A third is on standby to cope with equipment failure, whilst the fourth is on a planned maintenance period, a good example of the redundancy built into the safety systems.

The pumping stations are also provided with a dangerous goods sump. The prime purpose of the sump is to contain any dangerous goods spillages and to avoid them being pumped directly into the normal pumping network. Should dangerous goods enter the sump an alarm is sent to the Rail Control Centre and investigations are made as to the cause.

2.5 Power

Electricity for the catenary and all other services is fed from both the UK and French national grids. The design is so configured that should one supply totally fail - a most unlikely event - the other can supply sufficient power to operate the system, albeit it at a slightly reduced capacity. In the event of total failure of both national grids, diesel generators will support essential systems such as ventilation and drainage. Other essential safety systems are supported by local batteries, i.e. emergency lighting, computers etc.

To guard against axle boxes running hot and to detect the danger caused by equipment hanging down from a train, hot axle box and dragging part detectors are situated at key points in the system with alarms sent directly to the Rail Control Centre.

2.6 Signalling

In order to reduce the possibility of human error to a minimum, Eurotunnel has adopted a form of automatic train protection using speed codes and cab signalling. The usual configuration of track circuiting and overlaps is employed but the familiar lineside equipment of colour light or semaphore signals is replaced by independent marker boards.

Data is transmitted to the train via trackside equipment which can read the traffic pattern ahead, local gradients, and temporary or permanent speed restrictions. The ontrain equipment receives the data, compares it to the train characteristics, and calculates the instantaneous safe maximum speed. Warnings are given and eventually brakes are applied automatically if the speed goes above the 'safe speed'. This brings the train within the required braking curve, allowing the driver to regain control. Full reversible signalling of this type is available in both running tunnels and on the main terminal lines.

Track-side and on-train equipment is duplicated. This ensures that any train using the main tracks has all the necessary data required to control its speed at all times, and guarantees safe operation.

Signalling on secondary tracks is a relay-based local yard interlocking system. This is a conventionally based line-side aspect system with no cab signalling on secondary tracks. At the boundaries of the secondary tracks there are cab signalling arming and disarming loops ensuring that trains leaving the secondary tracks and entering the main tracks have their cab signalling equipment activated and armed. A similar position exists for national railways trains entering or leaving from Eurotunnel's signalling system on main line tracks.

Once the cab signalling equipment within Eurotunnel system is disarmed the tachometry equipment limits the speed to a maximum of 35 kilometres per hour. If the cab signalling fails to become successfully activated and armed, the 35 kilometres per hour limit is maintained. If the cab signalling fails to become successfully deactivated and disarmed, emergency brakes are applied on leaving the cab signalled area. All emergency brake applications are transmitted to the Rail Control Centre as an audible alarm.

3 OPERATING THE SYSTEM

3.1 Railway and Terminal Control

Central control of the railway system is provided by a main Railway Control Centre at Folkestone and a standby facility on the Coquelles terminal. The system is designed in such a way that the railway system can be controlled from either the main railway control centre or the standby facility with a minimum of handover delay. The main difference between the control rooms is the absence of a mimic panel on the French side.

A Terminal Control is located on either terminal ensuring not only a co-ordinated approach during normal operation but also a swift response in the event of an emergency, i.e. receipt of the Emergency Response Organisations' vehicles, redirection of traffic, etc.

At either end of the Tunnel are the Fire Equipment Management Centres. Their primary function is to monitor all fire detection and suppression systems in the tunnels and to alert the Railway Control Centre in the event of an alarm. On the UK side they are staffed by full-time firemen from Kent Fire Brigade and under contract to Eurotunnel and on the French side by Sapeurs Pompiers of the local fire brigade.

Incident Control Centres have also been built on each terminal, fully equipped with permanent communications links and facilities for all the Emergency Response Organisations. These rooms are built solely for use in the event of an emergency.

3.2 Communications

Apart from the usual internal telephone network, Eurotunnel has installed two further means of communication - concession radio and track-to-train radio, each with high in-built redundancy levels.

Concession radio is a UHF trunked mobile system, affording communications between all staff within Eurotunnel - a vital link in the safety chain since speed and ease of communication are prerequisites for good safety.

Track-to-train radio is a dedicated link between train driver and Railway Controller and involves both voice operation and dispatch and receipt of standard predetermined text messages in either French or English displayed in the driver's cab. Standard text messages are used to eradicate the possibility of misunderstanding spoken messages, although extensive training is also given on radio discipline. The individual shuttle/train number of the driver using track-to-train radio is shown on the Railway Controller's display thus ensuring correct identification.

Public address systems are also available for both Railway and Terminal Control Centres for communication to any part of the network.

3.3 Fire Safety

The potential hazard to which Eurotunnel has directed most attention is fire and it has applied the maxim 'prevention rather than cure' to its greatest extent possible.

In the running tunnels a fire detection system housed in 31 detector stations constantly samples and analyses the air, using optical and ionisation sensors to detect smoke, with ultraviolet and infra-red detectors to detect flame. Confirmed alarms are automatically transmitted to the Railway Control Centre and Fire Equipment Management Centre. All technical equipment rooms in the service tunnel are also monitored and equipped with an automatic extinguishing system.

The Eurotunnel shuttle trains are protected by a sophisticated fire detection and suppression system which is continuously monitored at the chef de train's (guard's) position.

Two independent systems are used for fire suppression. The first, intended for dealing with a fire alarm from a petrol leak from the engine compartment or petrol tank of a road vehicle, is an aqueous film-forming foam (AFFF) which operates in the central undercar channel of the carrier wagons. The second is a total gas deluge system which can be used if a fire starts in a road vehicles itself. This would only be used in extreme conditions and normally only after the wagon(s) concerned had been evacuated.

All materials used in shuttle wagon construction are fire-resistant and provide a 30-minute fire barrier. Fire doors at either end of each wagon are closed when running, thus a moving shuttle wagon can be evacuated longitudinally through passenger doors and provide 30 minutes' protection to passengers. Since the journey time portal to portal is 24 minutes, the safety philosophy is based on keeping trains running rather than stopping them in the tunnel.

3.4 Shuttle Rolling Stock

As well as the precautions mentioned above, other safety features have been built into the Shuttle rolling stock.

The tourist shuttle wagons are air-conditioned and have additional ventilation systems to purge vehicle fumes during and immediately after loading and unloading. The floors of the wagons are specially designed with skid-resistant surfaces and fuel spillage channels.

Communication between passengers and the *chef de train* is possible via a passenger communication alarm system. The *chef de train* has the ability to view each shuttle wagon independently through a video system which automatically displays the affected wagon in the event of a fire alarm sounding. The *chef de train* also has public address facilities throughout the train and a dot matrix system for text messages. Both safety announcements and safety information panels are standard throughout the shuttles. In addition, the tourist shuttles are constantly patrolled by shuttle attendants.

Disabled passengers are located in particular positions within the shuttle trains in order that the crew know exactly where they are should they need to be evacuated. Specially designed wheelchairs will be provided to assist in evacuation along the walkway.

Very few dangerous goods will be permitted to be conveyed through the Tunnel. A tracking system will be used for HGVs conveying dangerous goods in order that their exact position on shuttles is known. Both SNCF and BR have highly efficient computer-based systems which provide very full information regarding goods carried on their trains.

All trains using the Channel Tunnel with the exception of national railways freight trains will be provided with a locomotive at either end. This is to ensure that should one locomotive fail the other is available to haul the train out of the Tunnel. It is possible to uncouple wagons of the Tourist Shuttles in groups of three from inside the train to allow the unaffected portions of the train to be moved out of the Tunnel, using the locomotive at either end to drive each portion in opposite directions. It is for this reason that the *chef de train* will be trained also as a driver.

3.5 Operating Rules

In parallel with the design a comprehensive set of procedures has been established at various levels of detail to regulate the operation of the transportation system. It was a requirement of the Concession Agreement that the Safety Arrangements including Operating Rules and Emergency Procedures were approved by the Intergovernmental Commission; this approval was a precondition for the issue of the Operating Certificate.

Where hazards were identified which could not be dealt with in the design, measures to do this had to be included in these operating procedures.

3.6 Command Procedure Exercises

An on-going series of exercises tests the efficiency of the Rules and regulations. These exercises, based on a military formula, enable all Eurotunnel staff to rehearse their particular responsibilities in simulated conditions with a high degree of realism. Exercises have already been held both internally and with the Emergency Response Organisations. The benefits for safety have been immense bringing as they do a high degree of professionalism and confidence among the personnel concerned.

3.7 Safety Case and Safety Studies

As a first of its kind in the transport industry, Eurotunnel has compiled a full Safety Case which will contain a qualitative and quantitative analysis of the safety systems employed.

A whole range of safety tests and safety studies have been and will be carried out. They are designed to ensure that the claims of manufacturers and the targets set within Eurotunnel can be achieved with the equipment provided. The studies range from tests on fire detection systems and smoke control to evacuation procedures and human factors analysis, plus quantative and qualitative analyses of the system. Discussions with outside industries on their safety systems and safety initiatives are taking place constantly.

4 SAFETY MANAGEMENT STRUCTURE

4.1 Safety Directorate

In establishing the Safety Directorate within Eurotunnel, two important and perhaps paradoxical aims have been achieved. Firstly, the department has to be independent in order to give neutral judgement. Secondly, the department needs to maintain a close working relationship with other departments, particularly Operations, in order to keep in touch with day-to-day reality and maintain its influence.

For this reason, the Safety Director reports to the Managing Director and the Eurotunnel Safety Committee. The latter comprises Senior executives from both inside and outside Eurotunnel, and this structure permits a useful exchange of ideas from other industries.

It must be stressed that safety must remain in the line - the responsibility of each department and its line managers and staff. The creation of a Safety Directorate must not be regarded as removing that responsibility in any way. The Safety Directorate has been created to assist wherever possible to assist in legal interpretation, safety projects, safety investment, risk analysis, all health and safety issues, audit, enquiries and investigations, and particularly to develop our safety culture within the company.

4.2 Inter-Governmental Commission/Safety Authority

Due to the unique nature of Eurotunnel as the first truly binational company, a controlling authority, entitled the Inter-Governmental Commission (IGC), has been established jointly by the UK and French governments, comprising representatives of the two governments. The Safety Authority itself is formed by experts in safety and transportation matters from the two governements relevant departments or organisations. It operates through various working groups, covering such topics as dangerous goods, rescue and public safety, railway safety and technology. The relationship between Eurotunnel and the IGC is equivalent to that between the Civil Aviation Authority and the airlines. Eurotunnel is responsible to the Safety Authority/IGC on safety matters, and from them receives the Operating Certificate.

4.3 Safety Committees within Eurotunnel

The principal Safety Committee is formed of top level executives from Eurotunnel including the Safety Director and members of other industries. This committee continuously reviews safety policy and safety performance of the company.

A cascade system in the committee structure ensures that the chairman of one committee attends the committee above as a member and reports back on strategic decisions etc. Such a system facilitates effective upward communication.

5 SAFETY MANAGEMENT METHODS

5.1 The Human Factor

Overlooked by many companies although of equal importance to the design factors is the necessity of a proactive and cogent safety culture in which all employees feel committed to good safety. Eurotunnel has accordingly expended much effort in creating and maintaining a culture based on open reporting of incidents (undesired events that result in harm to people, damage to property or loss to process) and accidents (undesired events which under slightly different circumstances could have resulted in harm to people, damage to property or loss to process).

Incidents and accidents have the same cause. It has been calculated that for every one accident there may be 600 incidents, a point which will be amplified later in this paper. This is amplified later in this paper. It is vital therefore that both are investigated to obtain a clear picture of the critical few. To get details of incidents however, a caring trusting culture is required, since in a blame culture personnel are tempted to suppress incidents in case discipline is meted out.

Eurotunnel believes that if a genuine mistake has been made and information regarding that mistake and the reasons for it are communicated, then no blame should be attached. (However, a very strong differentiation must be made between genuine mistakes and gross misconduct. The latter must of course receive the punishment it deserves.) The whole point of managing safety is to identify the root causes of incidents and accidents, not to apportion blame.

5.2 Analysis of Information

Since Eurotunnel teaches that information on incidents and accidents is valued, an efficient and well-thought out management system to gather and analyse that information is vital.

Eurotunnel's Safety Management System (*En Garde*) has been designed to fulfill the following objectives: to be easy to use and accessible to all; to provide feedback to users; to track progress of incidents and accidents; and to produce trend analyses.

Each incident and accident report is converted into a catalogue of keywords which are fed into the computer system. It is these keywords that are analysed to identify root causes of incidents and accidents. The keywords also include information regarding the status of reports/enquiries/recommendations and provide an excellent tracking system for both management and staff alike. The system automatically replies to the person initiating the report, informing them of its progress and any recommendations that may have been made as a result of the initial advice. In addition, all incidents and accidents have a hazard rating applied to them in order that management can devote its precious time to those most worthy of its attention. By such a method it is possible to concentrate on major safety issues, and to extract information based on these ratings to assist in identifying trends. Using advanced computer technology, any incident or accident can be input into the system within a very short space of time.

The Safety Audit System, with its associated Safety Performance Standards, completes the picture. Since it is not possible to control what it is not possible to measure, a quantitative audit system is necessary. Eurotunnel has developed its own system, based on the International Safety Rating System. By allocating marks to safety achievements split into a number of elements, managers are able to note their successes and identify those areas capable of improvement to achieve a high safety record.

Whilst taking account of the human factors element of safety management, there is no doubt that the keystone to Eurotunnel's approach is the trusting and open reporting environment which has been created - without that the system would fail.

5.3 Safety Performance/Loss Control

To become a commercially successful business Eurotunnel must control losses in all forms. In safety performance terms this means that our quantification methods must reflect not only our actual losses, but more importantly our potential risk for loss.

Major studies into the causal factors of accidents have shown that for every accident resulting in serious injury there are many times more events leading to property damage, loss to process or near misses (incidents) which could have escalated into major losses. One such study was carried out by a team headed by Frank Bird, the then Director of Engineering Services for the Insurance Company of North America. The team analysed over 1.75 million accidents reported by 297 companies representing 21 industrial groups. Collectively these companies employed 1.75 million personnel who worked over 3 billion man hours during the period analysed. The result of this study showed that for every major injury resulting in death, disability, lost time or medical treatment, there were some 10 minor injuries reported. Further analysis showed that for every major injury there were 30 cases of damage to property. Finally, and perhaps most significantly, there were 600 incidents or near misses which under slightly different circumstances could have resulted in injury or damage to property. These ratios are represented in Figure A:-

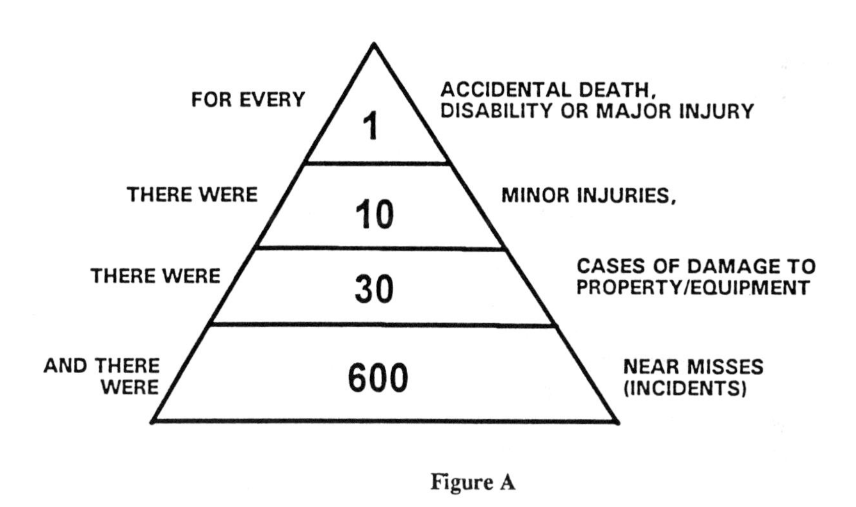

Figure A

It is clear from both the figure and the definitions of incidents and accidents themselves that incidents represent a very important source of information about a company's safety performance by pointing to the potential risk of an accident. This factor alone is however insufficient since the potential risk of loss will be unquantified. A method of quantifying the potential risk of loss, and for assessing risk for all operations in Eurotunnel, is set out in Figure B overleaf. Eurotunnel intend to treat the potential impact of accidents and incidents in the same way since they both have the same root causes. Thus the actual loss incurred in an accident will not influence the assessment of the potential for loss.

POTENTIAL RISK MATRIX

	EVERY 12 MTHS	EVERY 6 MTHS	EVERY 2 MTHS	EVERY 2 WKS	DAILY	PEOPLE	PROCESS * EQUIPMENT * ENVIRONMENT
E	30E	60E	90E	120E	150E	FATAL INJURY	*MAJOR* £500K + FF5M +
D	10D	20D	30D	40D	50D	PERMANENT DISABILITY INJURY	*SIGNIFICANT* £100K - 500K FFIM - 5M
C	4C	8C	12C	16C	20C	HOSPITALISATION INJURY 3 DAYS OR MORE	*MODERATE* £25K - 100K FF250MM - 1M
B	2B	4B	6B	8B	10B	MEDICAL TREATMENT LOST TIME INJURY UP TO 2 DAYS	*MINOR* £5K - 25K FF50MM - 250MM
A	1A	2A	3A	4A	5	SIMPLE FIRST AID INJURY	*TRIVIAL* £0 - 5K FF0 - 50MM

Horizontal axis = **POTENTIAL FREQUENCY OF RECURRENCE**
Vertical axis = **POTENTIAL SEVERITY**

Figure B

This matrix enables assessment to be carried out by evaluating the accident or incident against the two axes of Potential Severity and Potential Frequency of Recurrence.

On the vertical scale it allows the user to assign potential severity of loss using as an aid either injury or damage potential - the values assigned to each category are open to revision in the light of experience. Whilst on the horizontal scale the potential frequency of occurrence (from daily to annually) can be assessed. The figure calculated as a function of the two axes will represent the category of risk to which the company is, or has been, exposed. These categories are divided into three bands:

LOW RISK	-	1A to 4C
MEDIUM RISK	-	5A to 12C
HIGH RISK	-	16C to 150E

The long term objective of Eurotunnel will be to manage improvement in safety such that the vast majority of accidents and incidents occur in the LOW RISK category.

As an example of a particular incident, on 15 March 1994, four trouble-shooters from the Rolling Stock department were called to assist a train with apparent traction failure in Running Tunnel Two approximately 200m from the portal at Beussingue. Once the repair had been carried out, the trouble-shooters returned to the French Portal, walking along the Running Tunnel instead of using the Service Tunnel. Disregarding any extenuating circumstances, the Potential Hazard rating was set at HIGH - 30 - using the following methodology.

Potential Severity:	Personnel walking in the Running Tunnels without a Permit incorporating train protection, are potentially exposed to a permanent disability injury (refer to Matrix line D).
Potential Frequency of Recurrence:	Trouble-shooters may be asked to attend a stalled train in the tunnels relatively infrequently - say once every two months - thus at the junction of the two axes we arrive at the HIGH RISK category of HIGH 30.

The overall safety performance of each department in the company is expressed by calculating their Average Potential Risk Factor for each period, using the following equation:

$$\text{Average PRF} = \frac{(A \times B) + (A \times B) \ \ldots}{\text{Total } A}$$

where A equals: number of accidents/incidents in each hazard category in each department;

where B equals: hazard category rating.

Figure C below shows a contrived table indicating total incidents/accidents by Hazard Category, followed by Figure D - four contrived 'departmental potential risk factor graphs.

	January	February	March	April
High	4	6	5	11
Medium	5	5	6	17
Low	3	10	8	4
Monthly Total	12	21	19	32
Cumulative Total	12	33	52	84

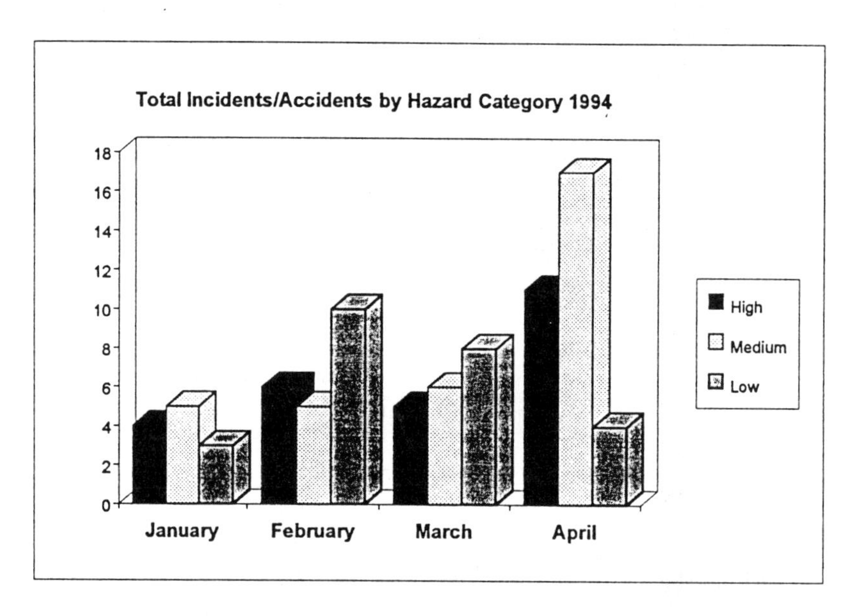

Figure C

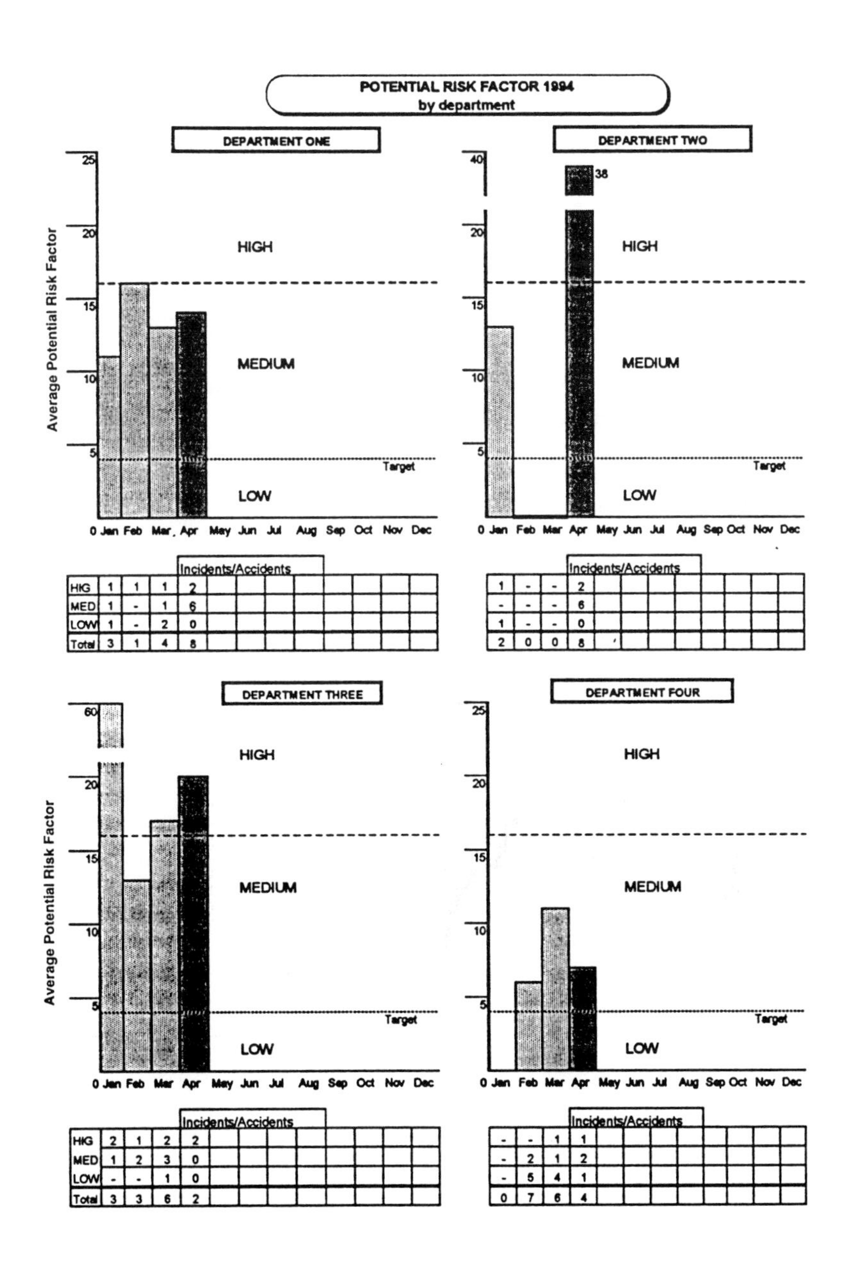

Department One – Incidents/Accidents

HIG	1	1	1	2								
MED	1	-	1	6								
LOW	1	-	2	0								
Total	3	1	4	8								

Department Two – Incidents/Accidents

1	-	-	2								
-	-	-	6								
1	-	-	0								
2	0	0	8								

Department Three – Incidents/Accidents

HIG	2	1	2	2								
MED	1	2	3	0								
LOW	-	-	1	0								
Total	3	3	6	2								

Department Four – Incidents/Accidents

-	-	1	1								
-	2	1	2								
-	5	4	1								
0	7	6	4								

Figure D

Eurotunnel is considering plotting actual risk factor analyses on the same tables to highlight the difference between potential and actual. Under active consideration also is the construction of a link between the incident/accident reporting system and the audit elements.

Every month a safety report is issued simultaneously to ALL managers in the company including the Joint Board, ensuring common provision of safety information. The report highlights audit results, major incidents/accidents, enquiry reports and quantified potential risk factors for the company as a whole and by department.

The objective is to manage the risk and thus control the loss within targets set.

6 CONCLUSION

From the outset, Eurotunnel has been fully committed to the safety of its system. In choosing the Eurotunnel scheme, the government considered it to be the safest from the traveller's point of view. The measures described above demonstrate the particular attention paid to the design and method of working to ensure that the transport system is safe. It is the belief of the company that we will achieve our aim to become a world leader in safety management.

Discussion on session 7

A. R. Thomas, *Mott Ewbank Preece*

What value to the authors place on Civil Engineering and at what level do they employ civil engineering staff?

N. Roth, *London Transport Planning*

Could the author state whether the STTS guidance system imposes left running or can it be used in either direction?

N. Roth, *London Transport Planning*

Could the author explain which of the hidden recommendations he thought were inappropriate to British Rail?

T. Mansfield, *British Rail Projects*

The 'report incidents without implied blame' for the individual could lead to persistent opportunists 'bending the rules' on the basis that they cannot be sacked. How does the safety culture deal with this situation?

A. Smith, *TTC Traffic and Transport Consultants*

When the Transit Shuttle is working at full capacity, i.e. a train every 15 minutes, I calculate this will require six trains. If one train is in the maintenance workshop this leaves only one train in reserve for emergencies. Is this not a very small back-up reserve?

B. Watson
Reply to A. R. Thomas

Eurotunnel values engineering qualifications highly, including those of civil engineers. Civil engineers are retained in the operating organization right up to Department Head level within Fixed Equipment Maintenance and some of our planning functions.

J. O. Kennedy
Reply to N. Roth

The normal running side is immaterial. The guidance can be engaged on either track in either direction. Left running was originally chosen to conform with the left running of trains in France, the UK and the tunnel.

R. Morris
Reply to A. R. Thomas

The authors place great value on civil engineering. They are employed at the highest managerial level in the company and civil engineers are not debarred from being a director.

Reply to N. Roth

The STTS guidance system can be used in either direction.

Reply to T. Mansfield

Persistent ‘offenders’ are not allowed the ‘bend the rules’. It is clear that a repetition is viewed in a different light.

Reply to A. Smith

Six trains to operate one departure every 15 minutes allows for one train to be in maintenance and one in reserve for emergencies, a small but achievable reserve.

Associated titles available from Thomas Telford

Cost effective maintenance of railway track. R. A. Vickers (ed.).
ISBN 0 7277 1930 0, £37.00 UK and Europe, £42.00 elsewhere by air

Engineering geology of the Channel Tunnel. C. S. Harris, M. B. Hart, P. M. Varley and C. D. Warren.
ISBN 0 7277 2045 7, £80.00 UK and Europe, £89.00 elsewhere by air

Heavy vehicles and roads: technology, safety and policy. D. Cebon and C. G. B. Mitchell (eds).
ISBN 0 7277 1903 3, £100.00 UK and Europe, £110.00 elsewhere by air

Light transit systems. B. H. North (ed.).
ISBN 0 7277 1590 9, £40.00 UK and Europe, £46.00 elsewhere by air

Modern railway transportation. B. H. North (ed.).
ISBN 0 7277 1973 4, £60.00 UK and Europe, £67.00 elsewhere by air

Rail mass transit for developing countries. Institution of Civil Engineers.
ISBN 0 7277 1560 7, £58.00 UK and Europe, £65.00 elsewhere by air

Track geotechnology and substructure management. E. Selig and J. Waters.
ISBN 0 7277 2013 9, £80.00 UK and Europe, £89 elsewhere by air

Urban transport. H. K. Blessington (ed.).
ISBN 0 7277 2084 8, £30.00 UK and Europe, £35.00 elsewhere by air